Search for the
Tourette Syndrome
and
Human Behavior Genes

by

David E. Comings, M.D.

City of Hope National Medical Center

Search for the Tourette Syndrome and Human Behavior Genes

by *David E. Comings, M.D.*

Published by ◯─☐ **Hope Press** P.O.Box 188
Duarte, CA 91009-0188 U.S.A.

Other books by Hope Press:

Tourette Syndrome and Human Behavior
by *David E. Comings, M.D.*

The Gene Bomb **Does Higher Education and Advanced Technology Accelerate the Selection of Genes for Learning Disorders, ADHD, Addicative and Disruptive Behavior?**
by *David E. Comings, M.D.*

Teaching the Tiger
by *Marilyn P. Dornbush, Ph.D* and *Sheryl K. Pruitt, M.Ed.*

RYAN and **What Makes Ryan Tick?**
by *Susan Hughes*

(to order these and others see back leaf forms)

Library of Congress Cataloging-in-Publication Data

Comings, David E.
    Search for the Tourette syndrome and human behavior genes / by David E. Comings.
       p. cm.
    Includes bibliographical references and index.
    ISBN 1-878267-36-1 (hb). -- ISBN 1-878267-41-8 (pbk.)
    1. Tourette syndrome--Genetic aspects. 2. Behavior genetics.
I. Title.
    [DNLM: 1. Tourette Syndrome--genetics. 2. Genetics, Behavioral.
WM 187 C733s 1996]
RC375.C658   1996
DNLM/DLC
for Library of Congress
                          96-16530
                          CIP

Dedicated to:

My patients

Who taught me all I know about Tourette syndrome,

and to:

The City of Hope National Medical Center

Without whose support none of this would have happened.

FOREWARD

The brain sciences these days are in something of a crisis. For years medical practitioners who deal with behavioral and emotional problems have sought to achieve the status of a hard science, and thus to gain admission to the swashbuckling, self-assured world of surgeons and cardiologists, so firm in their knowledge and heroic accomplishments. Recent advances in numerous fields, however, notably in molecular biology and psycho-pharmacology, have allowed researchers to amass a body of scientific knowledge about human behavior with a rapidity that has exceeded their capacity to integrate it into a satisfying theoretical framework. Every day, it seems, clinicians are forced to revise their understanding of the enigmatic relationship between biological mechanisms and human experience in the face of a steady stream of publications announcing the discovery of the genetic, chemical or structural bases of yet another aspect of our mental lives. This period of rapid transition has proven both a comfort and source of confusion for mental health professionals. The explosion of the knowledge base is certainly gratifying for psychiatrists, in that it has allowed them finally to take their position among colleagues who have done so much beneath the mantle of rigorous scientific methodology. At the same time, this new recognition of the infinitely variable expressions of a genetic etiology from one individual to the next has rendered diagnostic strategies obsolete. There are now many uncomfortably gray areas in diagnosing and treating mental illnesses, for the older categorical boundaries no longer hold true.

The relationship between the brain, genes, and the environment is far too complex for either a purely psychodynamic or a purely pharmacological treatment approach. It is an uncertain time for the world of psychiatry, for no new paradigm has emerged to replace the previous one. Obviously, this trend in the field would seem to require of clinicians an ability to tolerate a certain degree of ambiguity, a flexibility of mind that might allow them to work with what they know until a better working model comes along. Unfortunately, psychiatrists' overzealous attempts to become more scientific has, on the whole, led to just the opposite result, and the field is too often dominated by a disturbingly reductionistic kind of tunnel vision.

i

Out of a desire to ground psychiatry in hard science, those in power have clung to a rigidly orthodox theoretical framework that assumes the human psyche is easily and directly reducible to the terminology that they have devised.

This hubristic attitude has allowed the bureaucracy of the moment to claim a righteous indignation at the suggestion that their offerings might be too fuzzy, too speculative to accept as scientific fact, and researchers holding such opinions have often been shouted down by academic ridicule. Human behavior, pathological or healthy, is so variable as to elude completely any attempt at a rigidly precise description.

The intent of the status quo is laudable, to be sure, for the fields of psychology and psychiatry have long lacked a litmus test to guide clinicians in discerning and classifying psychopathology, and there has been increasing pressure to structure psychiatric theory according to a concrete scientific backbone. Driven by the need for certainty, by the self-aggrandizing desire to secure their own discoveries, the dominant school of thought has fallen into the practice of automatically discounting any new theory that challenges these fundamentals.

David Comings' new book is a story of one man's encounter with this psychiatric clergy, and of just what it took to introduce change into such an entrenched bureaucracy. It is at once a detective story, a scientific essay, and a study in the folly of human nature. It is also a love story. The book lays bare to the reader all the intrigue and meticulous care that occupies the life of a professional gene hunter, as Dr. Comings recounts the history of his latest foray into uncharted territory of the human genome. He was, and is, a hard scientist who got caught by his work as a clinician. David Comings moved into the study of Tourette syndrome, this strange condition of twitching and shouting, after a long and illustrious career exploring the genetics of better-understood, more clear-cut problems. He and others had long been convinced that there was a simple, straightforward genetic basis for this disorder.

Once he dove into the clinical world, however, and began to match his genetic research with the actual lives of his patients, he discovered that the lines between many conventional diagnostic categories were too smudged and vague to be useful. He essentially re-learned a valuable lesson, that all good medical research needs to be grounded in exposure to the patient population toward which it is directed. Motivated by a natural human desire for order, explanation and control, the ruling school of thought about Tourette's had at last found a way to classify the disorder as a matter of biology, rather than of moral corruption, and, fresh from this victory, was unwilling to confront the possibility of diagnostic uncertainty. To demonstrate a biological basis for twitching and shouting was quite a feat for the establishment; to link this disorder to the darker realms of misbehavior proved unacceptable.

Comings, with his essentially outsider's perspective, was able to look at not only Tourette patients, but also their relatives, and he realized that he had stumbled across a problem of far greater complexity than anyone had yet suspected. He observed that people with Tourette syndrome had a host of other problems besides the characteristic tics, and that there were many patients (or their relatives) who were without tics yet shared not only many of the other symptoms of the disorder, but also common genetic factors. Suddenly, by his tugging on a single strand, a sizable patch of the mantle of psychiatry began to unravel. What had before seemed to be distinct disorders, he realized, were etiologically related and were perhaps merely variable expressions of a relatively distinct set of genes. This kind of approach to the biology of mental illnesses now has gene hunters all over the world paying attention to the possible roles of a number of genes in contributing to a disorder, and looking at conditions ranging from autism to ADHD to the darling of the moment, PTSD.

This journey into the clinical world highlights a wonderful truism: by embracing the world as it is, in all its apparent chaos and complexity, one may eventually discover the non-random nature of things. Comings' opponents turned away from the ambiguity that haunted their research, for it threatened to undermine not only their claim to supremacy, but their funding as well. They had a handle on the disorder, they had defined it and, in a sense, they felt that it was theirs. By further genetic research, they felt sure, they would elucidate the exact etiologic mechanism behind it. Comings, however, confronted not only the genetic complexity involved, but the pain and chaos of Tourette's patients' lives, and saw the various ways that they tried to deal with the reality of their disorder. He realized that the truth is not always as neat and tidy, as simplistically-designed, as we would hope, and that any description of the motor symptoms of Tourette's must also include the behavioral troubles. By embracing this reality as he witnessed it and pursuing the truth for its own sake, Comings has set us upon the hunt for a much richer picture of behavioral biology.

David Comings tells the story of how far we still have to go in moving beyond the all-too-prevalent linear thinking of one gene, one neurotransmitter, one disorder. He shows us how dangerous it is to fall overly in love with our diagnostic labels, for it then becomes tempting to confuse them with actual disorders as they are experienced by individuals. Each and every diagnosis must be unique, for the boundaries of pathology are only conveniences in which to steer our clinical work in the right direction, and things often turn out to be to be other than they appear. This story of mystery, frustration, perseverance, and triumph demonstrates that the truth may ultimately prevail over any bureaucratic pettiness, and we are all the richer for it.

John Ratey, M.D.
Author of *Driven to Distraction*
Answers to Distraction and
The Neuropsychiatry of Behavior Disorders

Table of Contents

Foreward by John Ratey, M.D. i

Table of Contents...1

A Note About Reading This Book 5

Chapter 1. Introduction..7

Chapter 2. Before Tourette Syndrome...9

Chapter 3. The XYY Affair 13

Chapter 4. The Early Years 17

Chapter 5. The Exhibitionist..25

Chapter 6. The Genetics of TS 29

Chapter 7. Conduct Problems in Tourette Syndrome............................33

Chapter 8. ADHD and Tourette Syndrome 39

Chapter 9. The Controlled Study..45

Chapter 10. Serotonin and Tryptophan...49

Chapter 11. The Visual Field Studies..53

Chapter 12. The Pauls Letter 57

Chapter 13. The Presidential Address 61

Chapter 14. The Arno Episode 65

Chapter 15. The Controlled Family History Studies 69

Chapter 16. Is the *TDO2* Gene the "*Alcoholism* Gene"?....................73

Chapter 17. The Book...77

Chapter 18. The Hypothetical *Gts* Mutation 83

Chapter 19. The American Psychiatric Association TS Symposium 85

Chapter 20. The Dopamine Receptors and the "*Alcoholism* Gene" 89

Chapter 21. The Other *Tryptophan* Gene 97

Chapter 22. The Rebuttals of the Non-Believers...................................99

Chapter 23. The Regulatory Region at Last 103

Chapter 24. The GREs 105

Chapter 25. The Trip to South Africa 109

Chapter 26. The Summer of '91 117

Chapter 27. The Frustration Continues 125

Chapter 28. The Dopamine Receptor Studies Revisited 131

Chapter 29. Post-Traumatic Stress Disorder 137

Chapter 30. Drug Addiction 139

Chapter 31. A Gene for Obesity 141

Chapter 32. A Gene for Height 143

Chapter 33. The *Dopamine D3 Receptor* Gene 145

Chapter 34. Polygenic Inheritance 149

Chapter 35. SIDS 153

Chapter 36. The Genetic Loading Technique 157

Chapter 37. Yale "Confirms" Our Findings 163

Chapter 38. Irritable Bowel Syndrome – A Genetic Disorder? 169

Chapter 39. The *Gts* Genes and Drug and Alcohol Abuse 173

Chapter 40. The Genetics of Sexual Behavior 177

Chapter 41. The Genetics of Conduct Disorder 183

Chapter 42. The Genetics of Depression 187

Chapter 43. Tourette Syndrome as a Spectrum Disorder 189

Chapter 44. Selection for the *Gts* Genes 193

Chapter 45. *Dopamine Receptor* Genes and Smoking 201

Chapter 46. Pathological Gambling 205

Chapter 47. Monoamine Oxidase 207

Chapter 48. Cancer Genes and Human Behavior 209

Chapter 49. A Marker of the *TDO2* Gene 211

Chapter 50. Searching for the "Real" *TDO2* Mutation 215

Chapter 51. The *TDO2* Mutations in Patients 223

Chapter 52. The Yale Group Claims Depression and
Anxiety Are Not Related to *Gts* Genes 227

Chapter 53. The *Dopamine Receptor* Gene in
Tourette Syndrome – Again 231

Chapter 54. Dopamine β-Hydroxylase 237

Chapter 55. The *Dopamine Transporter* Gene 241

Chapter 56. The Polygenic Inheritance of Behavior 245

Chapter 57. Epilogue 251

References 259

Appendix: Update on New Medications 273

Abbreviations, Definitions, Glossary 283

Index 293

A Note About Reading This Book

It has been my experience that anyone can understand science as long as the jargon is left out and the terms and concepts are adequately explained; thus I have included a section called *Abbreviations, Definitions, Glossary* in the back of the book. It will help the reader not trained in genetics to liberally refer to it while reading the book. Many of the concepts have been extensively explained in my earlier book *Tourette Syndrome and Human Behavior*; thus in a sentence such as "TS is usually thought to be inherited as an autosomal dominant [p41] trait," the [p41] means the subject of autosomal dominant inheritance is explained on page 41 of the earlier book, which can be obtained by using the the insert order card. A reference to an article listed in the bibliography at the end of the the present book will simply have a superscript [33] without a p. A reference such as "(see page 100)" refers to another part of the present book.

As in the *Tourette Syndrome and Human Behavior* book, I have made every attempt to make all aspects understandable to the non-scientist. Where certain terms are critical for understanding the story, I have included a description of the concepts and terms involved, often with liberal use of diagrams. Despite this, if a section seems a little difficult, just skip that part until you get to easier reading.

I have often been asked if I was planning to write a second edition of the *Tourette Syndrome and Human Behavior* book. My usual reply was that the only thing I would change would be to add new information about the genetic studies, and discuss a few of the newer medications that have come on the market since the first edition. This book provides the new information about the genetics of TS, and I have also added an appendix entitled *Update on New Medications*; thus for those of you who asked, this book can be considered to have brought the *Tourette Syndrome and Human Behavior* book completely up to date.

Chapter 1

Introduction

*In mainstream psychology, it is not yet quite proper to hypothesize
that genetics may contribute something to behavior. It does not seem to be
illegal to do so, merely indecent.*

J.R.Wilson, 1988[218]

I am a human geneticist. This means that as a physician-scientist, my primary interest is in hereditary diseases that affect humans. I wrote this book simply because I thought it was an interesting story. The science involved potentially touches the lives of every reader and is relevant to all human behavior. Ironically, the story speaks as much about the behavior of scientists as the science of behavior. Sometimes reality gives us better stories than fiction.

This book essentially begins near the time I first became involved in studying Tourette syndrome (TS) in 1980. At that time TS was considered to be a very rare hereditary disorder consisting only of tics and compulsive swearing. As my wife and I began to study the disorder, we came to realize that TS was actually quite common, often misdiagnosed, and associated with a very broad range of other behavioral disorders. We quickly sensed that since TS was hereditary it could be the Rosetta stone for deciphering the mysteries of the role of genes in human behavior. Our studies of families eventually convinced us that most patients with TS received one or more genes from both parents. We felt the genes were common and played an important role in a very broad range of behavioral and physical disorders. This book ends after we had identified a number of the genes responsible for TS and other human behavioral disorders.

Many books about medical discoveries have been called *The Race for...*this or that discovery. By contrast, for a long time I considered calling this book *The Non-Race for the Tourette Syndrome Genes*. I thought this would be an appropriate title because virtually the entire genetic and medical establishment thought our idea — that the Gilles de la Tourette Syndrome or *Gts* genes could also be causing a wide range of other behavioral and physical problems — was totally crazy. As a result, in contrast to Huntington's disease, cystic fibrosis, neurofibromatosis, schizophrenia, and other genetic diseases, there was relatively little interest in this disorder or in the genes that caused it.

The idea that a common set of genes played an important role in a wide range of psychiatric disorders was considered so bizarre, that from 1984 to 1992, despite submitting over twenty-two different grant requests, I was unable to raise any funds from the National Institutes of Health, National Institute of Mental Health, National Institute of Alcoholism and Alcohol Abuse, National Institute of Drug Abuse, or the Tourette Syndrome Association for this research. While the Tourette Syndrome Association funded many other groups in an extensive effort to find the *Gts* gene, this was based entirely on the assumption that TS patients received a single gene from only a single parent. It seemed so clear to me that this approach would fail that I felt, in essence, there was no race. However, since I had written about our experience with TS in the book *Tourette Syndrome and Human Behavior*,[33] and since the genes we and others uncovered were important in a wide range of disorders, I eventually came to feel the title *Search for the Tourette Syndrome and Human Behavior Genes* was more appropriate.

While the path to finding some of the *Gts* genes was littered with obstacles, and even though I met outright hostility from many directions, I have written this, not as any form of "I told you so," but only because I thought it might be of interest to many people, both scientists and laymen. I have attempted to simply tell the story as it happened, with no malice toward any of those legions of people who thought I was off my rocker. (I suspect that even after reading this book, some may still feel that way.) This absence of malice comes from the fact that despite the problems, the fourteen years that it took to find some of the genes have been the most rewarding years of my career and I would not take back or change a single minute. I suspect if it had been easy, it would not have been half as exciting.

Chapter 2

Before Tourette Syndrome

I can't ever remember not being interested in science. In grade school I read everything I could lay my hands on that had anything to do with evolution, geology, anthropology, or biology. I collected rocks, minerals, fossils, butterflies, beetles, snakes, and salamanders. I stuffed every dead animal I could find. My room looked like a museum.

I attended the ultimate egghead high school, University High in Urbana, Illinois. We called it Uni High. This was a school run by the Department of Education of the University of Illinois and was filled with professors' children, of which I was one. In this arena, bird watching was a group sport, and my friends and I often spent many weekends traipsing through forests and farmlands pushing up our species count.

My father was a professor of chemical engineering and because of this, I had a chemistry set that was the envy of all my peers. If I wanted an esoteric chemical he would have it on my desk the next day. Usually, however, my interests were less in esoteric chemicals and more in things that burned in a flash and made a loud bang, like powdered charcoal and magnesium.

Mrs. Lindsey, my high school biology teacher, helped me to fine-tune my interest in biology. She was everything that a superb teacher was supposed to be. She was even able to get some of her students included in the biology field trips for the university students, and we were constantly hiking off to every major swamp or fossil field within six hundred miles.

I have always been an insatiable reader, and in high school one of the books included a college text on abnormal psychology. I found the theories of Freud and others to be an intriguing, almost unbelievable, look into the mysteries of behavior. All the neurotic disorders were considered to be due to some early childhood conflict. It seemed that all a therapist had to do was to cleverly expose to the patient what these conflicts were and, like magic, the symptoms would go away. It seemed so easy, like a detective story. Find the hidden conflict and bingo, the patient was cured. The book said the psychoses, like schizophrenia and manic-depressive disorder, might have some organic and even genetic causes, but the neuroses were definitely all caused by environmental factors.

By the time I was twelve, I knew I wanted to become a doctor. That seemed to be the best way to combine a fascination with both biology and psychology.

Other than the fact that my brother, Gordon, was also there, one of the reasons I attended Uni High was that they had a "sub-freshman" program. If you passed their test they let you take seventh and eighth grades together in one year and then enter the regular four-year high school. I also skipped my senior year because my father had moved to Purdue, and I didn't want to start my senior year in a strange high school. It was actually my mother's idea. By the time most people finish high school, they have far more credits than they need to graduate. My mother found out that if I took one summer school course, I could enter as a freshman at the University of Illinois at sixteen; so my parents moved away and I stayed in the town I grew up in to go to college. In those days it was fairly common to enter medical school after only three years of college, and this allowed me to begin Northwestern University Medical School at nineteen and graduate at twenty-three.

After an internship and two years of internal medicine residency at Cook County Hospital in Chicago, I took a fellowship in hematology at the same institution. This was during the time that the genetic code was just being broken and Vernon Ingram had just shown that sickle cell disease was due to a genetic mutation that changed a single amino acid in the hemoglobin molecule. In the hematology clinic I was able to see the direct effect that this simple mutation had on the patients. Their blood cells were distorted into sickle-shaped rods. They were anemic and often came to the emergency room racked in the pain of a sickle cell crisis. Other mutations, affecting still different parts of the hemoglobin molecule and producing different symptoms, were being reported monthly. I was witnessing firsthand the birth of the exciting new field of molecular genetics and the early beginnings of the explosive growth of human genetics.

Seattle

After the hematology fellowship, I was obligated to spend time in the Army and was assigned to an outpatient clinic at Madigan Army Hospital in Tacoma, Washington. One of the consultants to the hospital was Dr. Arno Motulsky, head of the newly-formed Division of Medical Genetics at the University of Washington in Seattle. Medical genetics was a newly emerging medical specialty, and at that time this was one of the best places in the country to train; thus after my Army service I spent two years in a human genetics fellowship with Motulsky.

This was also a time of great excitement in the field of cytogenetics — the study of abnormal chromosomes in human disease. Only a few years had passed since new techniques made it possible to spread and count all the different human chromosomes. Many new diseases caused by abnormal numbers of chromosomes, such as Down's and Turner's syndromes, had just been described. Some chromosomes were impossible to distinguish from each other until the techniques of chromosome banding were developed. These procedures produced a unique set of bands on chromosomes and for the first time allowed each chromosome to be clearly identified. I was particularly interested in investigating why these techniques worked and what the bands meant in terms of how chromosomes were put together.

City of Hope

After leaving Seattle in 1966, I became the director of the newly-formed

Department of Medical Genetics at the City of Hope National Medical Center in Duarte, California, and have been there ever since. I learned a valuable lesson very early in my time at the City of Hope.

Tay-Sachs disease is a classic recessive disorder. The affected child receives a gene from both parents, develops a fatal degenerative disorder of the brain, and dies in the first few years of life. This devastating disorder was especially common in Ashkenazi Jews. Dr. John O'Brien had just discovered that a defect in the enzyme called "hex A" was the cause of Tay-Sachs, and he developed a simple test to detect who was carrying the gene. This test, which allowed extensive screening programs in various Jewish communities, virtually eliminated the disease.

When I got to the City of Hope Medical Center, I learned some of the background about this discovery. A researcher there had spent many years trying to discover the cause of Tay-Sachs disease by carefully analyzing changes that occurred in the fat compounds of brains of infants afflicted with the disease. In scientific circles these are called studies of epiphenomenology. For example, genes code for enzymes and the enzymes cause a series of different chemical changes. Mutant genes cause defective enzymes that cause abnormal chemical changes – the chemical changes are the epiphenomena; thus:

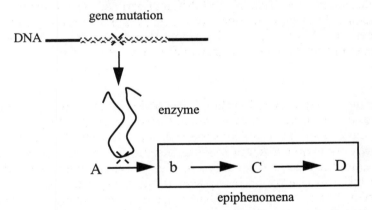

This diagram shows that the real defect is in the gene, not in the resulting chemical changes b, C, and D. O'Brien spent just a short time at the City of Hope. However, by thinking in terms of what gene and what enzyme were involved, he found the answer, while a senior scientist who had devoted years to studying the epiphenomenology had come up empty-handed. The lesson was clear. Think genetically. Think genes. Think abnormal enzymes. Just use epiphenomena to identify what genes to think about. Fifteen years later, after I became involved in TS, this lesson was still relevant.

Although I ran a genetics clinic and saw a variety of patients one afternoon a week, my primary interest was in basic research on chromosomes and deoxyribonucleic acid (DNA). We used a wide variety of sophisticated techniques in these studies. This early work was supported by several National Institutes of Health (NIH) grants. Between 1964 and 1980, my colleagues and I published over 210 papers on different aspects of chromosome structure and an assortment of other subjects. I was a member of the Genetics Study Section of the NIH for reviewing grants, and in 1978 became editor of the *American Journal of Human Genetics.*

Throughout this period my career was going the way I felt it was supposed to go. Theories were formulated and experimentally tested, papers were written and published, results were given at meetings, and grants were easily obtained to continue the work. Although the usual scientific controversies arose, they were quickly resolved by experimentation. It was then on to the next idea and everyone remained friends. Science was exciting. I was doing exactly what I had always wanted to do. However, by the mid- to late 1970's, many of the major questions about chromosome structure and what caused the chromosome bands had been largely solved. Some of the remaining questions, such as how the chromosomes were folded, began to seem like unimportant trivia.

My interests began to change to the role of abnormal genes and their effect on human behavior. I had just begun to see a few TS patients and had a few faint glimmerings of the importance of this disorder in the genetics of behavior. I was, however, sobered by the experience of a research colleague and friend. He had attempted some studies on the genetics of human behavior in relation to a chromosome abnormality called the XYY syndrome. This resulted in a chilling ordeal which I call the XYY affair.

Chapter 3

The XYY Affair

Women have two X chromosomes (XX), while men have one X chromosome and one Y chromosome (XY). This difference is what determines the sex of a child. In the early 1960's the examination of human chromosomes was a new science. Some patients were found to have abnormal numbers of sex chromosomes, such as XXY and XYY males and XO females. Many studies were done in institutions for the mentally retarded. This was based on the assumption that if chromosome abnormalities caused mental retardation or behavior problems, individuals with such defects were more likely to be found in these institutions. In 1965, Dr. Pat Jacobs and co-workers published a paper in *Nature* entitled, "Aggressive Behavior, Mental Sub-normality and XYY Male."[118] They reported that 3.5% of patients in a Scottish State Hospital for "mentally sub-normal male patients with dangerous, violent or criminal propensities" possessed an extra Y chromosome. This seemed to indicate that XYY males were "super males" and had more of the male characteristics of being tall and aggressive than XY males. The extra Y rapidly became known in the lay press as the "criminal chromosome."

Soon criminal lawyers were having chromosome studies done on their clients with the hope they would be XYY and this would free them on a plea analogous to "not responsible by reason of insanity." Richard Speck, the infamous mass murderer of nurses in Illinois, was tall, criminally aggressive, and widely reported by the press as being a case of XYY. This was incorrect.

The major problem of going to prisons or mental institutions for such studies was ascertainment bias. That is, since everyone in the prison had a criminal record, all XYY cases in such a study would be criminals. The real question was, what about XYY cases in the general population? Were they also aggressive and criminally inclined? Although further studies identified many XYY cases whose behavior was normal, this still left open the question of whether *some* XYY individuals were excessively aggressive.

If a connection between criminal behavior and XYY was to be made on the assumption that this variant was more common in prisoners, it was critical to determine how common XYY was in the general population. Examining placental blood from all consecutive newborn children at a specific hospital provided the most unbiased sample and was the easiest way to get blood. Several such studies indicated a frequency of XYY of between 1 in 2,000 and 1 in 4,000 newborns.

It was clear that to avoid the ascertainment bias problem, cases should be identified by a random screening of the general population. Many studies had indicated adults with aggressive behavior had often been aggressive when they were children, indicating that a tendency to aggressive behavior was a lifelong characteristic.

In the early 1970's, two physicians at Harvard Medical School, Dr. Stanley Walzer, a psychiatrist, and Dr. Park Gerald, a medical geneticist, initiated a study to determine if there was a relationship between the XYY chromosome and aggressive behavior in children and adults. To avoid ascertainment bias they found cases by screening all newborn children in the Boston Women's Hospital. Infants identified as having XYY or another chromosome abnormality, XXY, were to be examined at periodic intervals to determine if their behavior in childhood was considered normal or if it was associated with many of the symptoms of childhood conduct disorder.[p131] The study was funded by the National Institutes of Mental Health (NIMH) and approved by the internal review boards (IRB) of the hospital and medical school.

As the study progressed, two non-physician, basic scientists at Harvard who were members of an organization called Science for the People voiced concerns that the very fact that the children had been identified as having a chromosome abnormality and were being studied would cause their behavior to become abnormal; thus the study would become a self-fulfilling prophecy. They requested that the approval for the study be withdrawn. After a thorough re-review and some changes in the informed consent form, the study was approved by the full Harvard faculty (133 for and 35 against).

The general feeling among physicians who actually had experience taking care of children was that occasional follow-up visits did not have the power to cause children to develop a consistent pattern of aggressive behavior. In addition, the group of XXY children, who would not be expected to have such behavior, served as a control for this remote possibility.

By contrast, the Science for the People group was absolutely convinced this was an inherently evil study and was determined to stop it at any cost. They also believed that there was *no evidence in any study, ever, that genetic factors played a role in human behavior*. They were concerned that if any such evidence did appear to surface, then the social causes of violent or aberrant behavior, such as poverty and prejudice, would be ignored and never corrected. They were also concerned about a rebirth of the abuses of eugenics and Nazism.

When the review boards gave permission for the studies to continue, the protagonists were not satisfied and took their case to the public. One of the protagonists stated "...it was clear from the beginning that our initial idea was for publicity." A newspaper article in a leading Boston newspaper included the statement that the study was rejected by the full Harvard faculty by a vote of 133 against to 35 for (the opposite of the truth) but that these "scientists" were persisting in the study anyway. This resulted in a firestorm of criticism against the two principal investigators, including death threats.

In 1980, a Hastings Center conference was convened to study this whole affair.[222] In the proceedings Walzer recalled:

"It started as an internal affair in which one professor object-ed to the work of an assistant professor. There is a system of governance to manage this. In my instance, however, one party refused to honor this system of governance, went out on his own, disseminating documents, giving articles to mothers as they came into the hospital. Hastily-written articles appeared in jour-nals. The one-sided nature of this public debate destroyed the arena for the discussion and the opportunity for cool manage-ment.

"Throughout this entire two-year period there was never an opportunity for productive discussion. The major issues were never really presented or discussed. It was a bombardment, a cyclone in which every major and significant part of my life was torn apart."

At the Hastings Conference Dr. Michels, a psychiatrist from Cornell, stated:

"Why was this project picked on? My guess is that it had nothing to do with the project whatsoever. It had to do instead with a general concern about anything that could be used to jus-tify a biologically deterministic view about socially undesirable behavior.

".. the real cost of all this is that *I will tell every young psy-chiatrist or physician or medical student wanting to do research on anything of social relevance to recognize that it is immensely expensive in terms of time and personal career, because there are a lot of people in the world who are going to bother you if you do it*. It really would make sense, unless you have a terribly strong desire to do this project, to review whether there is some-thing you can't do in bean metabolism or some kind of pigeon behavior because it is safer to work that way in our present soci-ety. And that is expensive for all of us."

Since I was a cytogeneticist myself and since Gerald was a friend, I had fol-lowed these events with considerable interest. However, at that time I was doing research in a "safe" area — the basic mechanisms of chromosome banding. I sim-ply filed away in my memory the impression of how dangerous it could be to do research on the genetics of human behavior. The publication of the Hastings report in 1980 provided an opportunity to re-review the whole episode from both points of view. I noted that even at this late date, years after the events, there was still so much ill will between the two sides that they refused to attend the confer-ence together. As a result, two different conferences had to be held, with only a core of neutral staff present at both.

By this time I had already seen many patients with Tourette syndrome, and I fully realized that I was now beginning to embark on a course of study that might result in problems somewhat similar to those that my colleagues had endured. Unfortunately, my fears proved to be correct.

Chapter 4

The Early Years

I missed the diagnosis of TS in the first patient with this disorder that I ever saw. Because of this early fiasco, it is easy for me to understand, years later, the hundreds of times that my TS patients were incorrectly diagnosed, or the times when other physicians claimed the patients did not have TS after I had found that they fulfilled the standard criteria for making such a diagnosis.

This first patient, Sam, was a teacher who had been fired from his job because of multiple tics and inappropriate swearing. After trying for years to get another job in teaching, he gave up and turned to painting. When I saw him in the genetics clinic in 1979, the history of the tics and swearing since childhood led me to suspect the possibility of Tourette syndrome, but he showed no tics in the clinic and did not swear in my presence. The most striking feature about his behavior was that I couldn't get him to stop talking. He seemed anxious, depressed, and unable to break off the conversation. I finally had to mumble nice things about continuing the discussion next time as I slowly inched my way backwards out of the room, with words still pouring from his mouth. Because I didn't see him tic, and because I didn't hear him swear, I was reluctant to label him as having TS.

After a few visits and still without a definitive diagnosis, Sam stopped coming to the clinic. Years later, after I had seen many hundreds of TS patients, he returned. By this time I had come to realize that the majority of TS patients do not have tics in the doctor's office because they are unconsciously suppressing them, that the diagnosis often has to be based on the history alone, that less than a third of TS patients have compulsive swearing (coprolalia), that anxiety, panic attacks, and depression were common in TS, and that some talk a blue streak and have difficulty ending a conversation. In other words, instead of being a questionable case of TS, Sam was a classic case. When he returned he had a plethora of facial tics and grimaces.

Huntington's Disease

Since I had not diagnosed Sam as having TS, he was not the reason I became so involved with this disorder. The reason I became involved was due to my interest in another hereditary movement disorder – Huntington's Disease (HD). This is a relatively rare neurological disorder affecting about 1 in 10,000 adults. It is inherited as an autosomal dominant trait;[p41] that is, it requires only one *HD* gene to develop the disease, the gene is passed from generation to generation,

17

and there is a 50% risk that each child of a HD patient will inherit the gene themselves. Individuals who carry a *HD* gene usually begin to have jerky or snakelike movements of their head, body or extremities between thirty to fifty years of age. Like Alzheimer's disease, this is usually associated with a slowly progressing dementia, with loss of memory and eventually total incapacitation. It is an extraordinary distressing disorder because one gradually loses two of one's most precious functions – moving and thinking. The disease results in death in fifteen to twenty-five years.

Since I was trained as an internist first, then as a geneticist, when I opened the genetics clinic at the City of Hope, I had a predilection for seeing adults rather than children. Since HD was one of the more common adult genetic disorders, I began to see many HD patients and developed a research interest in the disease. I was an early member of the scientific advisory board of the Hereditary Disease Foundation founded by Dr. Milton Wexler. Wexler set up this organization after his wife developed HD. His daughter, Dr. Nancy Wexler, who was at risk for HD, helped her father steer the organization into major contributions toward finding that the *HD* gene was localized on the tip of chromosome 4.[106]

In 1977, Dr. Roswell Eldridge and co-workers published a paper describing the family histories of twenty-one patients with TS.[91] I was fascinated by the presence of not only tics, but many other disinhibited behaviors such as compulsive touching and sexual exhibitionism. Like HD, TS was a movement disorder and the movements were controlled by a drug called haloperidol.[p547] It was hereditary, and the inheritance appeared to be autosomal dominant. It seemed that if I could study a few cases of this very rare disorder I might learn something that would be useful in understanding and treating the more common, devastating Huntington's disease.

Los Angeles TSA

The local Tourette Syndrome Association (TSA) at that time was in somewhat of a disarray. Muriel Seligman, the past president, had spent a great deal of time producing *The Silent Intruder*, the first video film to explain the basic aspects of TS to new patients, parents, and other interested people. It was a high-quality production, narrated by Jack Lemon, and very well-done. This level of quality was possible because Seligman had many connections with the movie industry in Los Angeles. Although she was on the board of the National TSA, the reports that I, a newcomer to the world of TS, heard were that she was "burned out" on the day-to-day running of the chapter and, at that time, there was no official president. Nonetheless, there were occasional meetings.

The question of whether TS was a hereditary disorder was obviously of considerable interest to parents of TS children. From the pedigrees that Eldridge had published, it was apparent to me that TS was probably inherited as an autosomal dominant trait with reduced penetrance;[p42] that is, it required only a single *Gts* gene to develop TS, but some people could have the gene with no symptoms. Despite this, one group had just published a paper suggesting that TS was not even a hereditary disorder. I discussed this situation with Dr. Ken Kidd at Yale and decided to write a one-page note for the TSA newsletter pointing out that the evidence was very strong that TS was an inherited disorder and incomplete penetrance of a dominant gene was the most likely mechanism.

This question of inheritance was of considerable interest to Jerry, one of my earliest TS patients. He had a severe case of TS, with loud vocal noises, head jerking and swearing, but he had been told by his neurologist that TS was not a hereditary disorder and he could have children without worrying that they would get TS. When his son subsequently developed severe symptoms of TS, he was extraordinarily angry about the advice he had been given. Every time he would call about a new flurry of tics and confrontive behavior his son was displaying, it was inevitable that he would end the conversation with a few expletives about "that stupid advice." He and I would set up meetings of the Los Angeles Chapter of the Tourette Syndrome Association (LA/TSA), and one of the subjects we consistently put on the agenda was "The Genetics of Tourette Syndrome." This helped me to make contact with additional patients, and within a year I had seen about twenty TS families.

Support Groups

Another one of my early patients was Shela, the adopted daughter of Betty and Tom. In addition to her tics, she was having many behavioral problems, including refusing to obey parental rules, never bathing, carrying a knife to school in her hair, and repeatedly running away from home. Because of these and other behaviors which were similar to those present in many other TS children, Betty was a driving force behind trying to set up group therapy sessions for our TS families. Even though I had seen only about twenty TS patients, the trend of finding hyperactivity, conduct disorder, discipline problems, aggressive and obsessive-compulsive behaviors had become apparent. The parents repeatedly complained, "It is not the tics that drive us crazy, it is the behavior!"

Here I was, an internist, basic scientist, and geneticist, with no formal training in psychiatry being asked — or better, pleaded with — to set up and run group therapy sessions for families with some of the most difficult behavioral problems imaginable. I felt far more comfortable with test tubes, computers, scintillation counters, and pedigree-taking than I did with feelings, emotions, and behavioral problems. To me, the thought of running such a group engendered more a feeling of panic than of a new challenge. It was clear I needed professional help. The problem was there was no Department of Psychiatry or Psychology at the City of Hope. All we had in the realm of the behavioral sciences were social workers, and at that time they were more oriented toward intake and discharge planning than psychotherapy. My service had a social worker assigned to it, a man I will call Carl, and I thought at least I would start there.

I discussed with Carl what I needed, and suggested that in order for him to at least become familiar with the patients and their problems, he should attend the next meeting I was setting up. At this meeting we had a guest speaker, Dr. Abbuzahab, one of the early pioneers in the study of TS. After he spoke, Carl came up to me and asked if he could talk to the group. Although I had no idea what he was going to say, it seemed like a reasonable request. He then began to tell the group that he thought people could "will" cancer cells in their body to die, and he was certain TS patients could "will" themselves to stop the tics. I was dumbfounded, and stood there like the master of ceremonies of the Gong Show, wishing I had a hook to quickly whisk him off the stage. Many TS patients had told me that because they could voluntarily suppress their symptoms for varying periods of time, parents and teachers often had the mistaken idea that they had total voluntary control and could stop them permanently if they just tried hard enough. In truth, such voluntary suppression only led to increased internal tension, which eventually had to be expressed in the form of tics that were more intense than if there was no attempt at suppression. Here, suddenly, was a member of my "staff" telling them the same thing they resented hearing from teachers and parents. I glanced at Abbuzahab in embarrassment and diplomatically eased Carl off the stage. Fortunately, other aspects of his work were equally unsatisfactory and within a month he was mercifully gone from the scene.

Brenda

Within a month a new social worker had been hired to replace Carl. My secretary informed me one day that an appointment had been set up by the Social Services Department for me to meet her. Prior to my involvement with Carl, I had never even been aware of the social workers attached to my service. In typical doctor arrogance, I viewed them mostly as one more unnecessary delay in the bureaucratic process of signing in new patients. Since no one other than Carl knew of my need for help with the support group, it was a mystery to me why I was now being asked, for the first time in my fifteen years at the City of Hope, to interview this new person. Oftentimes social workers assigned to my service would come, spend several years there, and leave without my even knowing their name. I grumped to my secretary, "I suppose I'll see her, if I have to!"

When the interview came, in walked one of the most striking young women I had ever seen. She was wearing a fashionable brown wool suit with suede patches on the elbows and a chocolate brown cashmere sweater, all only partially covered by a freshly-ironed white coat. Every piece of clothing and jewelry were exquisitely matched. This was all the more striking for a man who occasionally found his way to work wearing one brown shoe, one black shoe, and blue socks.

Her name was Brenda. She related her past psychiatric experience as a probation officer, a family therapist in a Juvenile Hall, a stint at a State Children's Treatment center, her experience at a community mental health center working with mentally disordered sex and criminal offenders, social worker liaison between a university Department of Child Psychiatry and the Department of Pediatrics, and her experience in a busy emergency room.

I couldn't believe my luck. This was precisely the type of person I needed. As I began to tell her about TS and some of the behavioral problems I was encountering, her responses clearly indicated that there was a considerable amount of gray matter between her ears. She not only wanted to help with the support groups, she wanted to be actively involved in the evaluation and treatment of the patients. Within a few short weeks, we were interviewing all new TS patients as a team. Brenda had that intuitiveness for feelings and emotions that only comes from a combination of a natural gift of a third ear and years of experience with all types of emotional disorders. Having a social worker actually involved in the initial interviewing and care of patients was a considerable departure from the past of my not even knowing their name.

After we had seen an additional thirty TS patients, the behavioral problems they came in with were now even more apparent. Brenda also began to see the patients in individual psychotherapy to attempt to make some dent in these problems. Other than the tics, the most obvious problems centered around attention deficit hyperactivity disorder, learning disabilities, conduct disorders, and obsessive-compulsive behaviors. Because of the effect on school performance, we decided it was important to increase the awareness of teachers and parents about this disorder – especially since TS was treatable.

Brenda thought it would be useful to appear on a local TV show to talk about TS. I am sure that if I had tried, I would have gotten nowhere. She, however, was very good with verbal skills. Within a week she had arranged for a spot on a local TV show. It was in the morning and we only had about five minutes; however, this brief appearance resulted in a burst of phone calls – ninety-five in the next few days. Unlike "medical student's disease," where individuals only imagine they have what is being discussed, ninety-one of these turned out to be true TS. Many parents told us they only had to hear a few seconds of talk about "tics" and "vocal noises," and they knew that at last they had found the disorder that accounted for their child's symptoms. For the first time we began to realize that TS was not a rare disorder.

With Brenda's psychological expertise, we began having support groups about every two to three months. These were to continue to the present. We began to give presentations to any school district in southern California that wanted to hear about TS. Brenda also set up a "hot line" for parents in crisis to call for help. Selected mothers from several different areas were trained to answer these calls. We also started publishing a newsletter, called *Tic Talk*, to keep our parents informed about the latest TS findings, research, and methods of treatment.

Prior to the time that I became involved in TS, I had a single afternoon genetics clinic and spent the rest of my time in the laboratory; however, with all the TS-related activities, the time spent in the clinic was rapidly expanding. This initially made me uncomfortable, and I complained to Brenda that she was "dragging me kicking and screaming out of my lab into the clinic." This was a transition period when I was still heavily involved in other research activity and had little clue about whether studies of TS would lead to anything of significance. In a very brief period the time I was spending in the clinic increased to all day on Wednesday and Tuesday, Thursday, and Friday afternoons. We were soon seeing ten to fifteen new TS patients per week.

As my fascination with TS increased, and as I became aware of the rich lode of insights it held for understanding the genetics of human behavior, my anxiety about being pulled out of the lab began to subside. TS was becoming a full-time research and clinical interest. The work I had been doing on the structure of chromosomes began to seem boring and unimportant by comparison, and I felt less and less concerned about seeing it go.

On March 20, 1982, Brenda and I became a husband-and-wife team.

The First International TS Symposium

Soon after we became interested in TS, the TSA sponsored the first International Symposium on TS in May of 1981. We were so new to the field that we had relatively little to contribute – one paper showing that TS patients had no unique set of tissue antigens (HLA antigens)[70] and a paper done in cooperation with Dr. Israel Hanin suggesting there were higher levels of blood choline in some TS patients compared to controls.[69] We had, by this time, seen over 120 TS patients and it was clear to us that they had an unusually high frequency of compulsive behaviors, discipline problems, attention deficit hyperactivity disorder, and inappropriate sexual behaviors. We submitted a third abstract describing these findings. Of the three abstracts submitted, this was the only one that was not accepted for inclusion in the symposium proceedings. I did not think anything of it at the time, but in view of things that happened later, its fate may have been an early indication of the bias TSA had against recognizing any "psychiatric" problems in TS patients.

To Form or Not to Form a TSA Chapter

One of the subjects that consistently came up at our support group meetings was whether to take over and reorganize the quiescent LA/TSA chapter. Opinion was divided. Most thought we should, but only under certain conditions. My early patient, Jerry, felt that since there was a considerable research effort underway at the City of Hope, it was silly to raise money and send most of it off to the East Coast, three thousand miles away. He wanted a cure right here and right now.

Brenda felt that the goals of the two organizations were too different. TSA was primarily a lay organization. Its purpose was to raise money for TS research, increase public awareness about the disorder, provide referral lists of physicians in different states who were interested in caring for TS patients, and make available pamphlets summarizing various aspects of TS. By contrast, we were actually involved in patient care and research. Although some of the goals, such as public education, were similar, it seemed we couldn't do everything and should leave the fund raising to others; thus at one meeting, we concluded that if our patients and others wanted to revitalize the local TSA chapter, they should do it on their own. In hindsight, that was to prove to be a disastrous decision.

Soon afterward, a separate LA/TSA chapter was formed and a new president was elected. Unfortunately, when two groups have some overlapping functions, they often tend to compete more than to cooperate, and problems of "turf" can rapidly surface. For example, Brenda and I had worked hard on a series of two TV presentations about TS to be shown on consecutive nights on a major local channel. Brenda had contacted the station, gotten them interested in the subject, and all the preparation, filming and writing had been done at the City of Hope. The show was to end with a number people could call to reach our hot line or clinic, if they needed help.

At the end of the first show, there was, instead an announcement that all calls should be directed to the LA/TSA chapter, and their number was given. We called the station to find out what happened and were told that the president of the LA TSA had called and said that only he was authorized to receive calls. We called this new president and were told that he was going to receive all calls and was going to decide who would go to which doctor on the basis of zip codes. It was apparent that this new president wanted to be in total control of TS in Los Angeles, and he was going to tell doctors who they could or could not see. Our experience had already told us that people will spend hours traveling hundreds of miles if they perceive a certain clinic can provide the best care for them or their child. Good medical care was not a matter of zip codes. From then on, LA/TSA went their way and we went ours.

Unfortunately, it was not that simple.

Chapter 5

The Exhibitionist

From my very first involvement with TS, it was clear that one of the aspects of the disorder that was so fascinating was the glimpse it offered into the dark underbelly of human behavior. Some patients talked of their aggressive, violent, and sexual thoughts, their mind racing from one idea to the next, their inability to control their impulsive behaviors, their mood swings from elation to dark despair, their rages, and, of course, their inability to control their muscle-jerking. The parents were telling us over and over that unlike other children, their TS child was *often* angry, oppositional, and difficult to discipline. He talked back, often lied even when he did not need to, stole things, started fires, and was possessed by other seemingly driven behaviors.

Not all TS children had these problems. Some were absolute angels. However, the majority of those coming to the clinic had one or more of these problems. This was a genetic disorder and, to a geneticist, these behaviors seemed "driven" by some biochemical defect; I was constantly thinking in terms of what inherited disturbances in brain chemistry were fueling such difficult behaviors.

It was clear that if we could grow to understand this disease at a fundamental genetic level, we could understand many of the darker and disruptive forces of the human condition. Again, since I was a geneticist, I had never been heavily indoctrinated into the twentieth century psychiatric dogma that most behaviors were learned, and that the way you behaved was largely determined by your environment or how your parents raised you.

Time and time again parents would come in battered by the mental health system that blamed them for their child's atrocious and obnoxious behaviors. They were told that if your child was not behaving properly it was because you didn't discipline them enough, or you disciplined them too much, depending upon the bias of the present therapist. While it was certain that for some children this may have been true, for many of those with the most recalcitrant behavior problems, it was becoming obvious that this approach was flawed.

With the possible exception of recently trained psychiatrists, virtually none of the mental health professionals (social workers, marriage and family counselors, psychologists, and others) were being given more than lip service to the idea that genetic factors can play a critical role in these everyday behaviors. When Brenda took her course work for her masters in social work and her Ph.D. in psychology, there was only one course devoted to biological factors in human behavior, and even then almost all the facts presented were wrong and the role of genetic factors was often ridiculed.

These impressions continued to build as we saw more and more TS patients. Although I was not shy about publishing papers, it was not clear what aspect of our observations and thoughts we should report first. This problem was solved the day that J.J. walked into the clinic.

He was thirty-two years old at the time and was referred by a prison psychiatrist who noted the muscle tics. He was in prison for sexually molesting his son and for public exhibitionism. J.J. started having motor and vocal tics at age seven, and by age fifteen he had developed strong exhibitionist urges. He would attempt to satisfy them by going to the men's room in the park, waiting until he heard children approaching, then walking out pretending that his failure to "zip up" was merely a mistaken oversight.

One of the most fascinating aspects of this case was his description of how this urge totally overwhelmed him. It came on about once a week. J.J. said that once his brain began thinking about exhibiting himself there was absolutely nothing he could do to prevent it. Going to movies, jogging, watching sports — nothing even began to put a dent in the compulsion. It seemed undeniable to me that this incredibly driven behavior must be chemical rather than psychological in origin. Although psychotherapy was invariably the prescribed treatment — there was clear recognition that it almost never worked. This probably accounted for the horrible name given to these people — mentally disordered sex offenders (MDSO) — and why many were placed in institutions and, figuratively speaking, the key was thrown away.

If the exhibitionism was biochemical instead of psychological it should respond to chemical treatment. We began treatment with small amounts of haloperidol, and bingo, the exhibitionistic urges disappeared virtually overnight. J. J. said that as soon as the dose reached a certain level, not only did he stop wanting to exhibit himself, he even stopped thinking about it. This was exciting stuff — far more interesting than chromosome bands. Here was a disorder, classically believed to be due to some type of psychiatric trauma in childhood and untreatable, that we found to be associated with a clear-cut genetic disorder — Tourette syndrome. This implied it was biochemically, and not psychologically, caused and, sure enough, it responded beautifully to the best medication at the time for TS — haloperidol.

We wrote this case up and submitted it to the *American Journal of Psychiatry*. It was quickly accepted and published.[45] We had some reservations that the *Enquirer* might see it and emblazon their headlines with "Flashers Linked to Tourette Syndrome." Fortunately, that did not happen. What did happen is that over the next several years about ten cases of exhibitionism were referred to us. Of these, eight had TS.

About three years later, in April of 1985, a medical reporter somehow happened to uncover this article. She wrote a story about the link between TS and exhibitionism for a national wire network and it subsequently appeared in many papers around the country. Unfortunately, in Chicago, one of the bylines blared "Flashers may be Tourette sufferers." This caused some TS parents to be very upset. They called Sue Levi, then president of the TSA, and she called me. I agreed to write a letter to the editor to put a softer spin on the story and emphasize that this occurred in only a small minority of TS patients.

One therapist from Chicago, claiming to have worked with "many" TS patients, wrote a nasty letter questioning how I could make such a stupid statement, that no one else had ever reported exhibitionism in TS, and why was I using the newspaper instead of peer-reviewed journals. I wrote back pointing out that Eldridge and Nee had reported numerous cases of exhibitionism in TS long before we did, that our report had appeared years ago in a peer-reviewed journal, and that if he was not hearing about exhibitionism in TS it was probably because he was not asking the right questions. I got a nice reply stating he appreciated the letter, was now asking about and hearing about exhibitionism in some of his TS patients, and looked forward to our further studies.

This episode emphasized a problem that was to continue to haunt us for years. How do you talk and report about the disturbing behaviors that occur in some TS patients without appearing to stigmatize *all* TS patients? I have been pleasantly surprised that parents and patients themselves are able to make this distinction. We have had more trouble with professionals, including those in the legal profession, sometimes thinking that if a specific behavior is present in some TS patients, it must be present in all.

Chapter 6

The Genetics of Tourette Syndrome

In the early years of studying the genetics of TS, my primary interest was to ask whether any relatives of the patients had motor or vocal tics. These pedigrees seemed to fit a dominant pattern of inheritance in which people required only one gene to develop the symptoms. However, since some relatives that had to carry the *Gts* gene had no symptoms, it was necessary to assume a condition called reduced penetrance. This simply means that some people can carry the gene but have no symptoms. However, to rigorously demonstrate both of these features required a computer analysis of many families using a technique called segregation analysis.

This was not my area of expertise, so I collaborated with Dr. Robert Cloninger and his post-doctoral fellow, Dr. Eric Devor, at Washington University in St. Louis. I sent them the pedigrees on our first 250 families. They had available a new program called POINTER that was used in the analysis. The results suggested that, indeed, the most likely mode of inheritance was as an autosomal dominant trait with reduced penetrance. It also suggested that 1.2% of the general population carried the *Gts* gene.

We sent this paper to a prominent journal, the *New England Journal of Medicine*, since it was the first demonstration of a specific type of inheritance of TS. Kidd and his colleagues at Yale had published several prior studies on the inheritance of TS, but because of the relatively small number of cases, they had been unable to distinguish between the involvement of many genes versus a single major gene.

One of the reviewers of our paper had concerns about the new POINTER technique and raised many other objections. The paper was rejected. We then submitted it to the *American Journal of Human Genetics,* and the paper was accepted by both reviewers. A skeptic might say that since I was the editor of the journal at the time, of course it was accepted; however, both reviewers clearly approved it. In fact, one paper I submitted to the journal when I was editor was rejected, so I put that paper into the round file on the floor.

Linkage Studies Started

Once the computer studies indicated that TS was clearly a genetic disorder and seemingly inherited as an autosomal dominant trait, the next step was to find out which chromosome carried the *Gts* gene. This is done by the use of linkage studies[p53] and a computer program that gave a positive number when there was evidence that TS was linked to the marker being studied, and a negative number when there was clear evidence against such a linkage. Such studies required that we draw blood and isolate DNA from every member of about thirty different TS families. The diagnosis also had to be very accurate.

We started these studies in 1985, and the very first marker we used was a blood group called MNS. The computer program gave a very large negative number, indicating that the *Gts* gene was very unlikely to be near the MNS blood group. By 1987 we had accumulated 228 individuals and thought we had excluded TS from being on 40% of the chromosome regions.

As these studies progressed and kept coming up negative, I began having the uneasy feeling that linkage studies were the wrong approach. By mid-1987 I began to develop some strong ideas about what the specific gene causing TS might be. I gave up on the linkage approach just as the National TSA was beginning to put together a worldwide consortium to do linkage studies in TS.

Later Ideas

In later years we came to believe that TS was not inherited as a dominant trait, but as a semidominant-semirecessive trait.[p513] This meant that, in many cases the *Gts* gene came from both parents, not just one, as the autosomal dominant theory assumed. When I looked back at these early pedigrees I noticed that once we thought we had identified which parent the *Gts* gene came from, we often stopped asking questions about the other side of the family; thus some of the pedigrees looked like this:

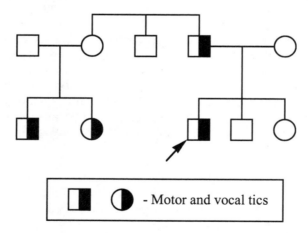

The proband, or initial patient, is denoted by the arrow. In this family the father (males are squares, females are circles) and the father's sister's children had TS. Clearly this patient's gene was coming from his father's side of the family. There was no need to spend a lot of time asking about the mother's side.

After taking many hundreds of additional pedigrees and developing an immense amount of clinical experience, we realized there was a lot more to TS than tics. Now, using this additional experience, a pedigree on the same family might look like this:

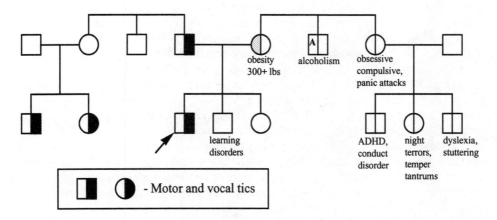

obesity 300+ lbs · alcoholism · obsessive compulsive, panic attacks

learning disorders · ADHD, conduct disorder · night terrors, temper tantrums · dyslexia, stuttering

- Motor and vocal tics

Although no one on the mother's side of the family had tics, there was a lot going on with other types of behavior. If the *Gts* gene caused a spectrum of behavioral disorders, then obviously the gene was coming from both parents. For years Brenda had been noticing this in the families she saw in therapy.

This taught me two important lessons. First, we tend to see what we are looking for. For example, in the first pedigree, since I thought the inheritance was autosomal dominant, I did not spend a lot of time asking about the mother's family and didn't take the kind of pedigree that would have been necessary to demonstrate a different type of inheritance.

Second, this reiterated the old adage about computer programs – "garbage in, garbage out." This is perhaps too harsh a criticism of our own early work, especially since everyone who later studied the subject came to precisely the same conclusion we had, that TS was inherited as dominant trait. However, this adage gave me the confidence to believe that our newer thoughts that TS patients actually required two or more genes was correct, even though every new study in the world was claiming we were wrong and that TS really was inherited as an autosomal dominant trait with reduced penetrance. As the reader will later see, there is an enormous difference between these two genetic mechanisms.

Chapter 7

Conduct Problems in TS

The one feature about Tourette syndrome that fascinated us from the very beginning was the effect this gene had on conduct. Although it was the motor and vocal tics that brought these children into the clinic, the parents complained most bitterly about the conduct problems. Although not present in every case, approximately half of TS children had problems with oppositional defiant disorder, showing some combination of constant talking back, not taking no for an answer, short temper, rage attacks over trivial things, lying, stealing, fire-starting, or aggressive behavior.[p131] As the medical half of the team, I would attempt to bring these behaviors under control with medication. However, if this was only partially successful, I would turn the child over to Brenda, the psychotherapist half of the team.

Her first response was to do what she had been trained to do — see the children individually and listen to their problems and complaints. The hope and the core of such therapy was that if they felt they had a sympathetic, understanding listener, and if past emotional conflicts were resolved, they would get better. It rapidly became apparent that for these children, this approach was almost totally ineffective. No matter how long the process went on, or how good the rapport became between patient and therapist, the behavior rarely changed.

It also became clear that these children seemed to be generally unaware of the effect their behavior was having on the rest of the family. When seen individually, they often claimed there were no problems. Brenda would then go out and say to the parents, "I hear everything was fine last week," only to be met with gasps and expressions of total disbelief. "Didn't he tell you about the twenty dollars he stole from us, or that he was expelled from school for three days for hitting children on the playground and talking back to the teacher, or about killing his pet hamster?"

It quickly became apparent that the whole family had to be present in the therapy session, if for no other reason than to hear the truth. An important aspect of family therapy was to involve all players. For a variety of reasons, divorce is common in TS families. The child's behavior has often been the cause of the divorce and usually continues to be a battleground, as the ex-spouse blames their partner for the child's poor behavior. Because of this it is critical to have both parents, or if they are re-married, both sets of parents, be involved in the therapy, so one does not sabotage what the other is trying to accomplish. This established the principle that the treatment modality known as family therapy was an essential first step. However, if there are severe marital problems, it is often necessary to resolve these before beginning to work on the parent-child problems.

Once the whole family was involved, the next revelation was that the TS child was often found to be ruling the entire household. The parents often disagreed on how to handle their disruptive child. One parent, usually the father, tended to be the conservative disciplinarian, while the other parent, the mother, tended to the "let's talk it out" approach. When the child did something that required a parental response, which was sometimes every few minutes, the parents ended up fighting more with each other than with the child.

The TS child very quickly learned to exploit this situation and soon became so adroit at manipulating the parents that, in essence, the child became the parent and the parents, the child — a situation called role reversal. If the parents refused to knuckle under, the tantrums became even more fearsome. The parents came to fear their child and to fear applying any discipline at all. One of the first things that was necessary in family therapy was to get the parents working on the same track, to take back their role as parents, and to stop being controlled by their child's behavior. This was no simple task, and sometimes one or both parents were so fearful of taking this first step that they simply terminated therapy. It was easier for them to let the child have her way than to confront her. Fortunately, most parents were able to make this transition.

Appropriate Consequences for Inappropriate Behavior.

The next aspect of dealing with those TS children with severe behavioral problems was the realization that nothing seemed to work for long. By the time these children needed therapy, the parents were saying, "If I give them positive reinforcement (rewards), that doesn't work; if I give them negative reinforcement (spankings), that doesn't work. Nothing works. What can I do?" The behavior in some TS children was best described as "driven." Just as some drug addicts simply cannot stop using drugs, *some* TS children simply cannot stop misbehaving. They have often stated this themselves —"I just can't seem to help it. I don't want to get in trouble all the time but I can't stop." Understanding that this is a genetically- and chemically-driven problem was one of the first steps in helping the parents to cope.

When a TS child massively misbehaves, most parents, and unfortunately everyone else, take this as an indication that the mother and father are poor parents and don't know how to control their children. Because of this, the parents react in anger and take the child's misbehavior as a personal affront to their parenting skills, ego, and self-esteem. This often leads them to join in the battle themselves, verbally or physically. "You can't behave this way, so take that!" — bam, shout, hit, scream — and a rapidly escalating war is on.

We found that the only effective way of avoiding this constantly recurring theme was to end the confrontations before they began. Statements such as "Go to your room and stay there until you calm down," "Go in the backyard and do twenty sit-ups," "Stand in the corner for five minutes," or "Go to the garage and take it out on the punching bag" provide a mechanism to give all parties a "time-out." If the child went to his room and trashed it, the next time-out might be to a room stripped of destructible items, such as the bathroom. If the yelling and screaming went on for two or three hours he still had to stay in time-out until that behavior stopped. We considered these neutral consequences since nothing physical or verbal was being done to the child — he was simply being allowed time for his raging brain chemicals to calm down and come back into some kind of equilibrium.

It was also important for parents to recognize that this approach would not immediately change or extinguish behavioral problems. Such an outcome might take years and depend as much upon appropriate medication and maturing of the nervous system, as upon this form of behavior management. At each family therapy session the out-of-control episodes were reviewed, and more appropriate ways of reacting were discussed. It often made a greater impact if the consequences fit the crime. For example, if a child broke a window with a rock, after the crisis period was over he had to help his parent repair it and then wash all the windows in the house. If he stole money from his parents, he would have to return the money, earning it if necessary. If the stealing continued, part of the consequences might include spending a number of hours in a situation symbolic of "jail," such as confinement to his room with no TV or stereo. An added twist might be to have one or two meals consist of only bread and water. TS children tend to be very concrete thinkers, and such concrete consequences tended to make more of an impression than simply saying, "These are things you shouldn't do."

Rages

For some TS patients, one of the most difficult things to deal with was the raging temper tantrums. Trivial frustrations or being told "no" sometimes sent these children into truly fearsome and prolonged rages of yelling, kicking, screaming, ripping clothing, and viciously hitting or punching anyone or anything in sight. In these situations almost nothing worked. Parents got hit, bruised and bitten, their glasses were ripped off and broken, and furniture was smashed. Over the years we had hundreds of frantic phone calls asking for advice. We could often hear the chaos in the background, like a war zone. We tried many approaches, such as holding them down or sending them to time-out Each had its drawbacks, such as parents getting injured, rooms getting smashed up, and children jumping out of windows.

Eventually we simply recommended calling the police during such totally out-of-control episodes. Usually the minute the police walked in the door the violent tantrums stopped. Calling the police, however, had a potential downside, in that the child usually accused the parents of abuse, and many times the children were removed from the home and the parents charged with child abuse. To attempt to prevent this, we told the parents to call us so we could talk to the police. This worked best if we were able to intervene while the police were still there.

During this period of time, Brenda had a family with a typically out-of-control TS child. Since the parents were divorced but shared physical custody, it was critical to have both sets of parents — the mother and her new husband, and the father and his live-in girlfriend — involved in the family therapy. Everything went well for many months and the child showed a rapid decrease in his "acting-out" behaviors. These split family situations, however, are often far more complex to manage than straight mother-father ones. Old, unresolved issues and persisting feelings of love and affection, alternating with hate and free-flowing blame, may produce a highly volatile, potentially explosive situation. In this case, the ex-husband and his girlfriend were having problems and Brenda was seeing them for a few sessions of their own. This made the ex-wife extremely angry. Perhaps she might have felt the marriage could have been saved if she and her ex-husband had been involved in similar therapy. All attempts at resolving a rapidly escalating war failed. The wife finally stormed out, saying to Brenda, "I will destroy you if it is the last thing I do."

Not unexpectedly, she found a sympathetic ear among a few individuals in the newly re-established LA/TSA chapter. We began to get feedback that a letter-writing campaign had been initiated, with letters sent to the National TSA complaining about Brenda and me. Since neither the local nor the national organization recognized that behavior problems had anything to do with TS, they didn't understand the need for "behavior management" therapy. This, in turn, made it easy for the letter writers to claim we were using discipline and "aversive techniques" to try to get the children to stop ticcing. They seemed to be well aware of the fact that TSA then had a rule that if they received three complaints about a physician on their referral list, they were simply removed from the list.

I had been invited to give a talk at the *First National Clinical Symposium on Tourette Syndrome* sponsored by TSA in New York City, on October 14, 1985. I recall sitting down as the morning meeting began, leafing through the pile of handouts provided by TSA. There were two lists — one of TS research centers in different states across the country, and a second referral list, by state, of physicians who were interested in TS, willing to see patients, and presumably had some knowledge about the disorder. I had always been on both lists.

As I casually perused the lists, I noticed that my name was no longer present on either list. I had been well aware, from numerous friends and patients in the LA/TSA chapter, of what had been going on and was not totally surprised that the local chapter had succeeded in getting us removed from both lists. Apparently the issue had been referred to the medical advisory committee and after much joint discussion, they decided to remove my name. What was especially disturbing was that they did so without ever picking up the phone and asking our side of the story. To me the situation was analogous to a national organization on schizophrenia removing a doctor from their referral list because a paranoid patient complained the doctor wanted to kill him, without ever calling the doctor to find out what was really going on.

From this it was clear that there were going to be two independent TS groups in the Los Angeles area, the LA/TSA chapter and the City of Hope Clinic and support group. Removal from the referral list had no discernible effect on the influx of new patients; if anything, it grew faster as we continued to give seminars to schools and hospitals throughout the area.

For years TSA had been fighting the outmoded idea, left over from Freudian psychodynamics, that TS was a psychological disorder, with the tics being the result of severe behavioral problems and repressed conflicts. The studies in the 1970s by Dr. Arthur Shapiro showed that most TS patients could be effectively treated with haloperidol. This, and the genetic nature of the disorder, indicated

TS was a neurological disorder and was not due to psychological causes; thus TSA fought vigorously the idea that TS was anything more than a tic disorder. All emotional problems, if any, were considered to be a result of trying to cope with the tics.

Then we came along and said, "Yes, TS is a genetic and organic disorder, but the *Gts* genes can also produce a wide range of behavioral disorders in addition to the tics. These other behaviors are often a far greater problem to most parents and patients than the tics." It seemed that TSA was having none of this and was fighting the idea tooth and nail. Unfortunately, the TS families were the major losers. They knew the behavioral problems they were having, but were repeatedly told these symptoms had nothing to do with TS.

For the next three years we remained off the TSA referral list, despite the fact that ours was becoming one of the most active TS clinics in the world. Even though this issue was eventually resolved, it seemed to us that TSA continued to do everything they could to discourage acceptance of the idea that TS was a behavioral spectrum disorder.

Unbeknownst to us, our problems had only just begun.

Chapter 8

ADHD and Tourette Syndrome

Attention deficit hyperactivity disorder (ADHD)[p73] is the most common behavioral disorder of childhood. Previously called "minimal brain damage" or "hyperactivity," it occurs in 5% to 8% of boys and 1% to 4% of girls. In addition to short attention span, hyperactivity, learning disorders and dyslexia, the child may also have many of the conduct problems previously described. It can be a devastating disorder.

Other than the tics, one of the first aspects of TS that immediately intrigued us was the high frequency of ADHD. It was present in over half of our first 250 cases. If we only looked at problems with attention, independent of whether the child was hyperactive or not, up to 90% of TS patients were affected.

We also noted that the ADHD was usually present for years before the tics began. However, in some TS children the tics didn't start until the teenage years, at which time ADHD symptoms also began. This was all the more striking because ADHD was generally defined as beginning prior to seven years of age. We also observed that many of the children we were seeing with just ADHD and no tics had one or more close relatives with tics, suggesting their ADHD was due to a *Gts* gene. Also, many of our TS children had siblings or parents with attentional or learning problems, but no tics.

To a clinician and a geneticist, these observations were fascinating. They suggested that TS and ADHD were genetically related. There was some evidence that ADHD was a genetic disorder, but it was not overwhelming and many health workers, teachers, and insurance companies considered it a psychological disorder. Most often it was simply assumed the parents were doing something wrong and it was all their fault. TS, however, was a clear-cut genetic disorder that was intimately associated with ADHD. To us this provided the strongest evidence yet that ADHD was also a genetic disorder.

Ritalin and TS

For many of our TS patients it was the ADHD that was devastating, whereas the tics were often just a trivial nuisance. We routinely treated these cases with Ritalin,[p573] the most widely-used medication for ADHD. On occasion, the tics increased after starting Ritalin, and this had been reported several times in the literature.[p575] In our experience this could usually be controlled with small doses of haloperidol.[p578] Oftentimes after treatment with Ritalin, the tics were either unaffected or sometimes even improved.[p576] We were thus surprised and even disturbed when, in 1982, Dr. Tom Lowe, Dr. Donald Cohen, and their colleagues from the Yale Child Study Center published a paper in the *Journal of the American Medical Association* entitled "Stimulant Medications Precipitate Tourette's Syndrome." It stated that Ritalin could cause TS and should never be used in patients with TS, or in patients with ADHD and a family history of TS. For example, they stated:

> "...motor tics or diagnosed Tourette's syndrome in a child should be a contraindication to the use of stimulant medication for alleviation of hyperactive symptoms.
> "...the development of motor tic symptoms in any child receiving stimulants...is a clear indication for the immediate discontinuation of stimulant therapy, in an effort to minimize the possibility of eliciting a full-blown case of Tourette's syndrome.
> "...the widespread use of stimulants may be increasing substantially the number of cases [of Tourette syndrome] requiring clinical diagnosis and intervention."

This paper was almost diametrically opposed to our experience. Many of our TS patients with ADHD virtually could not exist outside of an institution without the help of Ritalin or Dexedrine. However, as soon as the *JAMA* article appeared, many physicians who were treating children with TS and ADHD immediately stopped the Ritalin and refused to treat the ADHD, out of fear of a lawsuit.

The child was now out of control. The parents were desperate. These TS cases were often referred to us. We immediately put them back on the haloperidol-Ritalin combination and they did well. We also found that most of the children who apparently developed tics while taking Ritalin actually had tics before ever receiving Ritalin. They simply had never been asked about tics.

It was clearly important to investigate this issue further. Some of our TS patients with ADHD had been treated with Ritalin *before* they developed tics. Others had been treated with Ritalin *after* they developed tics. These two groups gave us the opportunity to examine the question, "Was the interval between the onset of the ADHD and the tics shorter for those who received Ritalin *before* they had tics than for those who received Ritalin *after* the tics had started?" If the Lowe-Cohen hypothesis was correct, the answer should be a definite yes. Taking Ritalin should have hastened the onset of tics. If Ritalin was not a major factor in causing TS, the answer should be no. Taking Ritalin should not have hastened the onset of tics.

In fact the answer was a definite no. The duration between the onset of ADHD and tics was much greater in those who had Ritalin before the tics had started. This suggested that in some cases the Ritalin might actually protect against the development of tics. There were theoretical reasons why this might happen.[30, p395]

The TS Symposium

Around this time, Cohen was planning a symposium on TS for the *Journal of the American Academy of Child and Adolescent Psychiatry* and invited us to submit a paper. I am not sure whether he was aware of just how much we disagreed with his Ritalin paper, but we thought this was a perfect time and place to present our theory about the genetic interrelatedness of TS and ADHD and the evidence that Ritalin could be very helpful in some TS patients who also had ADHD. We sent in a paper summarizing these observations for 250 patients and discussing the above points.

One of the editors was from England, where there was great skepticism that ADHD even existed. He felt that if it did exist, it was definitely not a genetic disorder, and he raised many objections to the paper. Enough changes were finally made that Cohen accepted the paper which was entitled "Tourette Syndrome and Attention Deficit Disorder with Hyperactivity: Are they Genetically Related?"[46] It has been widely quoted ever since.

Cohen was a member of the medical-scientific advisory board of TSA and intimately involved in formulating TSA thought and philosophy. Little did I realize at the time that this paper would be the start of a long and often acrimonious feud between the Yale group and us that would eventually become intermixed with the difficulties we were encountering with TSA.

The Ciba-Giegy Case

There had always been a great deal of emotion about the use of Ritalin. Opinions ranged from it being a God-given miracle drug that can allow severely impaired ADHD children to function in school and life, to being a "chemical straight-jacket" for a hypothetical, nonexistent disease invented by teachers and doctors to keep unruly children from being disruptive.

In such a setting, the Lowe-Cohen paper was the perfect gift to parents and their lawyers who wanted to sue doctors and Ciba-Giegy, the company that made Ritalin, if something went wrong. Here was an obvious "thing that could go wrong." Ritalin could cause TS. Any parents whose child developed tics while on Ritalin, and whose tics did not go away, would now have a reason to sue both their doctor and the company.

Since, in our experience, TS and ADHD were intimately related and many ADHD children developed tics whether they were on Ritalin or not, this was a potential disaster for everyone involved with treating ADHD. We worried that doctors could become so petrified of lawsuits that they would stop using Ritalin, or related medications. It would be the children with ADHD who would suffer the consequences.

In fact, it was not long before I got a call from lawyers at Ciba-Giegy asking for help. The first suit had been filed. A boy in Tennessee had developed TS while on Ritalin. The tics did not go away when the Ritalin was stopped, and Ciba-Giegy was being sued for $40 million because they had not warned patients that Ritalin could cause TS. The pediatrician was also being sued, and Cohen was testifying for the mother and her son against the doctor and Ciba-Giegy.

As soon as the Lowe-Cohen paper appeared and the legal implications became apparent, Ciba-Giegy put a disclaimer in the Ritalin insert stating "*Ritalin is contraindicated also....in patients with motor tics or with a family history or diagnosis of Tourette's syndrome.*" We thought this statement was overly cautious, because in our experience this would exclude up to half of the cases of

ADHD and all children with TS and ADHD.

The Tennessee case was based on the assumption that this disclaimer should have been put in the drug insert as soon as the first paper appeared suggesting that Ritalin could precipitate tics, even though it seemed to be a very rare problem.

Fortunately for the defense, the boy's grandfather had TS. I testified that TS was a genetic disorder, that TS was caused by abnormal genes, not by Ritalin, and that many children with ADHD developed tics because many cases of ADHD were due to the *Gts* gene. Shapiro testified that he often used the combination of haloperidol and Ritalin for TS and never had problems. The jury was out for only a brief time and returned a verdict that the boy's treating pediatrician and Ciba-Giegy were not at fault.

Pauls Says TS and ADHD are Unrelated

Our symposium paper was published in the spring of 1984. By June of that year, Drs. James Leckman, David Pauls, Cohen, Kidd, and other colleagues from the Yale Child Study Center submitted an abstract to the American Society of Human Genetics meetings entitled "Evidence Against a Genetic Relationship Between Tourette Syndrome and Attention Deficit Disorder."[162]

This study was based on twenty-seven TS cases and their relatives. Of these, 63% had ADHD, similar to the high frequency we had found in our cases. Pauls divided his TS probands into two groups, sixteen who had TS *with* ADHD and fourteen who had TS *without* ADHD. They found that in the first group, 25% of the relatives with tics also had ADHD, whereas in the second group, *none* of the relatives with tics had ADHD. From this they concluded that TS and ADHD were *not* genetically related, as we had suggested. They proposed that TS and ADHD were inherited separately and the apparent association was a statistical accident called *ascertainment bias*. This means that if a TS patient happened by chance to also have ADHD he would be much more likely to come to see the doctor than if he didn't have ADHD. As a result, the presence of ADHD in patients with TS was considered to be just accidental. The Pauls et al. paper claimed that if a TS patient did not have ADHD, then the frequency of ADHD in the relatives would be no greater than chance.

This paper was presented at the American Society of Human Genetics meeting the following November. Pauls is a Ph.D. and did not have the clinical responsibility of treating TS patients. To me – after treating hundreds of TS patients struggling with severe ADHD, seeing tics and ADHD simultaneously come out of nowhere in teenage years, and seeing many brothers and sisters of our TS patients also suffering with ADHD – the connection between TS and ADHD seemed as obvious as the hand in front of my face.

Letters to the Editor – Exchange #1

The full paper by Pauls and his colleagues appeared in the *Archives of General Psychiatry* in December of 1986. It was entitled "Gilles de la Tourette's syndrome and Attention Deficit Disorder with Hyperactivity. Evidence Against a Genetic Relationship."[165] After this paper came out many of our patients began telling us that their doctors were saying TS and ADHD were unrelated. The doctors were focusing on the tics and ignoring the more serious problems with ADHD and behavior. Because of this we felt, for the sake of these children, it was important to rebut the Pauls paper. We wrote a letter to the editor stating the following points:[49]

1. It is a common feature of all syndromes for only the most severe cases, with the full set of symptoms, to seek medical help. Because the less severely-affected relatives did not have the full syndrome did not mean these symptoms were there by accident.

2. The number of cases reported in the study was too small to draw any statistically valid conclusions. In statistics there are two types of errors. One is to say something is true when in reality it is false. Statisticians call this a type I error. Most scientists are so petrified about making this type of error that they instead make the second, less often-discussed error. This is to say something is not true when in fact it is true. This is called a type II error. Type II errors are often made when too few patients are studied. We suggested Pauls and colleagues were making a type II error.

3. We examined the families that we had been using for linkage studies, where each member had been individually interviewed for symptoms, including ADHD. This clearly showed that TS and ADHD did travel together in families, not separately as the paper suggested.

4. We also divided our cases into those with and without ADHD. When the proband had ADHD, 37% of the relatives with tics had ADHD. When the proband did not have ADHD, 21% of the relatives with tics had ADHD. This was much higher than the 0% Pauls and colleagues had observed.

5. Finally, we pointed out that Pauls and Kidd had been co-authors of a paper earlier that year with Dr. Roger Kurlan.[136] This was a study of a large TS family in Canada. Here the proband did not have ADHD, yet 31% of the relatives with tics had ADHD. This was inconsistent with the Pauls statement that if the proband did not have ADHD, then the frequency of ADHD in the relative with tics would not be increased.

In the rebuttal to our letter,[166] Pauls et al. restated their position and re-emphasized that they felt the association of TS and ADHD was simply due to ascertainment bias and the two were not genetically related.

These letters were published in November of 1987. That same month we published a series of seven papers which were just as vigorously responded to by Pauls et al. as our response had been to their article. The debate was accelerating.

Chapter 9

The Controlled Study

While the paper summarizing the clinical features of our first 250 cases of Tourette syndrome was being reviewed and published,[47] it was obvious to us that the next set of patients would have to be studied in a different manner. This was because many of the observations we had made about the problems TS children had with poor conduct, discipline problems, anxieties, phobias, compulsive, oppositional and other behaviors, could also be seen in normal children.

A phrase we often heard when discussing TS was, "So what? Sometimes my kids also do those things and they don't have Tourette syndrome." Mothers of the more severely-affected TS children repeatedly spoke of a similar frustration at trying to covey to others what they were experiencing. "No one believes us. The pediatrician thinks I'm just an hysterical overreacting mother. The teachers don't see it because he only misbehaves at home. Everyone thinks if there is a problem it is all my fault." For Brenda and me, who were listening to TS parents on a daily basis, it was obvious we were often dealing with behavior problems that were far outside the range of normal. In addition, the stories were all the same. About half of our parents complained their TS children could not take no for an answer, had rage attacks and outrageous temper tantrums, were constantly talking back, and had many other behavior problems.

It was clear we needed to compare the frequencies of these behavior problems in TS children to those in normal controls. Shapiro had compared behaviors of TS patients to other patients in a general psychiatric clinic. He used a psychological test called the MMPI and concluded TS patients showed no unique behavioral problems. This seemed to us analogous to studying behavioral aspects of lung cancer patients and using patients with all types of cancer as controls. It was clear to us that normal controls were required.

Such controls, however, were not easy to find. It was becoming increasingly apparent that we were studying a set of genes that were capable of manifesting themselves in a wide variety of ways. Taking our controls from patients who were attending other clinics was fraught with danger because they might be expressing symptoms of TS we were not aware of. For example, if compulsive smoking was one of the manifestations of the compulsive behavior caused by the *Gts* gene, we obviously could not use patients from a lung cancer clinic. In the same manner, if the *Gts* gene caused psychosomatic problems, we could not use patients from an asthma, peptic ulcer or spastic colon clinic. Almost any group of patients coming to see the doctor seemed potentially "contaminated." There was, however, one "disorder" which was immune from these problems – pregnancy.

Being born was a universal characteristic of every human being. There was a problem, though. There was no obstetrics service at the City of Hope. There would be much less criticism of the controls if they were drawn from the same patient pool as the TS families. However, I did see pregnant women coming for amniocentesis in my prenatal diagnosis clinic, and these were even my own patients.

The obvious solution to the problem of controls was to use these families. In many ways they were similar to the TS patients in that they came to the clinic knowing they were going to be asked questions about their family history, and both the father and the mother were usually present. I saw them twice, first for the initial interview, counseling, and family history. They then returned several weeks later for the amniocentesis. After the first visit I asked them if they were willing to participate as controls. If the answer was yes, they were asked to fill out the same questionnaire on their children that I gave to the parents of TS children. If there was more than one child, the one closest to the average age of the TS children was chosen. If they had no children they were asked to give the questionnaire to a sibling, thus providing a match for some of our older TS patients. The questionnaire was returned when they came back for the amniocentesis. This proved to be a highly motivated group of individuals and 98% of the questionnaires were returned.

The second item that needed to be changed was the questionnaire itself. The results of our study of the first 250 patients were based on a short questionnaire and a semi-structured interview of the patients and their parents. Semi-structured means that similar but not identical questions were asked of each patient, and the exact form of the questions might change from week to week. A structured questionnaire or interview is one where everyone is asked the identical set of questions. We needed a larger and more comprehensive questionnaire and one that used standardized questions. This meant using questions that others had already used, where they had examined the results, from a large group of individuals, to make sure the results were reproducible.

To help us in this, Brenda and I attended a tutorial given at Washington University Medical School in St. Lewis. This course taught us how to use what was called the Diagnostic Interview Schedule (DIS). This was an extensive, highly-structured interview designed to identify and diagnose thirty-two different types of psychiatric diagnoses based on the DSM-III, the diagnostic bible of psychiatrists.[86] The development of the DIS had been carried out by Dr. Lee Robins and her colleagues with a large grant from the National Institutes of Mental Health. Eventually the DIS was used in a large nationwide epidemiological study to determine the incidence of various behavioral problems in a general population.[182] Because it was supported by the government, it was a public domain instrument. Many of the questions used in our new larger questionnaire were taken verbatim from the DIS, and most of the others were modeled after the Diagnostic and Statistical Manual III (DSM-III). Some additional questions inquiring about specific TS behaviors were added.

Although the DIS was designed to be given orally by a trained examiner, we did not have the funds to do this, and the questions were given in questionnaire form. This resulted in a many-page questionnaire that was presented to all new patients (or their parents) and to all controls. (When this study was completed, the questionnaire was expanded still further. This final questionnaire is the version that is in print.)[33]

For the next several years, these questionnaires were simply piled away in a drawer as they came in and were not used for diagnostic purposes. The diagnosis itself was based on a history of behaviors from early childhood on, a family history, and a physical exam. After approximately three hundred questionnaires were accumulated, I wrote a computer program in BASIC that allowed the results to be entered into files for analysis with a statistical program available for the Apple IIe. A volunteer entered all the data, and we proceeded to spend the next year analyzing it.

Except for a single very small study of only 21 TS patients using a short Behavior Problem Checklist,[219] there had never before been a study of TS patients compared with normal controls, especially not of this size. When completed there were 246 TS patients, 17 patients with just ADHD, 15 with ADHD associated with a family history of TS,[p69] and 47 controls. There had also never been a study of such a wide range of behaviors. Most physicians taking care of TS patients still largely considered it to be just a tic disorder and either did not appreciate or did not ask about its behavioral aspects.

By the time the analysis was complete, we had eleven manuscripts covering ADHD, conduct disorder, phobias, panic attacks, depression and mania, sleep disorders, handedness, allergies, schizoid symptoms, obsessive-compulsive, and other behaviors. The very size of the results made publication difficult. Both the *New England Journal of Medicine* and the *Archives of General Psychiatry* returned them unreviewed because the study was too large. Neither the *Pediatric Clinics* nor the *Psychiatric Clinics of North America* would accept them, feeling they would not be of that much interest to their readers.

By this time, I had rotated off being editor of the *American Journal of Human Genetics*. Because there was no page limitation for this journal and because TS was a genetic disorder with many implications for the genetics of human behavior, this seemed an ideal place to submit them. After agreeing to condense the eleven papers to seven, they were accepted and published in the November 1987 issue.[28,30,48,51-54] (The interested reader is referred to the papers themselves or to the book *Tourette Syndrome and Human Behavior*,[33] where these and other results are described in detail.)

It was apparent that TS was associated with a wide range of other behavioral problems. Because there were so many different behaviors, because the pedigrees we had taken showed that they were also present in the relatives of the TS patients, and because there was little correlation between how bad the tics were and how bad the behaviors were, we felt the most likely explanation was that the chemical disturbance in the brain that was causing the tics was also causing the behavior problems.

It was obvious that TS was more than just a tic disorder.

Chapter 10

Serotonin and Tryptophan

In January of 1987, I saw a letter to the editor in the English medical journal *Lancet* which described an elderly lady in a nursing home. She was aggressive, angry, and abusive. The authors had found that her blood serotonin was low and had given her tryptophan, a common amino acid that acts as a precursor to serotonin. She got better. I was aware of the studies showing low levels of the breakdown product of serotonin in the spinal fluid of patients with depression, aggressive and suicidal behavior, and Tourette syndrome.[p457]

I had never considered doing spinal tap studies in our TS patients for two reasons. First, two such studies on a few TS patients had already shown low levels, and second, spinal taps were uncomfortable and this was not something I wanted to subject my patients to. Here was a note, however, suggesting that blood serotonin levels could be used to determine if serotonin was defective. I checked with our clinical pathology laboratory to see if a blood serotonin test was available. It was, through BioScience, a commercial medical laboratory in Los Angeles. After two more letters to the editor appeared in *Lancet* describing similar patients and similar low blood serotonin levels, I proceeded to have all new patients and their close relatives, and many old TS patients tested for blood serotonin levels.

By April 1987, it became apparent that the blood serotonin levels tended to be low in our TS patients, especially those not on medication.[p459] This raised the question, "Why were the serotonin levels low?" Because serotonin was made from tryptophan, and tryptophan levels could also be done in commercial testing labs, I started a second phase of examining both serotonin and tryptophan levels. By June, it was clear that the blood tryptophan levels were also low.

This was very exciting. Geneticists are trained to think in terms of genes and enzymes. There were many hundreds of papers in the psychiatric literature on serotonin and tryptophan in the spinal fluid, blood, and platelets of patients with various psychiatric disorders — the "epiphenomenology" of serotonin. Almost no one had considered what the defective genes were that caused these changes. This was probably due to two factors. First, most psychiatrists were not trained to think in genetic terms, and second, most of the conditions studied (suicide, depression, aggression, arson, and others) were not generally considered to be highly genetic disorders; however, the situation was totally different with Tourette syndrome. Here was a condition that was clearly genetic and clinically associated with all the disorders linked to defective serotonin metabolism, and these patients were showing low blood serotonin and tryptophan levels.

The metabolic pathway for serotonin is fairly simple.[p467] Tryptophan can be converted to serotonin by an enzyme called tryptophan hydroxylase, or tryptophan can be broken down by an enzyme called tryptophan oxygenase or tryptophan 2,3-dioxygenase (TDO2).

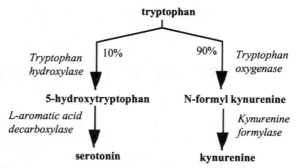

If the defective gene was tryptophan hydroxylase, serotonin would be low but tryptophan would be normal or even elevated. By contrast, if the mutation caused the *tryptophan oxygenase* gene *(TDO2)* to be overactive, both tryptophan and serotonin should be low — and they were. To this geneticist, the simplest explanation was that the low serotonin in TS was due to a mutation that caused an increased level of the tryptophan oxygenase enzyme. Because all of the symptoms of TS could be explained by low serotonin levels in the body and brain, *TDO2* could be the *Gts* gene.

The only way to prove it would be to isolate the human *TDO2* gene. This job was made easier by the fact that the rat *TDO2* gene had already been isolated and cloned by Dr. Schmid, Dr. Schültz, and colleagues in Germany.[190] By July 1987, we had started a second study of serotonin and tryptophan in TS to verify the preliminary study, and by August, I had obtained copies of rat *TDO2* clones from Dr. Schmid.

Cloning the Human *TDO2* Gene

One of the nice features about human genetics is that humans are not that different from "lower" animals. Darwin was right — life forms do evolve and thus they are related to each other. If someone clones a gene in the mouse or rat, there is usually enough similarity in the sequence of the DNA bases that such a clone can be used to find the human gene; thus we used the rat *TDO2* clone to find a similar sequence in a library of clones of pieces of human DNA. To get a copy of the expressed *TDO2* gene, we also began to search a library of clones to the messenger RNA from human liver. By early 1988, Donn Muhleman, one of my indispensable laboratory collaborators, had identified a clone for the messenger RNA of the human *TDO2* gene.

We began the process of sequencing this clone. In the laboratory we called it *HTO3*, for *Human Tryptophan Oxygenase 3*, the *3* being the third clone we had isolated. We chose the third clone because it contained the largest piece of DNA.

Determining the sequence of *HTO3* turned out to be a complex job. The DNA in the clone was rearranged, and initially we didn't realize it.[76] This sometimes happens either when the original clone is made or after it has been growing in culture. By the end of the year we had it all deciphered.

TDO2 is on Chromosome 4q31

One of the earliest goals we had was to find out what chromosome the human *TDO2* gene was on. To do this we did two things. First, we sent a copy of *HTO3* to Dr. Tim Donalan at Stanford University. He was an expert in the technique called "in situ hybridization." This involved hybridizing[p55] radioactive copies of *HTO3* to human chromosomes spread out on slides. They were then covered with a thin photographic film. After weeks of exposure, grains would appear over the chromosome regions carrying the human *TDO2* gene. Second, we obtained a set of DNA samples from hybrids between mouse and human cells from Dr. Mohandas at UCLA. These were mouse cells which also contained a variable number of different human chromosomes. By hybridizing the *HTO3* clone to DNA from the whole set of hybrid cells, we were able to determine that our presumptive human *TDO2* gene was on chromosome 4.

We then needed to determine what part of chromosome 4 the gene was on. To do this, we obtained a new set of hybrids between mouse or hamster cells and parts of chromosome 4 from Dr. John Wasmuth, at the University of California in Irvine. We also obtained cells from a baby with a broken chromosome 4 from Dr. Myora Smith, also at Irvine. Hybridization studies of these cells showed that the *TDO2* gene was on the long arm between bands 25 and 32. By this time we had heard from Donalan, and he had also found that the *TDO2* gene was on the long arm of chromosome 4 in bands 31 to 32. Combined, these results indicated the human *TDO2* gene was on chromosome 4 in band q31.

Within a few months, this seemingly obscure observation was to acquire some clinical significance.

Chapter 11

The Visual Field Studies

In December of 1987, we learned of some studies by Dr. Jay Enoch of the Department of Optometry at the University of California in Berkeley.[P513] We invited him to our lab to tell us of his work. His studies indicated there were some subtle visual field changes in patients with TS. The intriguing aspect was that Enoch seemed to be able to pick out parents who carried the *Gts* gene, even when they had no symptoms. Many of the families he studied showed these defects in both parents. This seemed to confirm our suspicions that the *Gts* gene was often coming from both parents and thus, in many cases, the TS patients were carrying a double dose of the *Gts* gene. The meeting with Enock was very friendly, and he invited us to Berkeley in January to watch the testing being done and perhaps learn to do it ourselves.

I was sufficiently enthusiastic about the potential of visual field defects as a possible marker for the *Gts* gene, that a few weeks later I found my way to downtown Los Angeles and a rundown warehouse of secondhand medical instruments. I spent three thousand dollars of our precious research funds to buy a used Goldman perimeter, the only instrument that could pick up these changes. In January of 1988, Brenda and I went to Berkeley to learn firsthand from Enoch how to use the machine.

The testing was not easy for either the examiner or the patient. So that I could see what it felt like, I had Enoch do the testing on me. After about fifteen minutes he showed me the results − perfectly normal eye fields. It should have been reassuring that I was not a *Gts* gene carrier, but it was just the opposite. Unknown to Enock, one of my sons had ADHD so severe that he never finished high school. A second son had a different set of problems that I felt fell within the TS spectrum. Because I had a brother and a sister with significant weight problems and some obsessive-compulsive behaviors, I was reasonably convinced I had to be a *Gts* gene carrier. I might claim that I was an asymptomatic carrier, but a predisposition to working sixteen hours a day might easily classify me as a bona fide workaholic, a symptom we knew to be a characteristics of some of our *Gts* gene carriers. If Enoch had told me I had abnormal visual fields and thus *was* a gene carrier, it would have considerably enhanced my faith and enthusiasm in the test. By contrast, the statement that I had normal visual fields and thus was not a carrier, made me worry that there might be a certain degree of subjectivity to the test. This is one of the reasons that blinded studies are so valuable in science.

Another fact added to my reluctance to wholeheartedly accept the utility of visual field testing. The results we were observing in our TS pedigrees and in our serotonin and tryptophan studies indicated that many TS patients received genes from both parents. We also had evidence that 1 in 90 boys had TS.[71] If these two assumptions were true, simple genetic calculations indicated that at least 13% of the population had to carry the *Gts* gene. Enoch however, was saying on the one hand that both parents of a TS child carried the gene, but on the other hand he kept reassuring me that these visual field findings were *rare* in normal people and were unique to TS and glaucoma, and glaucoma was easy to rule out by testing ocular pressures. As a geneticist rather than an optometrist, I worried that it could not be both ways. If both parents were *Gts* gene carriers, then the carrier rate for the gene had to be dramatically higher than if TS was a dominant disorder and required only one gene. The visual field defect could not be both very rare *and* a marker of the *Gts* gene.

To me these problems simply indicated that the visual field test was less precise than Enock thought it was. It did not, however, keep me from thinking this was a valuable contribution to the study of TS. After all, his findings supported our theory about the semidominant-semirecessive inheritance of TS, a theory that was more widely assumed to be incorrect than correct.

Enoch, Brenda, and I decided we would simultaneously submit a set of manuscripts to the *New England Journal of Medicine*. He would describe his visual field studies suggesting most cases of TS received a gene from both parents, and we would describe our family history, serotonin, and tryptophan studies which reached the same conclusion. We thought the two papers would tend to support each other, and the subject seemed important enough to send to a major journal, because it suggested the *Gts* gene was the most common abnormal gene affecting man and might be responsible for many cases of alcoholism, ADHD, obsessive-compulsive and other behavioral disorders. We finished our paper and sent it off to Dr. Enoch in case he wanted the results to help cast his own paper.

Somewhere in this grand scheme, Brenda and I had overlooked the TSA connection. During lunch in Berkeley, Enoch had told us that the newly-appointed executive director of TSA was a good friend of his, because both of them had previously been involved with a foundation concerned with a hereditary eye disease. They had just had dinner together. Brenda and I winked at each other, wondering what horrible tales Enock might have been told about us. We were not excessively concerned, however, because we had met the executive director at a symposium on on the behavioral aspects of TS that TSA had sponsored in August 1987. He had seemed very friendly and we were beginning to hope that our prior problems with TSA were behind us. While at that meeting we had presented the results of our controlled study showing a wide range of behavioral problems in TS, and these papers had just been published a few months previously.

After returning from Berkeley, I was waiting to hear from Enoch about the progress of our joint submission of papers. When his call came, I anticipated it would be concerned with some minor editorial changes he wanted in the manuscripts. Instead he simply stated that Brenda and I were "very controversial," and he felt that it was better for him if he discontinued our collaboration. He suggested that we submit our papers separately.

Enoch's whole demeanor had changed after talking to the executive director.

It seemed clear that our problems with TSA were still running full-force. I thought it was ironic that this lay executive director, new to TS and with no clinical or research experience in the field, and director of an organization supposedly devoted to encouraging research into TS, would work so energetically to destroy what might have become an important joint research project into the genetics of TS. If a cooperative study of the visual fields in TS patients and their relatives showed the test to be useful in identifying gene carriers, it would add power to the genetic linkage studies that were devoted to trying to find the *Gts* gene. If the cooperative studies had been carried out, they might have gone a long way toward assuring TSA that the hundreds of thousands of dollars they were soon to spend on linkage studies would be done correctly. We thought this craziness was simply a leftover from the old problems we previously had with TSA.

Little did we realize it was the first indication of a new and vigorous effort to totally discredit our controlled studies which suggested that a wide range of behavioral disorders were associated with TS.

Chapter 12

The Pauls Letter

"There is a tendency in the scientific tradition that when you do not like the results, the direction, or the implications of a research [study], you then attack the methodology."
President of the Hastings Center[222]

In March of 1988, four months after our series of papers on "A Controlled Study of Tourette Syndrome" was published, several friends around the country called telling me that they had received a form letter from TSA. The letter was a follows:

"March 28, 1988

To: Tourette Syndrome Researchers and Clinicians

From: Sue Levi, President Liaison, Scientific Affairs (TSA)

You may be aware of the considerable interest generated by the publication of a series of papers by Drs. David and Brenda Comings on Tourette Syndrome which appeared in the *American Journal of Human Genetics* (vol. 42:701-866, 87).

Drs. Cohen, Pauls, Leckman and Kidd have sent us the attached letter to the editor written in response to the publication of these papers. This letter has been accepted for publication, and will probably appear in the *Journal*'s September 1988 issue. The deadline for this issue is April 22, 1988....

You may wish to:

1. Write your own letter to the editor about the issues raised by the Comings' articles;

2. Join others who have indicated that they plan to directly notify the *Journal*'s editor, Dr. Charles J. Epstein, of their endorsement of the attached critique.

If you wish to suggest names of colleagues who might be interested in receiving this material, please give us a call.

Sue's letter had been sent to a wide range of Tourette syndrome researchers around the world. Soon afterward, Epstein sent me the Pauls et al. letter to the editor, asking if we wished to respond. The letter was entitled "Tourette Syndrome and Neuropsychiatric Disorders: Is There a Genetic Connection?" Two of the authors were the same as those who responded to our letter to the editor of the *Archives of General Psychiatry*, in November 1987, four months previously.

I told Epstein I would be happy to respond, under two conditions. First, that this would not set off a prolonged series of back-and-forth letters, and second, that Pauls et al. would not be allowed to retract their letter if they did not like our response. I requested the latter because I knew Levi had sent their letter to many people without asking for or including a response from us, and this was the only chance we had to present a rebuttal. Epstein agreed. The Pauls et al. letter began:[164]

> "In a remarkable series of papers by....Comings and Comings in the *Journal*, a number of claims are made that have profound implications for future research on Gilles de la Tourette Syndrome (TS). Their assertions fall outside the mainstream of the very extensive TS literature that has developed over the past two decades (see Cohen et al. 1988 for review). The novelty of the conclusions and the visibility of their presentation require that the papers receive thorough discussion."

Pauls et al. raised seven objections to our studies. They objected to the types of subjects we studied, our referral to a *Gts* gene when they thought there was no unequivocal evidence that a *Gts* gene existed, our use of questionnaires instead of standardized psychological or psychiatric tests, our statistical methods, and my comment in the seventh paper that because the *Gts* gene seemed to be common, there was probably Darwinian-like selection for the gene. They concluded that these problems

> "make it impossible to accept as valid any of the results presented and raise serious concerns regarding the integrity of the peer review process for these papers."

In other words, nothing in these papers was correct, and they were so bad that the editor and the reviewers should never have accepted them for publication. I will not reiterate here the details of our multi-page response. The interested reader can examine the original.[55]

By the time this exchange of letters occurred, our thinking about Tourette syndrome had undergone a considerable degree of evolution and change. We had come to be convinced that most TS patients required two genes for the full expression of their symptoms. Our unpublished results of the blood serotonin and tryptophan studies had suggested that the *Gts* gene affected serotonin production, that the *Gts* gene itself might be *TDO2*, and this serotonin connection was capable of explaining all of the behavioral disorders seen in association with TS. The papers describing the serotonin studies and the paper on this new theory about the genetics of TS were grinding very slowly through the review process. Here was an opportunity to leap over those hurdles and lay out our recent thinking in considerable detail.

This produced an ironic situation. By trying to discredit one idea – that TS was a broad-based spectrum disorder of behavioral disinhibition – the Yale group was now providing us with a chance to present an even newer idea – that TS was due, at least in part, to a common gene affecting serotonin metabolism. Better still, it would be impossible for them to review and reject this paper since, as a reply to their letter, it had already been accepted.

After the response was written, I sent a copy to Levi, along with a letter stating that, as she was an officer of a non-profit association that uses donated funds, I thought it was inappropriate for her to so blatantly take sides on a scientific issue. I objected that her letter could have a chilling effect on clinicians and scientists wishing to enter the field or to publish papers on the behavioral aspects of TS. Once president of TSA, she had now become "President Liaison, Scientific Affairs" and was directly responsible for overseeing the funding of research grants sent to TSA; thus her opinions held additional weight. Because grant money is the lifeblood of research scientists, she was sending out a powerful message. I felt that she was inappropriately using her position to manipulate the outcome of legitimate scientific research.

By the time these letters were published, this whole episode became all the more puzzling to me. By now the book on Tourette's Syndrome and Tic Disorders, edited by Cohen, Dr. Ruth Bruun, and Leckman was out. I received an early copy because we had been invited to write a chapter on ADHD and TS. The first chapter in that book was by Leckman and Cohen,[143] two of the co-authors of the Pauls et al. letter. Written before the Pauls letter, it lists the following behavioral traits (Table 1.3, p.10) associated with Tourette syndrome:

- Developmentally inappropriate inattention and impulsivity, disinhibition of thoughts and actions
- Motoric hyperactivity and restlessness
- Learning disabilities
- Emotional lability, increased irritability, maniclike behavior
- Obsessive-compulsive behaviors
- Heightened anxiety, phobias, separation anxiety
- Depressive reactions

These were almost the identical set of behaviors we had reported in our controlled study of TS. This seemed totally at odds with the fact that both authors had signed the Pauls et al. letter claiming these same associated behaviors "fall outside the mainstream of the very extensive TS literature."

Equally puzzling was the fact that only one month after the Pauls et al. letter and our rebuttal appeared, Pauls, Leckman, and co-workers published an abstract in the proceedings of the November 1988 meeting of the American Society of Human Genetics entitled "A Family Study of Tourette's Syndrome: Evidence Against the Hypothesis of Association with a Wide Range of Psychiatric Phenotypes."[170] In this abstract they stated that "the frequency of the other neuropsychiatric disorders in our proband sample are comparable to those reported by Comings and Comings..." This abstract had been submitted to the meeting barely two months after their letter to the editor saying the presence of these behaviors "fall outside the mainstream of the very extensive TS literature."

This strange series of events was, and still is, a puzzle to me. How could these authors write a chapter in late 1987 saying a wide range of associated behaviors were present in TS patients, then write a letter to the editor in March 1988 saying these same behaviors did not occur in TS patients, and "it [is] impossible to accept as valid any of the results presented and raise serious concerns regarding the integrity of the peer review process for these papers," then write an abstract in May 1988 agreeing with us that this wide spectrum of behaviors did occur in TS patients?

Chapter 13

The Presidential Address

In 1988, I was president of the American Society of Human Genetics. The president had the option of giving a presidential address to the members. By precedent, this usually involved an analysis of some aspect of either the American Society of Human Geneticists, or some larger picture of the role of genetics in society.

From my years of working with Tourette syndrome, I knew in general what I wanted to say. It had become clear that mental health professionals felt that genetics was almost totally irrelevant to their profession. Most problems were due to learned behaviors or poor parenting, and genetics had little to do with these things. By contrast, most geneticists were equally uninterested in behavioral problems. They found great scientific and intellectual stimulation in studying rare genetic defects that caused disturbing changes in their patients' appearance or physical health, but the prospect of very common genes affecting behavior seemed as remote to many of them as it did to most mental health professionals. I felt that if our ideas were correct, it would require a massive re-education of mental health workers into the mysteries of genetics and a re-education of geneticists into the mysteries of mental health. This was what I wanted to talk about, and the title was "The Genetics of Human Behavior — Lessons for Two Societies."[31]

I had started writing the address many months before I received the Pauls et al. letter and had then set it aside. By the time I took it up again, we had received and responded to the letter from Pauls et al., and this exchange was published in August 1988, only a month before the meeting at which I was to give the address. Some thought I used this opportunity to further respond to Pauls. While some small part of this may have been correct, in essence the messages I wanted to convey had been written almost a year previously. This exchange of letters to the editor did, however, stimulate me to start the address with a reference to the XYY affair ten years previously and the potential dangers of talking about the genetics of human behavior. This comment turned out to be disturbingly prophetic.

Other parts of the address covered the evidence we had begun to accumulate that the frequency of alcoholism, drug addiction, and compulsive eating was increased in TS relatives. I suggested that compulsive drinking (alcoholism) in men and compulsive eating (obesity) in women might be the alternative ways in which males and females could express a *Gts* gene. After reiterating the idea that a spectrum of disorders might be caused by the *Gts* gene, I suggested that the

61

new science of chaos could offer an explanation as to why different people could express the *Gts* gene in such different ways. Chaos theory had its beginnings in the science of weather prediction[103] and basically stated that when complex systems are involved, no matter how much one knows about the variables put into the system, it is impossible to predict the outcome. The usual theories of behavior suggested that a relatively small percent of behavior was controlled by our genes, and everything else was controlled by our environment. I suggested that in the presence of certain genes, such as the *Gts* gene, a significant proportion of our behavior was controlled by genetics, and both environmental factors and chaos theory accounted for the rest.

The talk was in the morning and was well-received. At least no one stood up and booed. I had seen from the program, however, that at 2:45 in the afternoon of the same day, the Pauls et al. abstract was being presented. After what I had said in the presidential address just that morning, the abstract was, in essence, saying I didn't know what I was talking about. The following is a large portion of the abstract:

> "In a series of papers, Comings and Comings (*Am. J. Hum. Genet.* 41:701-866,1987) claimed that in addition to chronic tics and obsessive compulsive disorder, attention deficit disorder, conduct disorder, major depressive disorder, manic-depressive disorder, panic disorder, phobic disorders, schizoid disorders, sleep disorders, specific reading disability, and stuttering were also variant expressions of the *TS* gene. We have completed a family study of 86 probands and their 338 first degree biological relatives. Our results do not support the hypothesis proposed by Comings and Comings. In our current study only the rates of Tourette syndrome, chronic tics, and obsessive-compulsive disorder are significantly elevated among first degree relatives of the TS probands when compared to relatives of control probands."

As mentioned in the last chapter, they did, however, seem to retreat from the extreme position they had espoused in their letter to the editor, by also stating:

> "While the frequency of the other neuropsychiatric disorders in our proband sample are comparable to those reported by Comings and Comings..."

They then ended the abstract by saying,

> "...the rates of those disorders among first degree relatives are not significantly elevated when compared to their frequency in the control relatives and the general population."

When the afternoon session came, the room was packed. Pauls started out describing how only first-degree relatives (parents and siblings) were studied and using a structured questionnaire called the DIS – the same schedule we had incorporated into the questionnaire we used for our TS patients. In addition, two independent evaluators had to agree on the diagnoses before they would be accepted. He then briefly flashed the slide showing the high frequency of a wide range of different psychiatric diagnoses that had been made in the TS patients themselves (the probands). I tried to write them down but the slide was quickly gone. He then showed a slide comparing the frequency of these different psychiatric disorders in the relatives of TS patients versus the relatives of control subjects.

Although the data were not up long enough to copy, one aspect of it was clear – for about twelve of thirteen categories, a higher percentage of the TS relatives were affected by a given disorder than the relatives of controls. The other dramatic feature of the presentation was that he did not independently present the rates of psychiatric disorders in relatives with tics versus those without tics. This was crucial to his conclusion that the *Gts* gene was unrelated to a spectrum of disorders. If most of the disorders were more common in relatives with tics than relatives without tics, their conclusion that TS was not a spectrum disorder would have been invalidated.

Pauls ended with a strong statement that their data clearly did not concur with our hypothesis that the *Gts* gene was associated with a wide range of other psychiatric behavioral disorders. Even though the TS patients themselves had a high frequency of many different behavioral problems, as with the ADHD story, he stated these were all due to ascertainment bias and were not caused by the *Gts* gene.

I was at the microphone before he stopped talking. My first question was, "In your letter to the editor you stated that we were grossly incorrect by stating that TS patients had a wide range of other psychiatric disorders, and now, barely a month since that was published, you are saying we were correct. How do you explain that?"

His reply was, "We never said that. We just said these things were not present in the relatives."

"You clearly did say that, and anyone can read your letter," I replied. Next I asked, "Given the small number of patients you studied, for each disorder the difference may not be great enough to be significant. However, if they all have a common genetic basis, as we suggest, they should be additive and you should be able to put then into an "any behavior disorder" category. Have you looked to see if there is a significant difference for a "any behavioral disorder category?"

"No."

By that time Brenda wanted to ask him if he was a clinician and actually took care of TS patients, the answer to which was "No."

As we got up and left, I was wishing I could see the data in manuscript form with the results separated into relatives with and without TS. I felt that, once again, Pauls was making a type II error, and the best way to show it would be to compare the groups by making an "any behavioral disorder" category. From what I had seen in his tables, I was certain that if this was done, their data would show a significant difference between the relatives of TS patients versus the relatives of controls. I also wanted to see what would happen if their relatives were divided into those with and without chronic tics.

Chapter 14

The Arno Episode

As I mentioned earlier, Arno Motulsky had been my professor during my medical genetics fellowship when I was in Seattle. Brenda had never met him. As we were coming out of the lecture hall, I saw him standing outside the door, talking very loudly to a group of people. This was my chance to introduce Brenda, and we strode toward him with broad smiles. When I got close enough to hear what he was saying, though, the smile quickly faded. He was talking, or, more accurately, almost yelling, to a group of reporters, and it was obvious from the gist of it that he did not agree with our theories about TS. However, to simply say he did not agree was putting it mildly.

When he saw us he said, "I have been talking to reporters, but perhaps you don't want to continue the discussion; it is not very flattering." I didn't know how long he had been talking, but from what little we heard, I felt we had no choice but to try to defend ourselves.

We had often experienced this situation before, where people with the least clinical experience with TS had the strongest opinions that our results could not possibly be true, simply because they conflicted with their prior opinions about the causes of disturbed behavior. After listening to Pauls, Motulsky was obviously more convinced than ever that we were wrong and he was not mincing any words in his conversation with the reporters.

"This harkens back to the years of eugenics, when prostitutes and criminals were all thought to have a single defective gene. This is what led to the atrocities of Nazi Germany. This Tourette gene couldn't possibly cause all these things. I don't believe their ideas about serotonin or the limbic system disinhibition."

Brenda, who was Jewish herself, didn't buy the Nazism argument and said, "How many cases of Tourette syndrome have you seen?"

Motulsky replied, "a few," which experience told us usually meant "very few."

Sensing the helplessness of the situation, Brenda said, "Interview over." As we walked away, Brenda said to me, "You look terrible, like you are in shock."

"I feel that way," I replied.

For a couple of weeks, nothing appeared in the papers. I could not believe that with at least four reporters standing there, no one would pick up on such a potentially juicy story. One of the reporters was Lois Wingerson. She was writing a book, *Mapping Our Genes*,[220] and had asked for an interview later in the meeting. The book came out two years later, and in it she covered TS and gave a balanced account of this episode in the chapter, "The Case of the Hypothetical Culprit."

The lull was short-lived. On December 1, it "hit the fan."

The headlines across the country read:

"California Scientists' Discovery Termed a Colossal Mistake"

"Scientists' Claim Raises Furor"

"Husband and Wife Take Flak for Theory"

"Clash Over Theory for Behavior Disorders"

"Behavior Disorder Theory Leaves Scientists Clashing"

"Tourette's Debate Boils Over"

Most of the stories were put out from the Associated Press by Paul Raeburn and had the following flavor:

"A California geneticist and his psychologist wife say they have linked mental disorders, including mania, depression, hyperactivity, compulsive overeating and alcoholism, to a single, inherited genetic flaw.

"If they are right, the finding could revolutionize the treatment of mental illness. Difficult and expensive psychotherapy could be replaced with new drugs that would compensate for the genetic defect.

"However, some geneticists say Dr. David Comings and his wife, Brenda, are guilty of a colossal mistake or careless misuse of science.

"An angry debate over their work erupted recently at the annual meeting of the American Society of Human Genetics where David Comings, president of the society this year, used his presidential address to defend his findings.

"He detailed a long list of behavioral disorders that he said occurred with unusually high frequency in the relatives of people with Tourette syndrome.

"David Pauls of Yale University presented similar research that directly contradicted the Comings' findings. Pauls and his colleagues found no unusually high incidence of other disorders in families with Tourette syndrome.

"After Pauls presented his data and responded to critical questions from David Comings, geneticists lingered to continue the discussion. 'I disagree with you completely,' Dr. Arno Motulsky, professor of medicine and genetics at the University of Washington, told Comings. 'You make these grandiose schemes without evidence.'

"In Motulsky's view, that is a misuse of scientific data — making hypotheses that cannot be supported by the facts.

"'You revolutionize genetics if it's true — but I think it's very unlikely,' he said. David Comings was visibly hurt by his criticism; Motulsky had been his teacher.

"'I think you are making claims of genetics...I think you're doing genetics a disservice,' Motulsky continued, referring to the early Twentieth century, when laziness, prostitution and criminality were said to be the result of bad genes.

"The implication was that it was a good idea to sterilize such people, thereby ridding the population of undesirable traits, said Daniel Kevles, an historian at the California Institute of Technology and author of *In the Name of Eugenics: Genetics and the Uses of Human Heredity*.

"Making such generalizations had led to wildly erroneous and damaging misuse of science in the past and could easily do so again, Kevles said. He said he had not read the Comings' report and could not comment on it directly.

"Not everyone at the genetics meeting was critical of the Comings' work. Some praised the pair for their courage in proposing such a daring hypothesis.

"Dr. Victor McKusick of Johns Hopkins University, a medical geneticist who had done extensive family studies with the Amish in Pennsylvania, said, 'I lean toward the view that David Comings is closer to the truth. He's a perceptive person.'"

If this had simply been a brief flurry of publicity about dissenting opinions it would not have been a problem. Unfortunately, it was not that simple. The Pauls et al. letter to the editor, followed by the Pauls abstract, followed by the Motulsky outburst, cast a cloud over the entire area of research into the role of the *Gts* gene in behavioral disorders. Up until that time, it might still have been possible, although difficult to obtain some funds for this work. From this point on, getting papers published became even more difficult, and getting grants funded became impossible. In the parlance of grants, one usually hears that a grant was "approved, but not funded." This is the polite way of saying the reviewers didn't quite like the work enough to give it a high enough priority to fund it. By contrast, after this episode, most of our grants came back "disapproved." It is generally accepted that this means "even if there were an infinite amount of money, this grant would not be funded."

The maddening aspect was that we knew from our several thousand TS patients and families that we were on the right track; yet because of the objections of TSA, the Pauls et al. strident letter to the editor and abstract of a study with significant flaws, and these remarks, individuals with TS or its spectrum of related disorders were being disenfranchised. Research on this subject was considered "not in vogue" or "too highly controversial" and money to fund the research disappeared.

Chapter 15

The Controlled Family History Studies

The major point of contention was whether the associated behaviors that everyone seemed to agree were present in TS patients were also present in the relatives of TS patients who also had TS, so-called non-proband TS subjects. If these behaviors were simply due to ascertainment bias, as the Yale group claimed, they should not be present in non-proband TS individuals. If they were a result of the variety of ways the *Gts* genes could express themselves, as we believed, the behavioral problems should be present in non-proband TS patients at a greater frequency than in the general population. If the studies were large enough, they might also pick up increases in relatives who did not have TS. Having completed extensive studies on TS patients themselves, it was clear we now needed to analyze behavior in their relatives.

Pauls and co-workers had used what was called the family study technique. This involved interviewing each relative with the structured Diagnostic Interview Schedule. This had the advantage that it was more accurate for detecting symptoms that might be known only to the person himself. However, there were many disadvantages to this approach.

• It is very expensive because each individual has to be interviewed for several hours.

• The most severely disturbed relatives are often the ones most likely to be unavailable for interview, especially if they are in a mental hospital, in prison, living on the street, or have simply disappeared.

• Since the number of persons interviewed is relatively small, family history studies are susceptible to type II statistical errors.

• A form of reverse ascertainment bias can occur. For example, family studies require families in which both parents are available for interview, and this selects against using the more dysfunctional families in which parents are divorced, separated, or never married.

• Pauls and co-workers examined only the first-degree relatives (parents and siblings). This eliminated from consideration second- and third-degree relatives (aunts, uncles, and cousins). In our experience these individuals often had more severe problems than the parents. The reason for this is as follows: if an uncle was a chronic alcoholic, or in jail for drug dealing, or has other severe problems that keep him from marrying, holding a job, and having a family, he will never be included because he has no children. Only relatives who are parents of a TS child are studied.

We used the family history technique. This simply involved taking a detailed family history based on directly interviewing the TS patient, usually both parents, and the siblings. The information on uncles, aunts, and cousins was obtained from these individuals. The advantages of this approach are that it is:

• Very inexpensive.

• Large enough numbers of subjects can be included to avoid type II statistical errors.

• Aunts, uncles, and cousins are included.

• The most severely-affected relatives are included,

• It is very sensitive to major behavioral problems such as severe alcoholism, drug abuse, depression, manic-depressive disorder, agoraphobia, panic attacks, ADHD, learning disorders, homosexuality, and others. I have yet to have a parent tell me that a relative had a significant problem and find it was not true when there was an opportunity to personally interview that relative.

The disadvantage of the family history technique is that it is less sensitive to problems that people don't show or talk about, such as minor symptoms of depression, anxiety, or obsessive thoughts; however, in our study, if the symptoms were minor they were excluded anyway. The family history technique is a time-honored procedure used by medical geneticists for decades. Whereas the family study technique is usually considered to be more accurate, we have found that people are often more likely to cover up their own behavior than the behavior of their relatives. This is a further way in which the family history technique can be more accurate than the family study technique.

Over the Christmas vacation of 1988, I entered into the computer data on our last 130 consecutive family histories of TS patients and 25 controls from our prenatal diagnosis clinic. This gave 1,851 TS relatives and 541 control relatives.

Similar to the study in the abstract by Pauls et al., we found that the frequency of many behavioral problems was always greater in the first-degree relatives of TS patients compared with controls; however, because the numbers were small, the differences were not significant. However, when all the relatives (aunts, uncles and cousins) were included, the differences between TS relatives and control relatives *were* significant.

There was still the problem that by dividing behaviors into many different subcategories, such as depression, alcoholism, drug abuse, panic attacks, etc., the power of the study to pick up significant differences in each subgroup was diluted in proportion to the number of subgroups examined. However, if we collapsed all the subgroups into a "any behavioral problem" group, we might then find that the differences were highly significant. Now a type II statistical error would have been avoided. The results are shown in the following diagram:

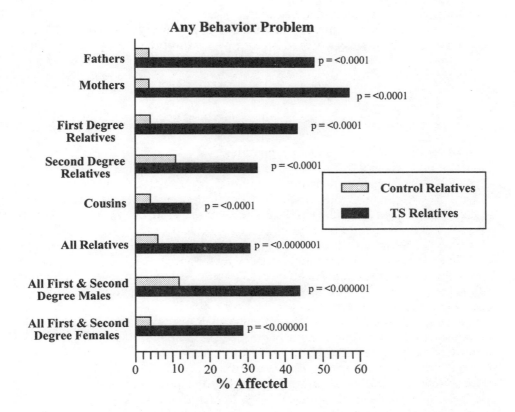

Any Behavior Problem

The differences between control and TS relatives were highly significant. This study went to the core of the controversy with the Yale group. They claimed that with the exception of obsessive-compulsive behaviors, the spectrum of disorders associated with TS was due to ascertainment bias and not to the *Gts* genes themselves. We claimed precisely the opposite — TS was a spectrum disorder and the *Gts* genes could cause any of a wide range of behavioral problems individually or in any combination. These family history studies on consecutive, unselected cases proved the point.

I submitted these papers with many detailed tables to the *Archives of General Psychiatry*. They were rejected. I shortened the manuscripts, took into consideration as many of the objections as I could, and re-submitted the three papers to the *Journal of Clinical Psychiatry*. Here the editor and reviewers were more sympathetic to the study, and they were published in August 1990.[57-59]

The *Journal of Clinical Psychiatry* also published a study that Ellen Knell and I had carried out, examining the prevalence of ADHD in the relatives of 131 TS probands.[131] By studying the relatives we avoided the problem of ascertainment bias in the probands. The high frequency of ADHD in the relatives with TS, but not in the relatives without TS, provided definitive proof that TS and ADHD were genetically related.

Chapter 16

Is the *TDO2* Gene
the "*Alcoholism* Gene"?

In January 1989, I was riding in the car to San Diego with Brenda. She had opened a part-time office in the area so the TS patients there didn't have to come so far for therapy. She was drove as I leafed through *Current Contents*, a listing of the table of contents of hundreds of medical and scientific journals. I saw listed under the *Journal of Alcoholism: Clinical and Experimental Research* a paper by Dr. Shirley Hill from Pittsburgh, entitled "Suggestive Evidence of a Genetic Linkage Between Alcoholism and the MNS Blood Group."[113] I knew this MNS blood group was also in 4q31, the same chromosome band we had found the *TDO2* gene to be on. The title literally leapt out at me.

When I finally obtained a copy of the paper, it reported a study of thirty families in which two or more members had early-onset hereditary alcoholism. By both linkage studies and a technique called "sib pair analysis," Hill had found preliminary evidence that this form of alcoholism was linked to the *MNS blood group* gene.

The exciting aspect of this for me was that our TS pedigrees repeatedly suggested that early-onset alcoholism was one of the most common ways the *Gts* gene was expressed, and we thought TS was due to a mutation of *TDO2* at 4q31. Here was a paper suggesting that an *alcoholism* gene was also on 4q31. The possibility that all this would happen by chance seemed remote. Here was objective evidence that the *Gts* gene and the *alcoholism* gene were in fact one and the same, as we thought. In addition, there were two studies that provided suggestive, but weaker, evidence that a gene for depression was also linked to the *MNS blood group*.[p679]

By this time, in the lab we had found a stretch of one hundred base pairs of the *HTO3 cDNA* clone that was 80% similar to the rat *TDO2* gene. This was a higher degree of similarity than usually seen between identical genes in rat and man. This gave us great confidence that we really had cloned the human *TDO2* gene. By the end of the month we had sent a paper off to *Nature* pointing out that a deficiency of serotonin was one of the major theories of alcoholism, that such a deficiency could be caused by a mutation of *TDO2*, that the human *TDO2* gene was localized to 4q31, and that Hill had found preliminary evidence that alcoholism was linked to 4q31. To me, the logical train of reasoning was clear-cut and exciting.

The reviewers were unimpressed. They felt that one hundred base pairs of similarity were not enough to prove that the *HTO3* clone represented the *TDO2* gene. This, despite the fact that it is generally agreed that twenty-five identical base pairs were enough to uniquely identify a gene sequence.

We then submitted the paper to *Science*. By this time the homologous region had extended to four hundred base pairs and the deduced amino acid sequences were 87% similar to those of the rat *TDO2*. *Science* also sent it back saying they would only be interested if we had found the specific mutation and proved that it was either the *TS* or the *alcoholism* gene.

To keep what I thought was an exciting development in the field of alcoholism from simply languishing in a series of unsuccessful review processes, I submitted abstracts describing these observations to the Tenth Gene Mapping Conference to be held in New Haven in June; to the American Society of Human Genetics for their fall meeting; and to the First World Congress of Psychiatric Genetics in Cambridge, England on August 3-5.

At the Gene Mapping Conference, this abstract, plus a second one with Donalan covering the in situ hybridization data, allowed the human *TDO2* gene to be officially placed at 4q31. Since two laboratories using two different approaches had gotten the same result, it was considered to have been confirmed.

The abstract sent to the American Society of Human Genetics was not accepted for presentation by either platform (a talk) or as a poster. This carried the implication that the program committee felt there were over six hundred abstracts that year that were more important than the possible identification of a gene for alcoholism — probably the single most common genetic disorder affecting man, and which cost society more than all of the other genetic disorders discussed at the meeting combined.

The First World Congress of Psychiatric Genetics

The third abstract went to a meeting that had been put together by Dr. Tim Crow, an English psychiatrist who was interested in the genetics of schizophrenia and had previously suggested that schizophrenia and manic-depressive disorders might share a common cause. He asked me to give summary comments on the Congress at the evening dinner on the final full day.

Several years earlier, Dr. Jeffrey Sverd had asked Brenda and me to present, with him, a symposium on Tourette syndrome at the American Academy of Child and Adolescent Psychiatry in Seattle. He is a psychiatrist and, as a member, was allowed to submit subjects for symposia. After the meeting, he and his wife became good friends. Our and Sverd's views on TS were identical. He also knew how to take detailed family histories and was seeing the identical patterns with many behavioral problems on both sides of the family, as we had observed. Sverd had a poster at this Congress that provided the first public, independent support for our hypothesis. In the abstract[205] he stated:

> "Comings and Comings argued that TS is inherited as a spectrum of neuropsychiatric disorders and that they may be expressed in the absence of tics. Evidence from clinical experience and research conducted at this center supports the Comings

and Comings' hypothesis that the wide array of disturbances in TS patients and relatives is an expression of the psychophysio-logic disturbance which underlies TS...A series of patients seeking psychiatric attention because of disabling psychiatric symptoms are presented. Diagnosis of an underlying TS diathesis was made for the first time as an incidental observation during the evaluation. Patients and families had never sought medical attention for tics. The pedigrees of the patients resemble remarkably those of the TS patients reported by Comings and Comings and include full-blown TS, chronic motor tic disorder, alcohol and drug abuse, major depression, bipolar disorder, obsessive-compulsive disorder, obesity, somatiform disorder, and pervasive developmental disorder. This experience cited suggests a significant relationship between TS and psychiatric disorders."

At least one person in the country believed us. We only had 250 million to go.

There were several other papers on TS at the Congress. They were all placed together in a short symposium. I led off the discussion by presenting the data suggesting that the *TDO2* gene was the *Gts* and *alcoholism* gene and possibly a major *depression* gene as well. The Yale contingent was barely able to suppress their extreme skepticism. Pauls presented the second paper. Everyone appeared to anticipate a renewed round of clashing, but he only reviewed his two-year-old study of the genetics of TS and its relationship to obsessive-compulsive disorder. No mention was made of TS and ADHD or TS and other psychiatric disorders. It was all very civil.

The Demise of the Manic-Depression and Schizophrenia Linkages

The most depressing aspect of the Congress was the report that the famous Amish linkage study, providing seemingly incontrovertible evidence that manic depressive disorder was linked to a gene on the short arm of chromosome 11, had fallen apart. Some additional members of the families had developed manic-depressive disorder who should not have carried the gene. In addition, new branches of the family had been added. Now, instead of strongly supporting the presence of a *manic-depressive* gene on chromosome 11, the evidence was even more strongly against it. In addition, no one could confirm the report of linkage of the *schizophrenia* gene to chromosome 5. Finally, a preliminary report suggestive of linkage of the gene for panic attacks had to be withdrawn.

The genetics of psychiatric disorders was in a massive state of disarray. Most Congresses are able to announce great progress in a field. The major message of this Congress was that the field had taken some giant steps backward. Many were discouraged and wondered if perhaps the diagnosis of psychiatric disorders might be so loose that linkage would never be found.

I now had the unenviable task of presiding over the wake. At the dinner I took the opportunity to point out that numerous abstracts at the Congress had suggested that different psychiatric disorders were part of a spectrum of related entities; that is, psychiatric disorders are rarely pure. Alcoholics often had

ADHD and conduct disorder as children, and as adults they frequently had anti-social personality disorder, panic attacks, and depression. The same type of multiple diagnoses, or so-called comorbidity, occurred in almost every psychiatric disorder. This, I suggested, was consistent with the possibility that instead of many separate, uncommon genes for each behavioral disorder, there were, instead, a small number of very common genes that, in different combinations, caused a wide range of different disorders. This could explain why the standard linkage techniques were not working. I suggested that chaos theory,[p651] other modifying genes, and a touch of environment, were adequate to explain why different people with the same or similar genes might have widely different symptoms. The applause was polite.

Continued Problems with the "Alcoholism" Paper

After returning home, I next took the *TDO2* gene localization paper to Dr. Gene Roberts in our institution. Roberts was a member of the National Academy of Sciences, and he submitted my paper to the *Proceedings of the National Academy of Sciences* for me. By now the region of homology between the rat and the human *TDO2* genes was over one thousand base pairs in length, and the similarity in the amino acid sequence remained high. There could be no question now that the rat and the human genes were the same, and the mapping part of the paper was straightforward.

One reviewer recommended acceptance with only minor revisions. The other reviewer had marked the box asking "Would this paper be of interest to a general scientific audience?" with "No." Roberts said he could not accept the paper.

I was incredulous. After some of the extraordinary esoterica that had been published in the *Proceedings*, here was a major clue to the cause of a disease affecting upward of 8% of the population, costing society billions of dollars every year, and "it was not of interest to a general scientific audience." Whoever this reviewer was, I wondered what he *would* consider to be of general scientific interest.

In the spring of 1990, I submitted the paper to the journal *Genomics*. One of the reviewers thought I should remove the speculation about its possible significance for alcoholism and TS. I fought this off, and after further revisions it was finally accepted in September 1990. It was over two years since first being submitted to *Nature* in January 1989 that the paper finally appeared in print.[76]

Chapter 17

The Book

By the fall of 1986, it had become clear to me that TS was such a richly complex disorder that it was impossible to present the whole picture in a few published papers. Only a book could do the subject justice. There were several books about TS, but they were all written for a professional audience, and none of them addressed the behavioral and other aspects of the disorder that we found so fascinating.

My patients were repeatedly telling me they would like to have a book about TS that they could understand. But they also wanted doctors to read it so there would be a broader understanding of the associated behaviors. It initially seemed that I would have to make a choice to write for one audience or the other. Over the years, however, I had come to develop a very healthy respect for the intelligence of my patients with TS and their families. Many of them had sought out and understood relatively technical material on TS. I knew that even the most complex subjects were easy to understand if they were explained without the shield of unnecessary technical jargon. It seemed that a step-by-step approach, explaining all new concepts as I went, would allow the book to be written for both audiences.

I started in August 1986. By July 1988, it was essentially finished, except for a few final chapters, writing an index, and proofreading. It was complete enough to begin to look for a publisher. Unfortunately, by this time the Pauls controversy was in full blossom, soon to be followed by the Motulsky affair.

The first publisher I tried was Plenum Press. I chose them because in 1972 I had written an extensive review of chromosome structure for their series *Advances in Human Genetics*. I liked the style of that book, and because this article was the most frequently cited one in the twelve years of the series, that seemed good for some brownie points with the publisher. Whether it was or was not, they were not interested.

My next try was with Oxford University Press. I chose them because my close friend, Dr. Richard Goodman, had published several books with them and was pleased. I had discussed the book with Goodman. He asked me what it was going to be called. When I told him I was thinking of *Tourette Syndrome – The Genetic Connection to Human Behavior*, he almost fainted.

"It needs a much sexier name than that," he said. "Most people have never heard of Tourette syndrome, and if they have, they think it is extremely rare. It will never sell. You need to call it *Genes and Your Behavior*, or something like that."

I had similar thoughts myself. I was caught between a loyalty to my patients with TS who needed to have doctors, teachers, and others become more familiar with their disorder, and the concern that such a title would doom the book to obscurity. In the end I thought I would be betraying my patients, their families, and myself if I left TS out of the title. I felt that with time, TS would gain more widespread recognition and, if it did not, the book would just have to remain as obscure as the disorder. I did, however, shorten the title to *Tourette Syndrome and Human Behavior*.

A potential problem with Oxford University Press was that, unknown to me at the time, Motulsky was the editor of their genetic books division. As expected, the reviews were both hot and cold.

> "Dr. Comings is a very bright and imaginative geneticist who has proposed revolutionary ideas on the pathogenesis and genetics of Tourette's syndrome. Most of these ideas are so new that they have not yet been fully evaluated or accepted by the medical community. Among his many concepts is one that would link many symptoms of aberrant behavior to the Tourette gene. He may well be right, and his ideas certainly are thought-provoking. The proposed book is one that expresses his personal view of Tourette's syndrome and does not express the consensus of opinion on this disorder; thus it will be very controversial.
>
> "One of my major concerns is that it is written for patients and their families, and I wonder if it would not be overwhelming for them. It may also frighten them to think that this one gene could cause so many behavioral changes. If a patient has one aspect of Tourette's syndrome, wouldn't he be fearful that he may develop all these symptoms sometime during his life?"

Although there some truth to this, our experience was mostly the opposite. When TS patients developed some of the associated behavioral problems, they often thought they were going crazy and that something was dreadfully wrong with them. This feeling was often enhanced when their doctor told them they were emotionally disturbed and needed to see a psychiatrist. Upon realizing these were all manifestations of TS, were treatable, and that they were not crazy, they experienced a feeling of enormous relief. Many of them truly understood the behavior problems in their relatives only after the diagnosis was made.

Another reviewer said:

> "It seems fairly clear that TS is a serious disorder, often familial, and sometimes associated with attention deficit disorder symptoms and obsessive-compulsive behavior. But, how common is the TS gene? In fact, is there really only a single TS gene? Is that single gene really responsible for most of the other forms of abnormal behavior found in other relatives of TS patients?
>
> "Furthermore, it is not yet generally accepted that TS is primarily a defect in serotonin metabolism, nor is it documented

that TS is primarily a 'disinhibition of the limbic system.' These two conclusions are likely to be overly simplistic at best, and completely inaccurate at worst.

"I should also note that Dr. Comings writes well, has evaluated a large number of patients with the diagnosis of TS and has clearly given a great deal of thought to this disorder. He may even turn out to be mostly correct! But I for one believe his speculations run far ahead of the available data."

A comment from a reviewer for another publisher, John Hopkins University Press, was one of my favorites. We had observed that many of the psychiatric disorders had overlapping symptoms and different relatives in a single family often had different disorders. To us this suggested a genetic relatedness. In response to this the reviewer stated,

"It is obvious that reasoning by analogy could be taken to the extreme which would allow you to say that a dog is analogous to a cat because they each have a snout with a wet nose, pointed ears, forward-looking eyes, fur, a tail, and four legs."

I wrote back that "if I found hundreds of pedigrees which contained both cats and dogs I would begin to seriously wonder if they were not genetically related." Another one of my favorites from the same reviewer was,

"There is a great deal of reasoning by analogy from animal experimentation and human brain lesions. This is a very weak approach. Lower animals are not human beings...and reasoning by analogy from human disorders is also a very weak approach."

I thought that if I could not use information from either animal or human data, what was that supposed to leave? I mused that the National Institutes of Health had spent billions of dollars on animal and human studies in the past thirty years and might find it interesting that this reviewer thought it was all worthless. I suspected I was experiencing a paradigm wall in which these ideas were so new, different, or controversial that no one was willing to say they should be published.

The editor for The University of California Press wrote back,

"As someone who is finding himself in the midst of a controversy, you will probably not be surprised to hear that we have had a little trouble finding dispassionate reviewers."

I replied to one of the editors,

"The basic concept I propose is remarkably simple, but, as has been stated by others,[132] entrenched scientific paradigms are extraordinarily hard to change. Such changes come in three stages. In stage one, everyone thinks the idea is crazy. In stage two, evidence begins to accumulate that the paradigm is correct. In stage three, the paradigm shift, the concept is considered so clear and so obvious, that people wonder what all the fuss was about. Unfortunately, this one is still in stage one."

It was clear from these four publishers that the idea that TS was a spectrum disorder and that a number of psychiatric defects might be genetically interrelated by common *Gts* genes was far too controversial for any of them to risk their reputations on. The ideas were "innovative and exciting," but there was too much of a possibility that I was wrong and too many people were offended by the thought that many behaviors could have a strong genetic component. Too many professionals were threatened by the idea that in some cases psychotherapy might be replaced by medication. Too many people who had never seen a case of TS or had never taken a behaviorally-oriented family history were convinced TS couldn't possibly be what I thought it was.

Hope Press

In February of 1989, I had a TS patient who was somewhat of a literary figure and had authored several books. We were discussing the problems I was encountering in trying to get the TS book published. I was caught in a paradox. The book was written to show that TS was more than just a tic disorder, was quite common, and had relevance to a wide range of behavioral disorders that most professionals thought were caused by environmental factors or a large number of different genes; yet the very misperceptions I was trying to fight were so deeply entrenched in the minds of those who were asked to review the book that I couldn't get it past them to get it published. I was caught in another Catch-22.

My patient asked me how I was writing and illustrating the book.

"On a Macintosh, of course," I said.

"Then that is your answer," he replied. "Computers are dramatically changing the world of publishing. Small publishers, with a select group of books, can now successfully compete with the largest publishing companies. Set up your own publishing company and publish it yourself."

It seemed like a formidable and almost impossible task. I went to the bookstore and purchased half a dozen books on publishing and setting up a small company. The more I read the more excited I became. I decided to call my new company "Hope Press," in honor of the institution I had been at for twenty-five years and the institution that had continued to support the research through all these difficulties, the City of Hope Medical Center. The logo was:

representing the genetic uncertainty of having children — the uncertainty of what we will get when we and our spouse mix our genes.

The process of producing a book was simpler than I thought. I purchased a copy of Pagemaker®, a desktop publishing software program, and set the entire book up in pages. This took three months. I then put together the index which took another two months. I called the copy editor who had worked for me when I was editor of the *American Journal of Human Genetics* and hired her to check the book for errors — a process that is never complete and which never removes all the errors. While she was doing this, I sent review copies to several experts on TS who actually saw TS patients. I also sent copies to Levi and several other medical and scientific advisors for TSA, asking them to write back if they found anything they didn't like. I never heard back from any of them. Once a pristine, corrected copy was in the computer, the next step was to send the disks off to have the pages directly printed in linotronic, high-resolution type.

A critical step was the design of the cover. I found a very talented graphic artist, also with a Macintosh, just a few miles away. I wanted the many disorders that TS was relevant to listed on the cover. The artist's job was to find a way to do this that was not overwhelming. I wanted the cover to be red, but Brenda's favorite color was purple. The artist did a remarkable job of pulling all these things together with a purple book listing the associated behaviors in red and a white title. We were both thrilled with the result.

By this time, I was so into the excitement of publishing that when one of my patients came to me with a superb book she had written about her son with TS, I decided to publish it as well. It was called *RYAN — A Mother's Story of Her Hyperactive/Tourette Syndrome Child* by Susan Hughes, which served as a perfect companion to the larger tome.

One of the most difficult tasks was to obtain cataloging in publication registration with the Library of Congress. This was critical for libraries who wanted to stock the book because it formatted the information about the book for the library cards. Two months of FAXing messages finally accomplished that

Once all of this was complete, the printer, Griffin Printers of Glendale, did the rest. The first copies of both books rolled off the press in January 1990. Only ten months from the time I thought the manuscript would never see the light of day, I had set up a publishing company and published two books. This was almost a year faster than the established companies were promising for a single book.

The entire operation of writing the 828-page book, making the 630 illustrations, setting up the pages, sending out letters, maintaining a mailing list, checking credit card numbers via modem, invoicing, billing, and accounting, was all handled by six programs on a single Macintosh IIx computer with a laser printer, occupying an office of less than six by ten feet in my home. This was a clear example of the electronics age run amok. Working a half-day a week, my step-daughter, Nicole, ran the mailroom in the garage.

By November of 1990, the red ink was gone, the books were ready for their second printing and were carried by the major wholesale book distributors. Hope Press was in the black, and we were working on a third and fourth book on TS, one written for children from a child's point of view by a child with TS, entitled *Hi, I'm Adam. A Child's Book About Tourette Syndrome* by Adam Beuhrens. The fourth book by the same child and his mother, Carol, was called *Adam and the*

Magic Marble. This was a delightful fantasy story about two boys with TS and a friend with cerebral palsy. They discover a magic marble that takes away their symptoms...and the adventure begins.

The fifth book was by AdamWard Seligman's, called *Echolalia*.

The sixth book was an anthology of short biographical stories by fourteen individuals with TS, edited by Adam Ward Seligman and John S. Hilkevich, entitled *Don't Think About Monkeys — Extraordinary Storied Written by People with Tourette Syndrome*.

Next to science and TS itself, publishing was one of the most exciting and rewarding adventures I had undertaken. Ironically, the book that no one wanted was to become, according to many patients, their "Bible." Many thousands of copies had been sold, and the profits helped to support the research no one wanted to fund.

Chapter 18

The Hypothetical *Gts* Mutation

By early 1990 we had sequenced the entire expressed part of the human *TDO2* gene. This is the part that forms the TDO2 enzyme. Normally, this would be enough to begin looking for a disease causing mutation. However, I strongly suspected that the mutation we were seeking was going to be in the regulatory region of the *TDO2* gene, not the expressed region. This is the part that is "upstream" to the expressed portion and contains the regions that control how effectively the gene works. This is due, in part, to the presence of short DNA sequences, called promoters, that interact with the enzymes that read the genetic code.

The sequence of the promoters of the rat *TDO2* gene had been published by Schmid and co-workers in 1982.[190] These sequences are similar for different genes and different species. There are also two regions called Glucocorticoid Response Elements or GREs. These are short stretches of DNA that bind to steroid hormones. Such binding activates the *TDO2* gene, which is the reason why this enzyme responds so well to these hormones.[p476]

Not only did I suspect that the *Gts* mutation was in the regulatory region of the *TDO2* gene, I even suspected which of only two base pairs were the site of the mutation. In 1986 Myers, Tilly, and Maniatis[152] published a report of a study of the promoter regions of the human hemoglobin gene. They showed that two unique mutations were capable of increasing the activity of the gene. Because this same promoter was present in the rat *TDO2* gene, and since in order for the *TDO2* gene to cause a decrease in serotonin it had to show increased activity or expression, I wondered whether a similar mutation might be the cause of TS and all of its associated behaviors.

To prove this we needed to clone the regulatory region of the human *TDO2* gene. By early 1990 we had isolated a very large clone that we thought would include this critical region. Unfortunately, after spending many months of cutting it up and sequencing the pieces, we concluded it did not contain the regulatory sequences we wanted. It was back to square one, and I asked Donn to search for another clone.

Another approach that we tried used a powerful technique called Polymerase Chain Reaction, or PCR. After the O.J. Simpson trial, the whole world had heard of PCR. It works as follows: If we know the sequence of a stretch of DNA, we can easily make or synthesize short pieces of DNA flanking both ends. Because these pieces contain only a small number of base pairs, they are called *oligo*nucleotides. *Oligo* stands for few, and nucleotides are the base pairs. We call them "oligomers" for short.

If we put oligomers A and B in a test tube and add an enzyme (DNA polymerase) that synthesizes new DNA, the region between the two oligomers can be amplified millions of times.

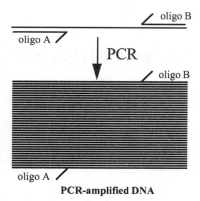

PCR-amplified DNA

The problem we had, however, was that we did not know the sequences "upstream" to the regulatory region; thus we had only one of the two oligomers (#14) needed to PCR the promoter region. Without its partner, it just sat there staring off in the direction region we wanted to sequence.

We began to wonder if we would ever be able to determine if our hypothetical mutation was really there.

[P.S. For those readers interested in more details, the map of this region of the rat *TDO2* gene looked like this:]

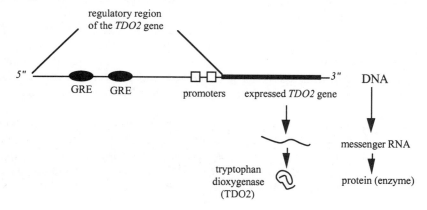

Chapter 19

The American Psychiatric Association TS Symposium

In 1989 we came to know Dr. Gordon Strauss, a psychiatrist at UCLA. Strauss decided to sponsor a symposium on Tourette syndrome at the American Psychiatric Association (APA) meeting in New York the following year. Having been aware of the uproar surrounding our studies of behavior in TS, Strauss wanted to get the major players together to discuss these issues. Because the organizers of the APA meeting actually preferred subjects involving some controversy, this seemed ideal. The symposium was entitled "Tourette Syndrome: Current Controversies." The speakers were Pauls, Kurlan, Dr. Mary Robertson, me, and Oliver Sacks, who at the last minute couldn't come and was replaced by Bruun.

Long plane journeys always provide me with an opportunity to catch up on reading journals, and on the ride to the symposium, I pulled the May issue of the *American Journal of Psychiatry* out of my briefcase. Fortuitously, in this issue there was an article of great relevance to the upcoming TS symposium. Drs. Hudson and Pope from McLean Hospital in Boston had an article entitled "Affective Spectrum Disorder: Does Antidepressant Response Identify a Family of Disorders with a Common Pathophysiology?"[116] Based on an extensive review of the literature, they noted that the following behavioral disorders all responded well to tricyclic or other antidepressant medications:

- attention deficit hyperactivity disorder
- obsessive-compulsive disorder
- major depression
- migraine headaches
- cataplexy (part of narcolepsy)
- bulimia
- irritable bowel syndrome
- panic attacks

They concluded that all of these disorders had a common basic cause, that the condition was one of the most common disorders affecting humans, and that there was a single etiologic step between the basic chemical defect and the symptoms. In addition, there were a number of disorders that almost fulfilled their criteria for inclusion. These were:

- post-traumatic stress disorder
- anorexia nervosa
- social phobias
- general anxiety
- Tourette syndrome
- obstructive sleep apnea

This article was of considerable interest because their affective spectrum disorder was a precise match to our Tourette syndrome spectrum disorder.[33] The only differences were that we also included alcoholism, drug abuse, and compulsive eating with obesity among the obsessive-compulsive behaviors. The concepts were identical, even down to the presumption that the basic cause was extremely common, involved serotonin metabolism, and that only a single step separated the defect from the effect on behavior.[p660] They left it as a common defect in metabolism. We saw it as a common gene or set of genes.

The symposium was held in the evening in the large ballroom of the New York Sheraton Hotel. As the initial speaker, I pointed out that we were beginning to see more agreement than disagreement about the clinical picture of TS. I noted that when the data in the two Pauls' papers on the issue of whether TS and ADHD were related were combined,[135,165] the results were identical to what we had obtained. I also reviewed what little I knew of his study reported at the American Society of Human Genetics meetings in 1987, claiming that first-degree relatives of TS patients did not show a significant increase in the frequency of a variety of behavioral disorders, compared to control families. This concurred with our family history-family study findings.[57-59] Because the number of first-degree relatives (parents, siblings and children) in both studies were relatively low, and because each individual behavioral disorder was relatively uncommon, there were not enough cases to statistically prove whether there was an increase of these disorders in first-degree relatives.

The striking feature was that in almost every category of behavior, more relatives of TS patients were affected than relatives of controls; thus if we looked at an "any behavioral disorder" category,[p645] the difference between parents and siblings of TS and controls was quite significant. Also, if we looked at all relatives, a total of 2,392, the differences in individual behaviors such as ADHD-learning disorder, depression, manic-depression, alcoholism-drug abuse, and others, were highly significant, indicating these disorders were all part of the expression of the *Gts* gene. I also pointed out the remarkable similarity between our TS spectrum disorder and the conclusion of Hudson and Pope, and presented some preliminary data on our findings concerning mutant dopamine receptor genes in TS (see next chapter).

Pauls was the next speaker, and for the first time I had a chance to copy down some of the results of the paper he first gave two years ago. He reiterated that when the TS patients themselves were examined, there was a significant increase over controls in a wide range of behavior problems, including obsessive-compulsive behaviors, attention deficit disorder, depression, anxiety, sleep, and other disorders. In looking at the relatives, there was an increased frequency in the TS relatives for twelve out of thirteen types of behavior problem. While they were only significant for obsessive-compulsive behaviors, the increased frequency in alcoholism was striking – 17% in the TS relatives versus 0% in the control relatives. However, because of the small number of total relatives, neither alcoholism nor any of the other behaviors, except obsessive-compulsive behaviors, were significantly different from controls.

Kurlan was the next speaker. He reported his studies with Pauls of the large Canadian TS pedigree. At the end he concluded, "We now believe that ADHD is part of the TS spectrum." After the meeting, he confided to Brenda that Pauls now seemed to agree with this idea.

The essence of this meeting was superbly reported in the July 21 issue of *Science News* by Bruce Bower, with the leader reading "Many mental disorders and a few crucial genes may tie into Tourette's syndrome." In a news report called "The Ticking Link," he led off with an eloquent 1902 description of a Frenchman identified only as "O" who bared his soul in print under the title "*Les Confessions d'un Ticquer.*" His physicians wrote that when the pressure to tic became too great, "O" would retreat to an empty room, "abandoning himself in his moment of solitude to a veritable debauch of absurd gesticulations, a wild muscular carnival, from which he return[ed] comforted, to resume sedately the thread of uninterrupted dialogue."

I was impressed because Bower had come up with an article I had never heard of before. He accurately described our studies of the epidemiology of TS in schoolboys, our family history studies of 1,851 TS relatives and 541 relatives of controls, and serotonin studies. He included some of the controversial issues that had been brought up, and concluded with a description of Oliver Sacks' "Super Tourette's."

After the symposium I was greatly encouraged by the comments in the TSA newsletter of Dr. Harvey Dean, the new TSA president. He stated that:

> "The public needs to know that there is more to Tourette Syndrome than motor and vocal tics. Behavioral aspects (i.e. obsessive compulsive behavior, attention deficit disorder, etc.) and other characteristics that are often a part of the Syndrome need to be integrated into the public's collective conscience. I frequently hear from parents about how the behavioral aspects of TS are far more limiting than the vocal and motor tics. We need to get this 'new' message across to what I hope is now a more concerned, educated and empathetic public."

It was also interesting to note that in the same newsletter there was a report of the Fifth TSA-Sponsored Genetic Workshop. Although I had participated in the First TSA Genetic Workshop, I had not been invited to participate in any of the subsequent ones. TSA had funded a number of laboratories around the world to attempt to find the *Gts* gene by linkage analysis.[p54] This approach assumed that TS was caused by a dominant gene. If our hypotheses were correct, none of the laboratories would be able find the *Gts* gene.[p680,61] Perhaps they didn't want to hear any of this heresy.

The newsletter report stated that the members of the workshop team had now excluded the *Gts* gene from 70% of the chromosomes and were looking forward to finding the gene on one of those few remaining chromosomes yet to be studied. I wondered how far toward excluding all 100% of the chromosomes they would have to go before beginning to realize that possibly the autosomal dominant theory might be incorrect.

Chapter 20

Dopamine Receptors and the *"Alcoholism* Gene"

In March 1990 I received a call from a reporter from the *Wall Street Journal* asking if I had heard about the discovery of the *"alcoholism* gene." She stated that Dr. Blum from the University of Texas and Dr. Noble from UCLA were reporting in the *Journal of the American Medical Association* that 69% of severe treatment-resistant alcoholics carried a genetic variant of the *dopamine D2 receptor*[p370] gene.[7] By contrast, this variant was present in only 20% of normal controls. She wanted to know what I thought of this report.

I have always dreaded these types of calls because reporters want an instant critique of a paper that one has not yet had a chance to read and digest. I said, "That sounds like an exciting result."

Her next question was, "Do you think this is ready to be used as a test for alcoholism?"

Attempting to be as prudent as possible, I replied that, "First, it is necessary to have the results verified by other workers." Because I was convinced that the primary defect in alcoholism was more likely to be a mutation in the *TDO2* gene affecting serotonin levels in the brain, I added, "There is also a possibility that the *D2 receptor* gene is modifying the action of another gene."

The next day, when the story appeared, a friend called, saying, "I see from the *Wall Street Journal* you think they have the wrong gene." I thought, Gulp. I hadn't meant to be that critical. I was just raising that as an alternative possibility.

A few days later, still before I had a chance to read the paper, a writer from the *British Medical Journal* called and wanted me to elaborate further on my statements in the *Wall Street Journal*. I stated that I had not meant to be that negative, and this time I suggested that the most likely connection between alcoholism and dopamine might be through the role of the dopamine on ADHD. A major theory of the cause of ADHD was that too little dopamine was present in the frontal lobes.[p394] One of the major disorders of childhood that predisposes to alcoholism in adults is ADHD.[p227] Because of these two observations, I suggested that the increased frequency of the dopamine D_2 receptor variant in alcoholism might actually reflect an increased frequency of the variant in ADHD.

Tourette Syndrome, ADHD and the Dopamine Receptor Variant

When I finally had a chance to read the original article, I was struck by the

89

similarity between the figures of Blum et al.[7] and what I assumed was going on in TS. For example, our genetic studies suggested that many individuals with TS inherited genes from both parents,[66] and our studies in a Los Angeles school district suggested that TS was present in 1 in 90 school boys.[71] If these two assumptions were correct, then up to18% of the general population would be carriers of the *Gts* gene.[33] This was remarkably close to the 20% of the population carrying the D_2A1 variant of the *dopamine receptor* gene. Since some, but certainly not all, alcoholism might be related to the *Gts* gene, it would be expected that about two-thirds of alcoholics would carry the *Gts* gene. These figures were remarkably close to those that Blum et al. were quoting. Linkage studies had reported that the *dopamine D2 receptor* gene was not linked to TS.[85,99] However, these reports were based on the assumption that TS was an autosomal dominant disorder. If, as we suspected, TS was inherited as a semidominant-semirecessive disorder, then these linkage reports could be in error. This led me to wonder, Is the *Tourette syndrome* gene actually the *dopamine D2 receptor* gene?"

A year prior to this, Dr. Oliver Civilli from the University of Oregon sent us the probe for the *dopamine D2 receptor (DRD2)* gene, so we already had it in the laboratory. We began to examine the frequency of the D_2A1 variant in DNA samples from over a hundred of our TS patients. For the controls we used subjects from a wide range of sources. Of the 102 controls, 23% carried the D_2A1 variant. Of the 114 TS patients, 48% carried the D_2A1 variant. This was a highly significant difference. If we just looked at those with severe TS, the frequency increased to 55%. If we examined children with ADHD but no tics and no family history of tics, the frequency of the D_2A1 variant was just as high as in the TS subjects.

By looking at how the D_2A1 variant traveled in families, it was evident the *D2 receptor* gene was *not* the *Gts* gene or the *ADHD* gene. However, it clearly had an influence on the symptoms because so many more TS and ADHD patients carried the gene than controls. This suggested it was what geneticists call a *modifier* gene, that is, a gene which modifies the effect of another gene.

These results were very exciting. After many years of searching for specific genes that played a role in TS and ADHD, here finally was a clear-cut example of a gene that was involved. In addition, it made great sense. The *D2A1* gene variant was associated with lower brain levels of the D_2 receptor.[155] This may have led to a relative deficiency of dopamine activity in the frontal lobes, which in turn released control over the lower brain structures, resulting in hyperactivity and tics.[p394] This helped to explain why Ritalin, Dexedrine, and Cylert, the three major medications used in the treatment of ADHD, were effective. These were supplying dopamine to the frontal lobes, compensating for the genetic deficiency of dopamine activity.

This was also good news for children with ADHD, since this is one of the most misunderstood disorders of childhood. Many health professionals, teachers, and others have claimed ADHD either does not exist or is so ambiguous that the term is meaningless. In fact, ADHD has as well a defined set of symptoms as any other syndrome. People just view it differently because the symptoms affect behavior rather than something one can see, such as eye color or height. Even though we had not found the primary gene causing ADHD, the D_2 receptor findings provided the first clear indication that ADHD was, in fact, a specific genetic entity.

Finally these results were also consistent with the possibility that the major gene causing TS or ADHD was still *TDO2,* which affected serotonin, because dopamine and serotonin tended to work together like a see-saw. Anything that decreased the level of serotonin or increased the level of dopamine, or at least the sensitivity of dopamine receptors, increased aggressive and sexual behavior.[p378] One of the things that could increase the sensitivity of the dopamine receptors in some parts of the brain was a decrease in dopamine, or dopamine activity, in other parts of the brain.[p393]

Within three weeks we had written up the results and sent an abstract in for the fall meeting of the American Society of Human Genetics[75] and a full report to the English journal *Nature.* I was somewhat surprised to get the *Nature* report back in the mail with a brief note saying they were not interested. Perhaps this reflected the long-held belief in England that ADHD was mostly an American disorder. In England they tend to label these children as having conduct disorder, emphasizing the behavior rather than the poor attention span. Or perhaps it reflected a new policy to avoid articles on the genetics of behavior, after they had to retract the report of apparent linkage between manic-depressive disorder and chromosome 11. Or maybe there were other "perhapses" we were unaware of. After a brief rewrite, I called one of the editors of *Science* to make sure they were at least interested in reviewing it. She assured me they were and it was sent off.

While this initial report was being reviewed, I became more and more excited about the implications of this work. Everyone agreed that the genetics of common behavioral disorders was going to be much more difficult to pin down and more complex than more clear-cut diseases with a well-defined mode of inheritance, such as Huntington's disease, muscular dystrophy, or cystic fibrosis; yet here was a major inroad into this murky area. I still felt that the *Gts* gene was going to be a major gene underlying a wide range of behavioral disorders, but here was a mechanism by which some of the variability in expression of the *Gts* gene could be explained by the added effect of a gene which regulated dopamine function. I also wondered if other disorders such as schizoid behaviors, autism, panic attacks, depression, conduct disorder, and compulsive eating would also show a significant increased frequency of the D_2A1 variant.

Schizophrenia

I was particularly interested in looking at schizophrenia, because it was widely believed to be due to abnormalities of dopamine, and was usually treated with haloperidol, a dopamine D_2 receptor inhibitor.[p370] We had DNA samples from the brains of individuals who had died of schizophrenia. Of twenty-six samples we examined, only a third showed the D_2A1 variant. Although this was not statistically significant, it was high enough to keep us interested. However, when additional cases were examined, the percent carrying the D_2A1 variant did not increase.

Autism

We also examined patients with autism.[p215] This was a relatively rare, but devastating, disorder characterized by a profound degree of social withdrawal, delayed speech, and many ritualistic behaviors. It is also called pervasive developmental disorder (PDD). In 1987, Drs. Larry Burd and Jacob Kerbeshian, from Grand Forks, North Dakota, had reported that of fifty-two children they had studied with pervasive developmental disorder, sixteen or 20% developed classic TS symptoms as they grew older.[16] By the time we began our studies of the D_2 receptor, we had also observed sixteen patients with Tourette syndrome who had previously been diagnosed as autistic.[60] Sverd, in New York, had observed thirteen similar cases.[201] These observations led us to believe that, in some cases, children born with two *Gts* genes could start out life with symptoms of autism. As they grew older, the motor and vocal tics would begin and the true diagnosis become apparent. This suggested that some cases of autism or PDD represented a severe form of TS and led to the question, "Why did these children have more severe problems than others?" One possibility was that, in addition to the *Gts* genes, they also inherited one or more modifier genes. I suspected that the D_2A1 variant would be a good candidate.

About two years earlier I had met Dr. Ray Crowe, a research psychiatrist at the University of Iowa. We were discussing a study he was doing on the possible role of X-linked genes in autism. Suspecting that some day the *Gts* gene might be linked to autism, I asked him if he would mind sending me some of the DNA left over from these studies, and he did. We pulled these out of the refrigerator and tested them for the D_2A1 variant. About 50% of the sixteen samples were positive, over twice the frequency in controls. This was consistent with the fact that some autistic children improved when treated with haloperidol. However, as with the schizophrenic patients, I needed more samples. I called Sverd at the Sagamore Children's Psychiatric Center. As a practicing child and adult psychiatrist, he was seeing children with autism, or PDD, on a regular basis and felt he could easily get some blood samples for me. When all of these were combined, along with samples of our own, 54.5% of thirty-three autistic children carried the D_2A1 variant, significantly different from normal.

Alcoholism

We were also interested in seeing if we could verify the finding of Blum and colleagues of an increased frequency of the D_2A1 variant in alcoholism. Because our family history studies in TS had also shown that both alcoholism and drug addiction were increased in relatives, we also wanted DNA samples from drug addicts. Here a friendship with Dr. James MacMurray of the Department of Psychiatry at the Jerry L. Pettis V.A. Hospital in Loma Linda was invaluable. MacMurray and I looked at the world of psychiatry with the same vision that many behaviors were biochemically driven. He also was particularly intrigued by the role of serotonin in many psychiatric disorders. After our preliminary results with TS and ADHD, I sent him a copy of the original manuscript, and we were both very excited about testing alcoholics and drug addicts. He was in a superb position to do this since he was head of the addiction unit at this V.A. hospital.

MacMurray related that these patients were extremely willing to participate in the research and would do anything to help understand their addictions. He told me one story that drove home the point.

He walked into the blood-drawing lab one day to find one of his patients hanging upside down with his legs wrapped around a pullup bar and a needle dripping blood from a neck vein. This patient was an IV drug user whose veins were so bad the technician couldn't draw blood. Not wanting to lose the opportunity to be studied, he hung himself upside down and put the needle in a jugular vein!

We also made further use of the National Neurological Research Bank in Los Angeles. This was an invaluable resource run by neurologist Dr. Wallace Tourtellotte. Many years ago, Tourtellotte had the foresight to realize that many of the important neurological and psychiatric disorders were basically chemical in nature, and to study this chemistry would require frozen brain samples. We already had a number of samples from alcoholics and other patients from this source, left over from our studies of Pc1 Duarte, a mutant brain protein we had studied years previously.[29] Blum had also used this resource in his study, and we called to make sure we were not studying the same patients. Using samples from MacMurray's clinic and from the brain bank, we found that 45% of forty alcoholics/drug addicts carried the D_2 variant. Although not as high as in the original Blum study, this was significantly higher than the controls. It did suggest to us that the D_2A1 variant probably played a role in some forms of addiction. We needed more patients and needed to determine if some sub-groups carried the D_2A1 variant, whereas others did not.

Conduct Disorder

Ever since we began to see significant problems with conduct disorder[p131] in one-third to one-half of our TS patients, I had been fascinated by the role of genetic factors in this troubling behavior. This approach was in stark contrast to the usual assumption that severe conduct problems were always learned behaviors and usually due to poor parenting or environmental factors. Parents are always blamed if their child misbehaves. Sometimes it is their fault; oftentimes it is not.

Most of the cases of severe TS and many of the children with ADHD we had already studied had conduct disorder; however, we had DNA on seven patients with conduct disorder who did not have TS or ADHD. Of these, six, or 86%, carried the D_2A1 variant. This was significantly increased over the controls. Although the numbers were small, the trend suggested this disorder would also be associated with the D_2A1 variant. This was not surprising, because dopamine had long been linked to aggressive behavior.

Other Disorders

Crowe's primary interest was in panic attacks. These are sudden episodes of anxiety that usually last only a few minutes but can be very frightening.[p175] Crowe was doing linkage studies trying to identify the chromosome carrying the gene for panic attacks. Since we felt that panic attacks were part of the TS spectrum,[50,54] I wondered if subjects with panic attacks would also tend to carry the D_2A1 allele. Crowe was able to send us DNA from thirteen patients. Of these, only 23% carried the D_2A1 variant, the same frequency as in our controls.

Although the numbers were small, this suggested that panic attacks were not going to be one of the conditions modified by the D_2A1 variant.

For testing depression and manic-depressive disorder, we examined the forty samples of DNA from the brains used in our studies of Pc1 Duarte. Of these, 27% showed the D_2A1 variant. This was not significantly different from the controls.

By this time we had gotten the paper back from *Science*. They had rejected it. Some of the reasons seemed incredible. One reviewer thought there might be differences in the DNA from lymphocyte cultures versus lymphocytes from the blood. If there was one clear principle from genetics, it was that a person's DNA was the same, regardless of which type of tissue it was taken from. Except for rare exceptions, such as the proteins involved in making antibodies, the DNA from different tissues is identical. I felt there was not a single comment that was not easy to rebut.

There was, however, a positive side to the rejection, in that since submitting the paper to *Science*, we had now examined more than twice as many subjects and had data on autism, alcoholism, drug addiction, schizophrenia, panic attacks, depression and additional patients with ADHD. It was now a much stronger paper. We sent the revised manuscript to the *New England Journal of Medicine*.

After returning from combat in Vietnam, many veterans had a wide range of problems, including alcohol and drug addiction, anxiety, panic attacks, obsessive-compulsive behaviors, sleep disorders, night terrors, and vivid flashbacks of combat experiences. By 1980 a new diagnostic category had appeared in the DSM-III – Post-Traumatic Stress Disorder (PTSD), to cover this entity.

There was, naturally, considerable interest on the part of the V.A. to understand PTSD. Was it entirely due to combat stress or were sufferers somehow genetically predisposed to react poorly to such stressful events? Because so many of the symptoms are part of the TS spectrum, for years I have felt that individuals who carried one or two *Gts* genes might be at risk for developing PTSD. TS patients are particularly susceptible to stress, and I was aware of at least three TS patients with severe PTSD. Finally Hudson and Pope included PTSD in their affective spectrum disorder, which I felt was identical to the TS spectrum disorder.

Two days after I had sent the D_2 paper to the *New England Journal of Medicine*, MacMurray called. We were discussing where to go next with the patients in his addiction clinic. I mentioned my fascination with the possible role of *Gts* genes and PTSD, and he replied, "Many of the samples I sent you were from patients who also had PTSD." After several calls we had put these data together. Of eleven veterans who had PTSD, 64% carried the D_2A1 variant. More studies were clearly needed (see Chapter 29). This was also very exciting. It was the first time that a clear genetic defect seemed to be associated with susceptibility to PTSD.

Modifying Genes in Human Behavior

I was very excited about all of these findings. The D_2A1 variant was present in too many normal individuals and absent from too many affected individuals to be the primary gene responsible for any of these conditions. I still felt defects in serotonin, probably due to mutations in the *TDO2* gene, were going to turn out to be more important in these conditions. However, it was equally clear that the D_2A1 variant was acting as a modifying gene. For example, if someone had a gene causing defective serotonin metabolism and also inherited this D_2A1 variant, they would be more likely to have symptoms than if they did not have the D$_2$A1 variant.

This all made sense by visualizing a serotonin-dopamine axis by which decreases in serotonin or increases in dopamine activity had an additive effect on aggressive, sexual, and other behaviors.[p378]

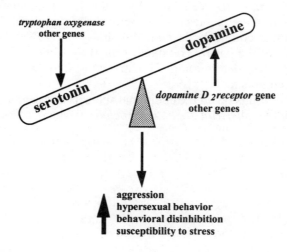

The decrease in serotonin was important, but the effect on dopamine played an exacerbating or modifying role. There were many possibilities for other modifying genes having a similar effect. These findings seemed to open a new era in psychiatry, where testing for such genes might help to diagnose and understand many of the behavioral disorders.

We had sent the paper to the *New England Journal of Medicine* on September 6, 1990, with a request for a quick decision to either accept or reject so we could send it elsewhere if necessary. Six months later, despite numerous phone calls, letters and pleas for action, we still had not gotten a decision. In the meantime we had a chance to examine thirty-three patients from MacMurray's unit with PTSD and more subjects with TS, ADHD, schizophrenia, and alcohol and drug addiction. All the previous observations were holding up. The percentage of subjects carrying the D$_2$A1 allele barely changed more than a few points up or down as the new cases were added. In December Bolos and his colleagues from the National Institute of Alcohol Abuse and Alcoholism reported in the *Journal of the American Medical Association* that the D$_2$A1 allele was present in 38% of forty living alcoholics versus 30% of controls. These were not significantly different and they concluded the D$_2$A1 did not play a role in susceptibility to alcoholism. They did find that the D$_2$A1 allele was present in 45% of severe alcoholics compared to only 30% in milder alcoholics. In addition, in two families they studied there was no evidence that the *D2 receptor* gene was linked to alcoholism.

This was widely reported as a failure to confirm the earlier studies of Blum and co-workers. We found this particularly frustrating, because our studies, stuck in editorial offices, would have explained these apparently conflicting results. The *D₂ receptor* was not the gene for alcoholism, it was just a modifying gene that made it more severe. It would not be present in mild alcoholics, moderately increased in more severe living alcoholics, and most frequent in those who had died of complications of severe alcoholism. We felt both studies were correct when viewed from this perspective.

Finally on February 10, we received a letter from the *New England Journal of Medicine* rejecting the manuscript. None of the reviews were particularly negative. One reviewer complained about the "hodgepodge" of disorders studied, missing the point of the paper. The intent was to examine a wide array of disorders for the purpose of determining if the increased frequency of the D_2A1 allele was unique to alcoholism.

We added the results on all the additional subjects and sent the new manuscript to *The Journal of the American Medical Association,* where it was accepted.[67]

Chapter 21

The Other *Tryptophan* Gene

After the studies of blood serotonin and tryptophan in TS suggested that *TDO2* might be the *Gts* gene, we began to clone and sequence this gene. The literature indicated there were two forms of *tryptophan oxygenase*. The form we were studying was present in the liver, worked only on tryptophan and used oxygen (O_2) as part of the reaction. However, there was a second form which was present in the intestine and brain, worked on tryptophan and other chemicals, and used oxygen in the form of O- instead of O_2. It could break down a number of tryptophan-like compounds, called indoleamines. Because of this, it was called *indoleamine dioxygenase,* or *IDO*. Since the two enzymes were so similar, and even had the same size sub-units, we thought they might both be made by the same gene or at least closely related genes. We assumed that by sequencing the *TDO2* gene we would simultaneously be sequencing the *IDO* gene.

Thus, it was a surprise when Donn walked into the lab in July 1990 with two papers in hand reporting the complete sequence of the expressed *IDO* gene. One was by Tone and his colleagues[207] from Japan, and the second was by Gupta and Dia,[105] of the Hibble Cancer Center in Dayton, Ohio. The Gupta report listed several hundred base pairs of "upstream" regulatory DNA. Since this was the part of the *TDO2* gene we had been trying to sequence, we thought our attempts to find the regulatory sequences of *TDO2* had been done for us, and now we could immediately begin searching for the possible *Gts* mutation. I took the papers home and entered the sequence into my Macintosh. Donn was doing the same with the computer in the lab.

As soon as we saw each other the next morning we simultaneously blurted out the same observation, "They are completely different genes!" There was not a single region of the sequence of our *TDO2* gene that matched the sequence of the *IDO* gene. We obtained a copy of the *IDO* clone from Dr. Gupta and, with the help of an old friend, Dr. Vesna Najfeld, we showed that *IDO* was on the short arm of chromosome 8.[153] It was remarkable that two enzymes with very similar function and similar size would have evolved from totally different sequences.

Usually when two genes have a similar function, at least part of the sequences are similar, indicating that at some point in evolution they evolved from the same gene. This was not the case and immediately raised the question, which was the *Gts* gene? We suspected that the *TDO2* gene was the *Gts* gene, because it was localized to band 4q31, the same band that appeared to contain an *early-onset alcoholism* gene. Since alcoholism seemed to be the most common way for the *Gts* gene to be expressed, we assumed the *TDO2* gene, the *Gts* gene, and an *alcoholism* gene, were the same. Nonetheless, it was possible we were wrong and the *IDO* gene was the *Gts* gene. Alternately, mutations of the *IDO* gene might act as modifiers of the *TDO2* gene in the same way that a variant of the *D2 receptor* gene was modifying the expression of TS, ADHD, conduct disorder, autism, alcoholism, and PTSD.

If *IDO* was involved, the expression of the enzyme would have to be increased and these mutations should also be in the regulatory region. It seemed we now had two candidate genes where the regulatory regions in controls and TS patients needed to be compared. However, we quickly uncovered a *Taq* I polymorphism of the *IDO* gene and found no difference in the frequency of the two alleles in controls versus subjects with TS. This suggested we could safely continue to place our major emphasis on the *TDO2* gene.

Chapter 22

The Rebuttals of the Non-Believers

Since our 1987 papers, a number of published studies of ours and others strongly supported the concept of TS as a broad behavioral spectrum disorder. [17,19,31-33,57,59,60,66,71,121,125,126,143,147,148,150,175,180,187,195,196, 199-203, 205] In the clinic, as pedigree after pedigree showed the same pattern of a multitude of behavioral problems among the relatives of both parents, we were increasingly confident that the *Gts* genes were very common, that they produced a spectrum of behavioral disorders, that defects in serotonin metabolism were involved, and that mutations of the *TDO2* gene would play a role in TS.

Despite this, five reviews of TS quickly appeared. Each one strongly supported the Yale group's position that, with the exception of obsessive-compulsive behaviors, all the other disorders present in TS patients were simply a fluke and due to ascertainment bias. Four out of five were written by individuals who had recently been awarded TSA grants.

The first, in 1989, was by Mary Robertson from England.[178] After reviewing our studies she stated:

> "At this juncture it must be stated that the majority of Comings' and Comings' findings and suggestions are not in accordance with the current literature on TS (Pauls et al., 1988[164])...or the opinions of several specialists in the field who met in 1987 in Washington,D.C. at a workshop to discuss TS and associated behavior."

After this statement, Robertson went on to give a nice review of how the same behaviors we had reported were increased in frequency in TS patients. In fact, it seemed somewhat unusual to make this statement and then provide evidence that exactly what we suggested was true. For example, in the very next paragraph, attempting to support the Pauls et al. theory, she stated:

> "Minderaa et al.(1988[150]) found that twelve out of fifty (24%) children with TS were referred to their clinic for reasons other than simple motor or vocal tics, examples of the reason being conduct and/or learning disorders, sleep disturbances, stuttering, hyperactivity and/or difficulty with interpersonal relationships."

This was exactly the point we had made in the 1987 papers, that the tics were often a trivial part of the problem, and it was the behavior and learning disabilities that were frequently the focus of attention. The concept of ascertainment bias is predicated on the assumption that patients who identify two different sets of symptoms are more likely to seek medical care than those with a single disorder. The point was that if these twelve children were referred for things other than tics, and the TS was discovered later, this in fact avoided the ascertainment bias that Pauls et al. claimed was the reason these behaviors were present. In this respect, the Minderaa findings were similar to the study Sverd[200] had published showing that ascertainment bias was not the explanation of the spectrum of behaviors in TS. Sverd reported many cases who had not been previously diagnosed as having TS. They came to the clinic for a variety of psychiatric complaints and were only later found to also have TS. Since they were referred for a non-TS diagnosis, this avoided the ascertainment bias problem.

I was also amused that Brenda and I were at the workshop Robertson referred to. We were quite pleased with the degree of agreement among the participants with the concept that, in addition to the tics, there were many other behavioral problems in TS.

The second paper, also in 1989, was by Kurlan.[133] After reviewing our studies he stated:

> "This conclusion, however, must be interpreted with significant caution (Pauls et al., 1988[164]). Data were generated using indirect interviews that have obvious inherent diagnostic inaccuracies. Just because a certain behavior is observed more commonly in association with TS than in the control populations does not necessarily imply that the two are etiologically related. For example, the high frequencies of depression, antisocial behavior, or other behavioral disturbances observed in TS patients may reflect ascertainment bias or simply represent the consequences of living with and adapting to the latter disorder. The control groups used in these studies may have been inadequate to detect this possibility."

Kurlan later came to doubt the Pauls et al. explanation and asked us to write a chapter called "Comorbid Behaviors" for his book on TS.[63]

In a third review in 1990, Dr. Gerald Golden[104] stated:

> "The hypothesis has been put forward that many forms of behavioral, psychiatric, and social pathology, including attention deficit hyperactivity disorder, are due to a commonly occurring gene for Tourette syndrome.[46,48] This rather global hypothesis has been criticized, however, and is not widely accepted (Pauls et al., 1988[164]). The lack of a genetic relationship between Tourette syndrome and attention deficit hyperactivity disorder has been demonstrated in a family study (Pauls et al, 1986[165]). The investigators found that there was not an increased frequen-

cy of attention deficit hyperactivity disorder among relatives of
children with Tourette syndrome compared with the general
population prevalence of attention deficit hyperactivity disorder....The hypothesis of a genetic relationship was not supported. The authors concluded that the association of the two disorders is most probably a function of ascertainment bias."

By the spring of 1991 two additional reviews of TS appeared. The first was
by Devor,[84] one of the co-authors on our 1984 paper[65] on segregation analysis
of TS. Devor's paper had the catchy title "Untying the Gordian Knot: The
Genetics of Tourette Syndrome." In discussing our Tourette syndrome spectrum disorder concept, he stated:

> "Comings' views have been criticized on several grounds
> (Pauls et. al 1988[164]). The majority of the criticisms are
> methodological. The response offered by Comings and Com-
> ings (1988[55]) is inadequate. Until Comings' study no evidence
> of increased risk for any disorder apart from ADD and OCD
> was found either in individuals with Tourette syndrome or fam-
> ilies (Shapiro et al., 1988[193]). Yet Comings claims to have
> observed a pattern of comorbidity consistent with his view that
> a single gene defect is at the root of all these disorders."

Later in the paper he stated that Pauls' and Leckman's (1986[167])

> "....analysis should be regarded as the final word on the
> genetic transmission of the syndrome, particularly in view of
> the fact that, among all previous genetic family studies, theirs
> is the most clinically consistent and statistically satisfactory."

By this, we presumed he meant it best presented the position that TS was
an autosomal dominant trait and just a tic disorder.

The last review was by Drs. Harvey Singer and John Walkup from Johns
Hopkins University. In an article published in the journal *Medicine*,[197] entitled
"Tourette Syndrome and Other Tic Disorders," they made the following state-
ment:

> "A possible genetic relationship between TS and ADHD is
> at present controversial. Evidence based on the less sensitive
> 'family history' method supports a genetic relationship (Com-
> ings and Comings, 1984, 1987[18,48]), whereas family studies
> based on the rigorous 'family study' method have suggested
> that ADHD is not related to TS and that the traits segregate
> independently (Pauls et al., 1886 a,b[165,167]). It is hypothesized
> that ADHD is a comorbid condition and that the high incidence
> of ADHD in TS patients is due to ascertainment bias (Pauls et
> al., 1986[165]). Similar arguments (Pauls et al., 1988[164]) have

also been used to *refute* a suggested genetic association between TS and other behavioral disturbances identified by direct interview, including anxiety, conduct disorders, depression, dyslexia, mania, panic attacks, phobias, and stuttering (Comings and Comings[30,48])."

I found Singer's statements particularly interesting since just prior to this review he and his colleagues had published an article entitled "Development of Behavioral and Emotional Problems in Tourette Syndrome."[196] This study used a standardized test called the Ackenbach Child Behavior Checklist to determine the frequency of behavioral problems in seventy-eight TS patients. This showed that male TS patients very often placed above the 98th percentile on scores, indicating many were obsessive-compulsive, schizoid, uncommunicative, delinquent, aggressive, hyperactive, depressed, socially withdrawn, immature, hostilely withdrawn, and complaining of bodily aches and pains.

The severity and frequency of many of these problems were even *greater* than what we had described in our 1987 papers. In addition, in the *Medicine* paper, they had examined the question of sleep disorders in TS children using a Sleep Behavior Questionnaire. They found a much greater incidence of insomnia, dreams, bedtime rituals, and other sleep disorders[195] in TS than non-TS children.

Despite this clinical experience confirming what we had been observing for the previous ten years, their acceptance of the yet-unpublished study by Pauls et al.[164] prevented them from making what to us was the simple logical leap — these behaviors were all part of the expression of the *Gts* genes.

It was the study of thousands of TS pedigrees that convinced us that many psychiatric disorders were linked together by a common set of genes and kept us from seriously considering another possibility — that everyone else was right and we were wrong.

Chapter 23

The Regulatory Region at Last

Within a month of the time I asked Donn to start searching for another genomic clone to try to find the regulatory part of the *TDO2* gene, he found a match. We called this new clone *TGH09*, indicating it was the ninth genomic clone we had isolated. It contained ten thousand base pairs. However, for technical reasons, we were suspicious that this one would also not contain the regulatory region, but we went ahead and started sequencing the ends of this new clone.

When the data came in, I stood over Donn's shoulder as he compared the new sequences to those of the *HTO3* clone. The good news was that one end perfectly matched exactly the area we wanted. The similar sequences started about one hundred base pairs inside of the *HTO3* clone and continued in the direction of the regulatory sequences. I held my breath, hoping the sequences would reach into the regulatory region. Unfortunately, the sequences stopped about twenty base pairs short. Disappointed again.

Donn then looked up and said, "Wait, this is the inverted end." I was ecstatic. This meant we had run out of sequence *not* because we were at the end of the clone, but simply because the sequencing process didn't extend *into* the clone any further. This meant our new clone contained the entire regulatory region of the *TDO2* gene. *At last we had cloned the region we so desperately wanted to see.*

On that morning, September 11, 1990, Donn told me that the sequencing into the regulatory region had worked. The output from the sequencing machine is in beautiful red, blue, green and black lines, with each peak representing a different base. There in my hand were 350 sequences of the regulatory region of the human *TDO2* gene. After years of work, with very limited resources, we wondered if we were finally close to finding the mutation causing TS.

We checked the new sequence against the published regulatory sequence of the rat *TDO2*. Since the computer was comparing the rat against the human, only the important regulatory sequences would be conserved across the many millions of years of evolution that separated the two species. The regions between the regulatory sequences that were relatively unimportant would have evolved into noise. These sequences would not match and there would be no diagonal lines. The sequences that were critical to regulating the *TDO2* gene would be conserved, and these would produce diagonal lines. The result we expected to see was a broken diagonal line.

As we waited for the computer to do its job, what slowly showed up on the monitor screen was absolutely gorgeous. The pattern was exactly as we expected.

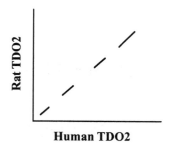

Human TDO2

We then ran a second program that put "*" signs between matching bases. This showed that the dashes were indeed the TATA box, the CAAT box, and a few other regulatory regions that were conserved. Perfect! Next I wanted to see what the two bases next to the CAAT box looked like. This was where the two bases I thought would be causing the *Gts* mutation were located (see Chapter 18).

In the rat this region was: GG TAATAA
In the human it was: AG TAATAA
In the human globin gene it was: GG CAATAA

The fact that any mutation of the two GGs in the *human globin* gene resulted in a threefold increase in expression of the gene, and that the rat was GG but the human was AG, was intriguing. If my speculations about the frequency of the *Gts* genes were correct, then up to 18% of individuals could be carrying the *Gts* mutation. This meant there was a one-in-five chance that the chromosome library was made from a person who carried the *Gts* gene. Was the G 'A the *Gts* mutation? To find out, we sequenced this region in three controls and four TS patients. All showed the same AG sequence, suggesting this was not the *Gts* mutation.

My idea about the *Gts* mutation being next to the CAAT box was clearly wrong. Finding the *Gts* gene was not going to be that easy.

Chapter 24

The GREs

By mid-October 1990, the sequence data on the regulatory region provided us with an interesting observation. The human sequences matched many of those of the rat up to 285 base pairs upstream from expressed *TDO2* gene. This contained all the regulatory sequences to control the rate at which the gene was expressed. However, from this region on, the similarity disappeared, even taking into consideration the fact that the rat and human species diverged many millions of years ago. As a result, when we got to the region where the first critical glucocorticoid response element (GRE) was located in the rat (see Chapter 18), it was totally missing from the human DNA.

The *TDO2* gene had long been touted as the primary example of how the rate of synthesis of an enzyme dramatically increased in the presence of steroid hormones acting on the GRE; yet the human *TDO2* gene seemed to be missing the very DNA segments that were supposed to allow this to happen. We wondered what was going on and whether this had anything to do with TS.

One thing we did observe was that at 850 base pairs out, there was a segment of DNA that contained a set of thirteen GTT repeats. This type of region is of interest in human genetics because repeated sequences tend to be unstable and the number of repeats may be different in different people. Geneticists take advantage of this variability and use these polymorphisms as genetic markers for linkage studies. This was exciting since, despite much effort, we had been unable to find any markers of the *TDO2* gene.

A second feature of the sequence data was that the GRE was missing because a rather large piece of DNA had been inserted into the human DNA. We wondered how big this insert was. We assumed that eventually we would find the two GREs comparable to those present in the rat, but by the end of October we were 1,300 bases pairs out and still had not found them.

On Friday, November 8, I took home the printout listing the new sequences. The first task was to check it for regions that matched the rat regulatory sequence. That produced nothing. However, there was one region of a series of short broken lines. After initially ignoring them, I decided to examine them more carefully. This showed that a region of the new human sequence matched twenty-two of twenty-five base pairs at the very end of the published rat sequence. This was 1,600 base pairs out from the start of the expressed human *TDO2* gene.

Like zipping up a sweater, I used this as a starting point and began working backward toward the *TDO2* gene. At 1,560 base pairs out I found a GRE that matched the one that was 1180 bases out on the rat. In this region fourteen of the sixteen base pairs matched those of the rat. The zipping process continued to show some degree of homology back to 950 bases out from the start of the rat gene. The homology then disappeared. There was no second GRE. Instead, the whole area was replaced by a large DNA insert of random sequences.

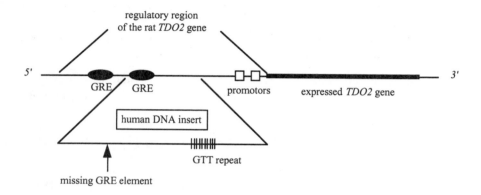

The GREs are short palindromes. A palindrome is a sequence that repeats itself as an inverted copy, like WORD–DROW. In a study of the GREs of several different genes that responded to steroid hormones, the most common or consensus sequence was TGTTCT. The complementary palindrome was AGAACA. The two halves are separated by any three base pairs to produce the following sequence: AGAACA- - -TGTTCT. In practice, the left side tends to be more variable than the right side, and the average or consensus on the left was GGTACA. Thinking that I might have missed a GRE within the DNA insert, I used a program that could detect any short sequence in a long segment of DNA. I first checked to see if there were any TGTTCT segments within the insert. None.

I then checked for a match of five out of six of the bases. The screen flickered like someone had given it a shot of adrenaline. There were thirteen matches in a stretch of 601 bases. This was not totally unexpected on a random basis, but the striking thing was that eight of them were all right next to each other; in fact, they were overlapping. This was the GTT repeat region. When the right part of the GREs from other rat genes and our human GRE were compared with the GTT repeat, the average or consensus GRE sequence was TGTTCT. By comparison, the sequence for the GTT repeat was TGTTGT.

Thus, the GTT repeat was identical to the consensus GRE sequence except for a single G in place of a C. In addition, there were five identical copies of it end to end. We thought this could be substituting for the second GRE we were looking for. If it was even more efficient than the rat GRE, the human *TDO2* gene might be producing much more enzyme than the rat. If there were more GTT repeats in TS patients this could be the mutation causing an increase in TDO2 function, which in turn caused TS.

The next task was to determine if TS patients had more GTT repeats or other mutations in any other part of the regulatory region. We tested this by PCR amplification and sequencing of these regions in TS patients and controls. By early March Donn had completed this study. There was no evidence that mutations in the GTT repeat or other parts of the regulatory region of the *TDO2* gene caused TS.

Thus, the idea that TS was due to a regulatory mutation in the *TDO2* gene seemed dead. Four years invested in cloning and sequencing the *TDO2* gene had produced nothing.

Soon afterward, Brenda and I left for a long planned trip to South Africa. It was a good time to get away.

Chapter 25

The Trip to South Africa

In February 1990, Brenda and I received an invitation from Dr. George Gericke, president of the South African Society of Human Genetics, to give a workshop and symposium on Tourette syndrome at their Congress in late March 1991, in Pretoria. With President DeKlerk now in office, there had been a great deal of movement toward abolishing apartheid. Since Margaret Thatcher had lifted England's economic ban, and since there was increasing sentiment in the U.S. to do the same, our social conscience allowed us to go. We also felt that enhancement of knowledge about this disorder would benefit children and adults of all races, so we accepted. I sent Gericke a copy of our newly-published book, *Tourette Syndrome and Human Behavior*. Over the next several months, I was intrigued by some of the correspondence indicating that they had developed a considerable interest in Tourette syndrome and "had some biochemical findings that I might find interesting."

We left on March 19, 1991. After a pair of eleven-hour plane rides we arrived in Pretoria very grungy and tired. After a bath and a few hours' sleep, I met Gericke. He told me that after reading my presidential address (see Chapter 13), he had become intrigued with the concept of TS as a spectrum disorder and had begun to treat patients with TS. Similar to our experience, the number of patients began to rapidly increase to the point that he felt there may have been a founder effect among the Afrikaners who had settled in South Africa from the Netherlands. Founder effect means that if a gene is present in a small group of immigrants (founders), its frequency may be very high in their descendants.

TDO2 Levels are Increased in Tourette Syndrome

After Gericke had received the copy of the book and read of our theory that an increase in TDO2 activity might be responsible for TS and its spectrum of behavioral disorders, he approached Dr. Siegbert Bissbort, in the University of Pretoria's Department of Chemical Pathology. Bissbort had years of experience in working with genetic variants in red blood cells, as well as studying oxygenases. Based on the insight that only specialists in an area have, Bissbort knew that kynurenine, the breakdown product of tryptophan, was present in red blood cells and that many enzymes were present in red blood cells that one would never expect to be there. This led him to the hunch that TDO2 might be present in red blood cells. He had just invented a new technique to test oxygenases and had studied twenty-five patients with TS. *All showed the marked increase in TDO2 activity we had predicted*! I was incredulous. Our predictions about the cause of TS appeared to be coming true.

We met Bissbort the next day, March 22 at 2 P.M. He was a slim, soft-spoken man who was clearly in command of his subject. As he began to tell us of his findings, I could sense the great excitement he felt for the work. First he showed us a tracing, taken directly from the spectrophotometer, comparing the enzyme levels from a control and a TS patient. In this assay a straight line meant no activity. The more rapidly the line dropped, the higher the activity.

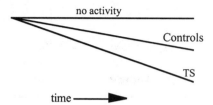

This indicated the TS patient in this run had a much higher level of TDO2 activity than the control. Next he showed us the results summarizing the twenty-five TS patients they had studied, and controls. All of the TS patients showed 150% of normal levels of TDO2 activity.

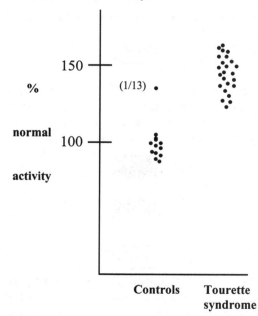

Equally exciting, all of the controls except one had normal levels. The one with elevated activity was undoubtedly a carrier and this tiny sample alone suggested a high carrier rate for the gene, again verifying what we had suspected.[33,71]

The next findings were even more exciting. Bissbort had also developed an electrophoretic test for the TDO2 activity. Here extracts of the red blood cells were placed in an electric field (electrophoresis). If there were any changes in the amino acid sequence of the TDO2 enzyme, it would have a different electric charge and would migrate faster or slower in the electric field than the normal enzyme. This provided a technique to look for such mutations and to determine if they were present in single copy (from only one parent) or double copy (from both parents). Bissbort had found that all the TS patients had a more rapidly-moving enzyme variant, and five of the twenty-five carried it in double dose, i.e. were homozygous, again confirming our predictions that many TS patients carried a double dose of the gene.[66]

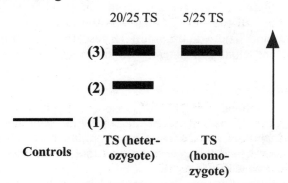

The controls showed a single band (1) representing a pair or dimer of two normal TDO2 enzymes.

The heterozygotes showed three bands: (1) the dimer of normal enzyme, a second band (2) consisting of a dimer of normal and mutant enzyme, and a third band (3) consisting of a dimer of two mutant enzymes. The bands with the mutant dimers were thicker due to greater enzyme activity.

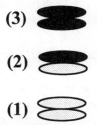

Like the controls, the affected homozygotes showed only a single band, but now the band was thicker because it was composed of a dimer of two mutant enzyme molecules with increased activity.

In addition, the homozygotes tended to have a family history indicating the TS spectrum of disorders was on both the mother's and father's side of the family, while in the heterozygotes, the family history usually showed problems on only one parental side.

In one afternoon I had seen results that verified our thinking over the past six years that TS was due to a mutation causing increased levels of TDO2, that it was a very common mutation, and that many TS patients carried it in double dose (recessive-like) but they could have symptoms with a single dose (dominant-like).

I was naturally anxious to try out these new techniques on our own TS patients in California. Much needed to be done. I wondered if this mutation would also be present in our patients in California, or was this mutation unique to Afrikaners? Were there different types of mutations in other geographic or racial groups, or were they all the same? What was the DNA mutation causing this electrophoretic variant? The whole field of TS research, and, if our TS spectrum theory was correct, psychiatry in general, had just taken a giant leap.

Where is the Mutation?

One of the most immediate results of Bissbort's results was that it suggested we were looking in the wrong place for the DNA mutation. Genes come in two parts, the *regulatory part* that controls how rapidly, and in what tissues, the enzyme is to be made, and the *expressed part* that determines the amino acid sequence of the enzyme itself. As discussed in the previous chapter, we were assuming that since the *Gts* mutation appeared to result in increased levels of TDO2, the mutation would be in the regulatory part. Bissbort's electrophoresis results now suggested the mutation was actually in the expressed part of the gene and affected the sequence of the amino acids. This is because if the mutation was in the regulatory part of the gene and simply resulted in an increase in the amount of a structurally normal enzyme, the electrophoresis results would look like this:

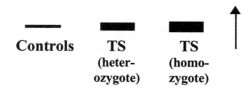

Controls **TS** **TS**
(heter- (homo-
ozygote) zygote)

Thus, since the amino acid structure of the TDO2 enzyme would not be affected if the mutation was in the regulatory part of the gene, it would migrate in an electric field at the same rate as the normal enzyme. Only the amount of the enzyme would be increased. In contrast to this, the mutation in the TDO2 enzyme that Bissbort found traveled faster in the electric field, indicating that both the structure and the activity of the enzyme were affected by the DNA mutation. This indicated to us we were looking at the wrong part of the gene. We should be looking for the mutation in the sequence of the exons, not in the regulatory sequence.

Where Next?

The technique for the determination of the enzyme activity of TDO2 and the electrophoresis of TDO2 were based on a new concept that Bissport had developed just months before. The basic idea could be generalized to many other enzymes, and he was also examining the role of other enzymes in TS. None of these studies could have been done without this new procedure that no one else had thought of before.

I suggested we could proceed in one of two ways. Bissbort and Gericke could publish their findings and let us use the technique on our California patients, which we would report separately. Alternatively, we could take the techniques home with us to study our patients in California to help answer some of the above questions and publish the results together.

At that initial meeting we seemed to be in agreement that the latter approach was the most desirable. This was late afternoon, Friday, March 22. We had to give the all-day workshop on TS that Gericke had set up for Saturday and then leave to attend the South African Congress of Human Genetics, an hour's drive from Pretoria. I was anxious to get copies of the laboratory protocols to FAX back to our lab so Donn and George could begin to set up the techniques. I asked Bissbort for a copy of the procedure. He said it had not been written up yet, but it might be available when we returned from the Congress on Thursday.

Although crammed with activities, the days until Thursday seemed to go by slowly. I spent many nights getting up at 5 A.M., writing and thinking about what I had learned. I was very eager to get started on the new studies and began to be concerned about whether Bissbort would actually give us the procedures when we got back to Pretoria.

Thursday finally arrived. I had a brief meeting with Gericke to discuss some cooperative research projects. I said my fond goodbys to him and said to Brenda, "Let's go down to Siegbert [Bissbort]'s laboratory so he can give us the protocols."

We pulled our chairs in a circle in Bissbort's office. After some idle chatter he began, "We are very eager and willing to completely share this technique with you; however, I must ask one thing. We are planning to patent the basic principle and I don't want to release any of the techniques until we have obtained that protection. We anticipate that will take one to two months."

I was quite familiar with patent law, since in 1987 we had filed a patent concerning the use of tests for *TDO2* mutations in behavioral disorders. Patents had to be filed before any of the ideas were made public in any way. We had filed the *TDO2* patent before any of our papers on the controlled study of TS were published. However, I didn't immediately catch on to what Bissbort was saying. I thought he meant we were not to reveal the technique to others or publish any of the papers until he had filed for a patent on the broader technique on which the assays were based.

I replied, "Of course, that is no problem. As first author you will have total control about when the paper is published." I then picked up my pen and pad of yellow paper and said, "Well, why don't we just go over the procedures step by step and I'll write them down?"

After Bissbort smiled again, it finally began to sink in. What he actually meant was that he was not releasing the procedures to us until the patent was applied for. I was disappointed but understood his position.

Making the best of the situation I said, "Well, that will give us a month or two to collect samples and get ready to set up the technique."

We had thousands of DNA samples on our patients, collected over the past ten years, but I had no blood samples suitable for testing the red blood cell enzyme levels. That two months could be spent collecting such samples. We could also be working on trying to find the DNA nucleotide substitution responsible for the mutation. Based on our sequence data, we knew the expressed part of the *TDO2* gene was divided into many exons. One approach to finding the mutation was to make oligomers spanning each of the exons, amplify each exon by PCR, and examine the DNA sequence in controls and in blood samples of TS patients. This, however, was an expensive proposition, at least, for our very meager budget. The studies would require us to synthesize about twenty-four new oligomers. At one hundred dollars per oligomer, that would deplete much of our tiny budget.

I knew that TDO2 was a heme protein; that is, like hemoglobin, it was not active until it was bound to a heme molecule. TDO2 needed to bind with oxygen to break apart tryptophan. The oxygen was bound to iron molecules and the iron, in turn, was bound to heme. The mutations in hemoglobin, known as hemoglobinopathies, had long been of interest to me. Dr. Richard Goodman had asked me to write a chapter on the hemoglobinopathies for his first book, *Genetic Diseases in Man*, published in 1972. Based on this article, Dr. Ernest Beutler, then head of our Division of Medicine, had asked me to write four more chapters on the hemoglobinopathies for his *Textbook of Hematology*, published in 1976; thus the whole area of the hemoglobins and heme-oxygen interactions was familiar to me. I knew that the heme was bound to globin by the amino acid, histidine.

When I got back to the hotel I sat down to write out a FAX message to Donn and George. I explained the results Bissbort had shown me about the enzyme levels and the electrophoretic patterns using figures identical to those shown above. I suggested that the exons containing the histidine amino acids would probably be close to the active site in the enzyme. This should be the region for us to focus on trying in to find the mutation. I was still thinking in terms of TDO2 being a dimer as Bissbort had suggested.

Brenda and I were to get up at 6:30 the following morning to take the bus to the Kruger National Park for a safari weekend, and we turned in early. I woke up with a start at 3 A.M. It had suddenly hit me. I remembered from the early literature on TDO2 that it was composed of four sub-units. Hemoglobin was also composed of four sub-units. Both used heme. Both bound oxygen. I also remembered studies showing that tryptophan induced (increased) the activity of TDO2 by causing it to bind more tightly to heme. There were a whole group of hemoglobinopathies where the interaction between heme and oxygen was altered. These were largely mutations of the histidine amino acid to some other amino acid. TDO2 might be functioning like hemoglobin, and the mutation was just like the mutations that altered heme function. Such mutations could result in a marked increase in TDO2 activity, because heme would be tightly bound to the enzyme all the time, and not just when tryptophan was around. Such mutations could permanently activate the TDO2 enzyme. This mechanism was a far more powerful way to cause increased levels of TDO2 than anything that could be happening in the regulatory region that we had been so obsessed with.

I couldn't get back to sleep and went down to the lobby to write another FAX to Donn and George.

"The more I think about the hemoglobin analogy the more I like it. Hemoglobin is a tetramer (four parts) with heme at the center. The *TDO2* mutation might be similar to the hemoglobinopathies that affect heme binding."

I suggested that to save money on the oligomers, they should focus on the exons that contain the histidines, similar to those in hemoglobin. Now I could relax and enjoy the upcoming weekend in the Kruger Park. It would take time to order the oligomers. Things wouldn't go any faster even if I was home.

Chapter 26

The Summer of '91

After we got home from South Africa, there were several things that immediately needed to be done. These included collecting whole blood samples on our patients, buying the instrument for the TDO2 assays, and a Macintosh IIx computer, so the database I was keeping on my computer at home could be shifted to the lab. In the lab we needed to shift our search for the *Gts* mutation from the regulatory region to the expressed portion of the *TDO2* gene.

Bissbort had given me a formula for a glycerol-phosphate solution that could be used to freeze blood samples and preserve the enzyme activity. This allowed us to begin to accumulate whole blood samples on all of the old and new patients in the clinic. Since I was seeing forty to sixty return patients on Wednesdays and ten to twelve new patients the rest of the week, these samples rapidly began to accumulate. Within a few months we had over six hundred samples. This might seem like overkill, but I wanted to obtain samples from as many different nationalities and racial groups as possible. The question of how many different *TDO2* mutations there were was critical. Only by knowing them all, could we confidently tell a patient they did or did not have the *Gts* gene.

Equipment

The second problem was obtaining funds for the equipment. We had a spectrophotometer in the lab, but it was ancient – purchased in 1972 and usually in the repair shop. To do the TDO2 assays we needed a modern, computer-controlled, automatic machine. These cost between $25,000 and $30,000, several times our operating budget. I told MacMurray about what we had learned in South Africa. He and I were on the phone almost every day, discussing our *D2 receptor* results on his addiction clinic patients. It was clear the *D2 receptor* gene was not the *alcoholism* gene, and I was convinced the *Gts* mutation might be an *alcoholism* gene. He suggested we send a letter to some of his friends who knew of some wealthy ex-alcoholic patients who might want to help. We tried this, but to no avail. I also attempted to get some funds from some private foundations, but again to no avail.

I decided I could at least buy the Macintosh IIx with Hope Press funds. The spectrophotometer, however, was another matter.

Next I went to our CEO. The City of Hope had continued to support our research when most of the rest of the world thought our ideas were bizarre. I explained what I needed and why. They promised to do what they could, despite the recession and tightness of funds. A week later I had the funds for the spectrophotometer. The City of Hope had come through once again.

This expensive instrument would not be of any value without the protocol from Bissbort, and I still did not have that. However, a day later a molecular biologist from the Pretoria laboratory called me. She was planning to come to California the following October and asked if I could set up a schedule for her to meet some of the geneticists in the area. She told me that after my visit there had been a number of newspaper articles on TS in the local papers, and they were so flooded with new TS cases, their clinic was backed up for months. She also said Bissbort seemed to have ironed out the assay and would be giving them a seminar on the technique, and I should soon be getting the protocol. That was good news.

The Tourette Syndrome Symposium

In 1981, TSA sponsored the First International Congress on Tourette Syndrome. Ten years later they were now sponsoring the second in Boston, June 16-18, 1991. I was scheduled to give a paper in the session on genetics. Five different groups funded by TSA were reporting their results to date of linkage studies in TS. These linkage studies were using the widely-accepted autosomal dominant model of TS. To date, 80% of the genome had been assumed to have been excluded. I was scheduled to discuss the "alternative hypothesis" that TS was inherited as a semidominant-semirecessive oligogenetic disorder. I was convinced they would never find the gene using the autosomal dominant model.[p680] In fact, we had also done linkage studies in 1986. One of the first markers we used was the MNS blood group. This gave a strongly negative result at chromosome band 4q31, precisely the site that I now felt was the location of one of the major *Gts* genes.

I was in a dilemma. Should I discuss the preliminary results from South Africa? It was very tempting to do so because they verified all our theories. On the other hand, we did not yet have the technique in our laboratory and had not yet independently confirmed the South African studies. We had been so thoroughly criticized by TSA and the entire community of TS researchers for our ideas to date, I didn't want to make such a startling announcement and then have it not be correct. We needed time to study many more patients without having everyone breathing down our neck. I decided I would only re-present our belief that TS was a spectrum disorder with a semidominant-semirecessive mode of inheritance, that other common genes affecting serotonin and dopamine were involved, and that if these observations were correct, the linkage studies many groups were doing all around the world would never give the answer.

The conference itself was wonderful. Paper after paper verified our theory that TS was a behavioral spectrum disorder. The data from other laboratories was showing that obsessive-compulsive behaviors, ADHD, conduct disorder, anxiety, phobias, panic attacks, agoraphobia, sleep disorders, learning problems, and even stuttering were present at increased levels in TS probands *and* their relatives.

I was never able to identify in my patients any difference between the obsessive-compulsive behaviors present in TS patients and those present in patients with "pure" obsessive-compulsive disorder (OCD). However, many others, including Dr. Judy Rappaport, the author of *The Boy Who Couldn't Stop Washing*,[174] felt there were differences. She reported a study of fifty-four patients with "pure" OCD without TS. They re-examined these patients five years later and, to their astonishment, found that 59% had tics. The only differences in the OCD patients with tics and those without tics was that the OCD symptoms started earlier in those with tics.

In a study of the Israeli Defense Force, among those soldiers identified as having TS, 59% had some other psychiatric diagnosis, compared to 6% of the soldiers without TS. This avoided the ascertainment bias question and was a beautiful verification of our studies.

One of the most exciting papers was a study of neurotransmitters in the brains of TS patients who had died. The only change present in all different areas examined was a decrease in the levels of tryptophan and serotonin. This perfectly matched our blood studies and was consistent with *TDO2* being one of the mutant genes.

Finally, the five different groups studying linkage now felt they had excluded the TS gene from 80% of the genome – and found no linkage between the 550 markers used and TS. They were beginning to openly worry that they were doing something wrong, such as perhaps typing some of the patients incorrectly. I suggested the problem was that their model for inheritance of TS was wrong and that the frequency of the *Gts* genes in the general population was fifteen to thirty times greater than what those using linkage techniques were assuming. Under these conditions, their studies would reach 100% "exclusion" and never find a linkage.

Trying to Get the Assay

I was hoping that by the time I got home from the TSA conference, Bissbort's assay would be sitting on my desk. Instead I had a FAX from George saying:

> ...Siegbert [Bissbort]...apparently is still working on some technical imperfections before he sends out the technique. I personally feel that we are wasting valuable time but am unable to speed up things, as Siegbert does not work in my department...
>
> Finally, I may come to California after the Washington Congress [International Congress of Human Genetics] and could visit your department on 17 and 18 October, 1991, if convenient. I could perhaps earn my visit by talking on our local observations regarding Tourette syndrome, and have promised myself to do everything to bring over Siegbert's technique if you have not heard anything from him before.
>
> Best wishes,
George

The thought of having to wait until October to get started on testing our TS patients for the *TDO2* mutation was unsettling. To see if I could speed things up, I called Gericke at home the following Saturday morning, June 22. We both felt that if Bissbort continued to worry about perfecting the assay before sending it to us, valuable time would be lost. I also told Gericke that if we found the *Gts* mutation at the DNA level, we wouldn't even need his assay anymore, except as a confirming test. I suggested it might help loosen things up if I sent a FAX pointing these things out and outlining our progress on finding the mutation. Part of the FAX read as follows:

> Dear George and Siegbert,
> Just thought I would bring you both up to date on our progress in finding the *Gts-Pretoria* mutation at the DNA level. I have enclosed a copy of the genomic map, compared to the rat map, showing the exons and introns. We have now sequenced the beginning and ending of many of the introns and we have made oligomers that allow us to PCR-amplify most of them. The map also shows the regions of the histidine residues that are conserved across time between the rat and the human. There are two major clusters of them. Each of these clusters also contains a sequence that closely matches known heme pocket sequences in other heme-binding proteins. We strongly suspect most of the *Gts* mutations are going to lie in these two regions.
> We have cloned these amplified regions from controls and two TS patients that are products of consanguineous matings. The latter should insure that the mutation is homozygous. We should have the sequences on all of this back soon and also hope it will lead the way to a simple, allele-specific PCR test.
>
> Best regards,
> David

I also pointed out that, on my promise to soon have the TDO2 assay in hand, the City of Hope had come up with the money needed for the spectrophotometer, and it was now sitting in my lab. This hinted that we would like to get the procedure as soon as possible.

By the following Wednesday, June 26, I received the following FAX from Gericke:

> After discussing your urgent dilemma as well as some of the recent exciting developments with Siegbert, he has promised me that by next week you will be in possession of the TDO2 technique as well as a nondisclosure agreement which he wants to modify slightly in some way that I have yet to see. The most practical contribution from my side is that we must keep our fingers crossed behind our backs.
>
> Warmest good wishes,
> George

I hoped that the procedure would soon follow. Unfortunately, it did not and additional weeks dragged by.

Searching for the *TDO2* Mutation

After I learned that the *Gts* mutation was probably within the coding region of the *TDO2* gene rather than in the regulatory sequences, we busied ourselves in the laboratory making a series of oligomers that would allow us to amplify the exons of *TDO2* in controls and TS patients. These amplified DNA regions were to be cloned into the Blue Script vector to allow them to be sequenced. This, in turn, would tell us specifically which DNA base pairs were mutant in TS patients. We had picked on the regions of *TDO2* that contained histidines because this was the amino acid that bound the heme molecule.

However, as is usually the case in the laboratory, things don't always go as smoothly as planned. We were having trouble cloning the PCR-amplified fragments into the Blue Script vector. There were good technical reasons why this was difficult and we were trying all of the known tricks to make it work. I had assigned Donn the long histidine-containing region near the tail of the *TDO2* gene, and George Dietz, the histidine-containing region near the head of the gene. Finally, on Friday, July 13, both had successfully cloned their respective regions and the sequences had just come back from the sequencing lab that morning. We all clustered around the computers, entering and comparing the sequences from controls and our TS patients.

Donn finished his first, and out of almost four hundred bases, there was a single pair that was different in the DNA from TS patient "A." This mutation resulted in the change of a proline amino acid to a serine, in the heme region near the tail of the molecule. This was intriguing because proline is considered to be a "hinge" amino acid. The amino acid chains in proteins often form coiled regions, or helices. Proline molecules break these rigid helices and allow the amino acid chain to bend. The loss of a proline could have resulted in a significant change in the shape of the protein. This, in turn, could have resulted in increased heme binding and thus increased activity of the TDO2 enzyme.

Within a few minutes of the time we finished examining Donn's sequences, George had his analyzed. We carefully compared them, base by base, to the master sequence and again found only a single difference. This time it was in an amino acid right next to a histidine amino acid. Since the same DNA from patient "A" had been used for sequencing both regions, it was unlikely both mutations would be correct. George went back and examined the sequences on three other patients, two with TS and one control. None of these, including a repeat testing of patient "A," showed the mutation. This seemed to rule out George's mutation. It was probably just a PCR artifact.

We still didn't know if Donn's was real or also just an artifact of the PCR process. It was necessary to check it several more times and examine additional TS and control patients. I suggested a rapid method of doing this. The mutation was such that the restriction enzyme would cut the normal sequence but not the mutant sequence. This meant that instead of needing to go to the trouble of recloning additional samples, we could simply amplify this segment in TS patients, cut the amplified region with a restriction endonuclease, then examine the results by electrophoresis, a process which would take days instead of weeks.

I went home that night hopeful, but not sufficiently excited to even mention the results to Brenda.

Wednesday, July 17, was a typically busy clinic day. After seeing fifty-five return patients, I was exhausted. I returned to the lab at 4 P.M. and asked Donn how the test was coming.

"I will have the results by 5 o'clock," he said.

"I'm so tired I'm going home. Call me if you get anything exciting."

"Don't hold your breath," Donn replied, voicing his usual conservative approach based on the fact that in the past all such "tests" of possible *Gts* mutations had failed.

"You are probably right," I said, with quiet resignation to the realities of research. I went home and walked in the door at 5:10.

Nicole met me at the door. "Donn just called from the lab. He said it worked!"

I jumped into the car and raced back to the lab. The results showed that all the DNA from the TS patients had been cut, suggesting they all carried the mutation. However, we needed to look at more TS patients and controls but had run out of the enzyme needed to cut the DNA. It would take several days before the new supply came in.

Bissbort Finds a Second Gene and Wants to Market a TS Test Kit

On Sunday, July 21, I called Gericke at home. His wife answered the phone and said he was in the bathroom, could I call him back in ten minutes. When I called back, the line was busy. I suspected he was talking to Bissbort.

A few minutes later he answered and said, "If the line was busy it was because I was talking to Siegbert."

"I assumed that was the case."

He apologized about the fact that despite Bissbort's promise to send us the technique within a week, almost a month later we still hadn't gotten it. I emphasized how useful it would be to have the TDO2 assay up and running in our lab.

Gericke suggested I call Bissbort directly, which I did. This conversation was a jolt to what I thought were plans for mutual cooperation. Bissbort said he had identified a second gene that also controlled serotonin levels and might be just as important for TS as the *TDO2* gene. He thought both genes were important in producing TS. Bissbort also said that in two months he was planning to come out with a commercial kit that could test for both genes, and that he would not send us either of the techniques until they were ready to release the kit. He did say I would be one of the first to receive the kit.

"We also feel there is a second important gene," I said. "What is the gene you are looking at?" I was referring to our thought that the *IDO* gene (Chapter 21) might also play a role in TS and related disorders, and some patients might carry a mutation for both genes.

Not unexpectedly, he replied, "I don't want to tell you now, but I can say it has a direct effect on serotonin levels." I wondered if it was *IDO*.

I called Gericke back. "Did you know Siegbert has identified a second gene he thinks is important in TS?"

"Yes, but he wanted to tell you himself."

I said "The serotonin pathway in man is so simple there are not many possibilities. I doubt if it is tryptophan hydroxylase.[p417] I remember someone already ruling that out, at least in depression. Do you know what his gene is? Siegbert didn't want to tell me."

"I think it is a methyl transferase."

"Is it COMT [catechol-o-methyl-transferase]?"

"No, that works on dopamine and norepinephrine metabolism. I think it is a transmethylase that breaks down serotonin — a serotonin transmethylase."

"That makes a lot of sense," I replied. "If TS is a serotonin deficiency disorder, people could have low levels either because they didn't make enough serotonin, because the *TDO2* gene was overactive, or because what serotonin they had was broken down too rapidly because a serotonin transmethylase was overactive."

Gericke was going to try to dig up further information and get back to me.

When I got back the following week, I had hoped there would be a FAX on the machine. There was none. I called Gericke on Saturday, July 28. He had been busy. He talked to the dean, to Bissbort's boss, and to the attorneys. The latter assured Bissbort that a non-disclosure agreement signed by us would protect his invention. Things looked better, but I was not going to count my techniques until they came across the FAX machine.

Back in the laboratory, while I was out of town, the "mutation" disappeared. Donn had compared the mutant sequence to the sequence in the rat and found they were the same. This suggested that our original master sequence was in error. Instead of finding a mutation, we had found an error in the original sequence. All we had accomplished was to rule out another exon as being the site of the *Gts* mutation.

Within a week we had ruled out the third exon that contained histidines as the site of the mutation; thus to date we had shown that exons 1, 2, 3, and 11 did not carry a mutation in TS patients. There was only one more histidine-containing exon to go, exon 10.

The Second World Congress on Psychiatric Genetics

The Second World Congress of Psychiatric Genetics was meeting August 14-16, 1991 in London, England. I had sent in three abstracts, one describing some of our molecular studies of the *TDO2* gene, a second describing the results of the *dopamine D2 receptor* gene studies, and a third entitled "Common Genes for Spectrum Disorders." In the latter we suggested that the reason no one was finding linkage to any of the psychiatric disorders was because the mechanism of inheritance people were using was all wrong. Instead of each disorder, such as alcoholism, schizophrenia, depression, Tourette syndrome, dyslexia, panic attacks, etc., being due to a fairly rare dominant gene, we suggested that most psychiatric disorders were actually all interrelated, forming a spectrum disorder that was caused by very common *Gts* genes.

Previously this idea had almost always fallen on deaf ears. However, by the summer of 1991 the field of psychiatric genetics was in chaos. The reported linkages of genes for manic-depression and schizophrenia had fallen apart. The Tourette Syndrome Association-funded consortium had not found linkage for TS on over 80% of the chromosome regions. No linkages had been found for any of the other psychiatric disorders. Despite this, most of the scientists attending were still actively involved in such linkage studies, and I was suggesting they would never find linkage because most disorders were caused by a different mode of inheritance.

More Delay

When I returned from the London conference, I called Gericke to check on progress. The news was good and bad. The good news was that once Bissbort's patent was finalized, the Pretoria group was going to send him to our laboratory to set up the assay and electrophoretic technique for examining TDO2 and the other enzymes. The bad news was that the patent probably wouldn't be in place until early November, and thus, Bissbort wouldn't come until mid- to late November.

The progress in our laboratory toward finding the mutation at the DNA level was steady but slow. Problems arose from almost every direction — the automatic DNA sequencer broke down for three weeks, the cloning vector stopped working and had to be remade from scratch, some segments of DNA proved to be so rich in GC or AT bases that the PCR process failed to work, and the absence of knowledge about flanking sequences kept us from amplifying some of the exons. We had slowly worked our way around most of these problems.

Exon 10 was the last histidine-rich exon to be examined. The sequences were complete by late September. I had great hopes that we would have found the *Gts* mutation by the end of the summer so we could proceed with the studies whether we had Bissbort's technique or not.

It was not to be.

Chapter 27

The Frustration Continues

The International Congress of Human Genetics occurs every five years. The eighth one met in Washington, D.C., from October 6-11. Gericke came in from South Africa and we had a chance to discuss Bissbort's upcoming November visit to our laboratory. Gericke was quite concerned that Bissbort might decide not to come. He was so involved with fine-tuning the technique and examining other enzymes that very few of Gericke's TS patients had been tested for the *TDO2* mutation, and he had yet to see a copy of the technique himself.

I suggested that if Bissbort had reservations about coming all the way to California, he should just send the technique and give us a month to try to get it working. If that failed, then he could come.

After the Congress, Gericke came to California to visit the lab. During the visit I took him to San Francisco to see that beautiful city and then attend the American Academy of Child and Adolescent Psychiatry Meetings, where I was presenting essentially the same talk I had given that summer at the Second World Congress of Psychiatric Genetics. After we returned to Duarte, Gericke spoke to our TS support group, telling them that TS in South Africa is very similar to TS in the U.S., with patients presenting the same spectrum of tics, attention deficit disorder, obsessive-compulsive behaviors, conduct disorder, anxiety and all the problems we had struggled with in our patients.

As I took Gericke to the airport bus on Monday, October 21, for the beginning of his long trip back to Pretoria, I told him I would call when he got settled.

I called him on November 2. This call finally gave me the clues I needed to began to understand the delays with Bissbort in setting up the TDO2 technique in our laboratory. Both Gericke and I had been under the assumption that Bissbort had submitted the patent application the previous July, and he was just waiting until it was granted to release the technique to either of us.

The thing we couldn't understand was that since patents are protected from the date of submission, why couldn't we go ahead and receive the technique and start the clinical studies? It now seemed apparent that the patent had not yet been submitted. In addition, there was a rule in South Africa that the applicant has a year from the time a patent is submitted to perfect the technique. If the procedure is not working perfectly as proposed within a year of submission, the patent is denied.

Now all the delays made sense. The extensive "fine-tuning" Bissbort seemed so consumed with was because he wanted to make sure the technique was perfect when submitted, rather than take a chance that if it wasn't perfect it might take more than a year to perfect it. Gericke also stated that Bissbort was afraid that the "non-disclosure agreement" we signed might not be valid internationally; thus he didn't want to send the procedure overseas until it was submitted.

This was all confirmed in a FAX I received from Gericke on November 15.

> Dear David,
>
> 1. Siegbert is happy that his technique is working well.
>
> 2. Early in January this will be handed in at his international law firm patent attorneys.
>
> 3. Simultaneously they will supply a nondisclosure agreement.
>
> 4. It takes one year before the seal is broken, during which there is time to further refine this technique with "patent pending."
>
> 5. Once the patent had been handed in, he thinks he should come and demonstrate the technique in your laboratory. He is willing to come for two weeks and thinks it will be better for him to visit you than handling any problems by FAX or phone.
>
> This will enable you not only to measure TDO2, but at least also serotonin methyl transferase, which we suggest may be the *OCD/tic* gene.
>
> 6. If we remain lucky, this implies that he will spend the last 2 weeks of January 1992 in your department.
>
> 7. I sometimes get the feeling that I have been a little mongrel trying to catch a bus (Siegbert) or have it change its direction, while the bus has been steadily chugging along and has always known when and how it will reach its destination. Not even the screaming passengers could divert the grim resolve with which the bus driver was independently charting his courses. I sincerely hope that we have come to the stage where the driver looks up, smiles and says, "We've arrived."
>
> Regards,
> George

Still No DNA Mutation in *TDO2*

By the beginning of 1992, we still had not found the DNA mutation in *TDO2*. We had finished comparative sequencing of all but three exons — 4, 7 and 8. These were hard to examine because we didn't have any information about the introns on both sides; thus we couldn't PCR across these three remaining exons.

I couldn't believe our bad luck. Was it possible that the mutation would be in one of these three final exons? Was it possible that we had simply missed a mutation in one of the exons we thought we had excluded? Was Bissbort putting us on and there was no mutation in *TDO2*? Perhaps we had missed some other type of mutation that did not involve the exons.

One possibility that did not involve a mutation in any of the exons but would still alter the amino acid structure of *TDO2* was that the mutant gene started in a different place. Was some type of a mutation adding an extra exon onto the front of the gene?

In the rat there was an alternative start site for the mRNA that was located 181 base pairs "upstream" from the usual start site. This was preceded by another TATA box. The sequence in the human showed the identical extra TATA box.

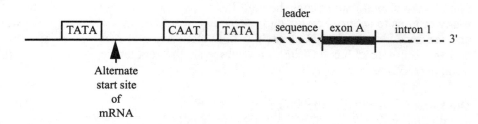

There was only one problem with this. The new sequence was out of register with the rest of the *TDO2* gene. The genetic code uses three base pairs for each amino acid. If additional amino acids are to be added in front of the old, the new code has to be in the same "triplet frame" as the old. This was not the case. However, Donn decided to look carefully at the sequences that determine where the exons start and stop. What he found was consistent with the presence of an additional "upstream" exon that was in the correct "triplet frame" with the normal gene. If this was happening, many new amino acids would be added to TDO2, including an extra histidine. This dramatic change in the enzyme might be the *Gts* mutation.

To check this, I had Donn compare the sequence of this region in several controls and TS patients. Disappointingly, there were no differences.

There was one more possibility. It seemed more than coincidental that the DNA insert we had found in the regulatory region of *TDO2* that contained the GRE like GTT sequence (see Chapters 18 and 24) was only about one hundred base pairs "upstream" from the new TATA box. Could it be that some of the variations in this region were capable of activating the alternate start site and thus producing a mutant TDO2 enzyme with many new amino acids added? Unfortunately, tests showed this was not occurring.

Although Bissbort was supposed to come by the end of January, it was now January 27 and I had yet to hear if he was coming. I waited until mid-February and called Bissbort himself. Once again, things were being put off. Now he wanted to wait until May to come. He needed still further time to perfect the different tests.

I pointed out that we had now accumulated over one thousand blood samples to test, and if we had the TDO2 procedure we could get these finished before he came and then concentrate on the other genes when he got here. This didn't work.

I felt that the only way out of these frustrating delays would be to find the mutation in the DNA sequence. Of course that had been our plan all year and we had still come up with nothing. Since we had not found any mutations or markers of the *TDO2* gene by sequencing, I sent our probes to Dr. Mark Grey in Indiana. He had published several papers about a technique called "Denaturing Gradient Gel Electrophoresis," or DGGE. This allowed the entire segment of DNA covered by the probes to be tested for genetic variants or polymorphisms. George Dietz from our lab had previously tried this technique but had trouble getting it to work. Grey had many random DNA samples cut with various restriction endonucleases, electrophoresed and already transferred to filters. Since the filters could be reprobed many times, he could test in a few weeks what would take us many months to set up. I called and asked if he would be willing to help. He was, and we sent him the *HTO3* clone, the *IDO* clone we had received from Gupta, and the genomic clone (*GTH09*) containing all the regulatory sequences of the human *TDO2* gene.

We Look for the Dye. Is it NBT?

I called Gericke back and suggested that I send George Dietz to South Africa instead of having anyone come here. Since Dietz had a lot of experience with spectrometry, this would save training time. Gericke said he would set up a meeting the following week with Bissbort and the head of the Pretoria Pathology Laboratory to examine this possibility.

I called back a week later to find Gericke even more frustrated than before. The meeting had taken place and gotten nowhere. Bissbort now wanted to return to some work he had started in 1983 on a different genetic disorder, porphyria, uniquely common in South Africa. Gericke suggested that Dietz could still come, but Bissbort complained that this would take time away from his porphyria work. When Gericke pressed more, Bissbort threatened, if pushed, to drop the TDO2 work entirely. Gericke was so frustrated he could not even call to tell me what was going on. He suggested I call the head of the lab myself to emphasize the potential importance of this gene for millions of people around the world.

I called the lab head and pointed out that if Bissbort would simply send us the technique, we could work out the bugs, test some patients, and Bissbort could still be first author. It would only take him a few seconds to send us the protocol.

The lab chief agreed to approach Bissbort about it, but nothing came of it. In discussing this dilemma with Gericke I said, "George, if we could just get the name of the dye, I could develop the technique myself. I suspect the oxygenase causes the dye to change color and the rate of change is related to the level of TDO2 activity."

Gericke replied, "Yes, Siegbert calls it the 'Kalahari reaction.'"

"Why is that?"

"Because, like the Kalahari desert at sunrise, the color changes from brown to blue."

I now had four important clues:

    1) TDO2 was apparently present in red blood cells.
    2) The enzyme activity could be detected by a dye reaction.
    3) The reaction was characterized by a decrease in color, and
    4) The color changed from brown to blue.

All I had to do now was find a redox (reduction-oxygenation) dye that was brown in solution and changed to blue as it was oxidized. It took very little looking to find that a dye called NBT (nitro blue tetrazolium) fulfilled these characteristics; however, there was a major problem. NBT was primarily used to detect reactions that interact with another chemical, called NADP, and there was nothing in the literature to suggest that oxygenases interacted with NADP. Oxygenases were supposed to convert molecular oxygen, O_2, into two oxygen molecules, each attached to the broken ring of the tryptophan molecule. To interact with NBT it was necessary to have an intermediate step of O_2 to O^- or to hydrogen peroxide (H_2O_2). These were reactions produced by a related group of enzymes called oxidases.

There was no evidence that TDO2 worked like an oxidase. I thought, maybe TDO2 does have oxidase activity and we just don't know it. Using NBT was clearly worth a try, so I ordered a supply from a chemical supply company called Sigma. In their catalog they had two references listed next to the chemical. Since I had to go to the clinic, I asked Karen Mercer, my secretary, to pick them up from the library for me. It was raining heavily that day, however, so she promised to pick them up on Monday.

I spent the weekend pondering the two major hurdles. 1) We had no evidence the TDO2 acted as an oxidase, and 2) even if it did, there was no evidence oxidases could interact with NADP, a step we thought was necessary to make the dye change color. I pored over my supply of the world's literature on the chemistry of TDO2. Of the many dozens of papers, a single study from Japan suggested that during an intermediate phase of the reaction O^- might be produced. However, there was no clue that TDO2 could interact with NADP.

Karen dropped the references in my briefcase on Monday, but it was not until Tuesday that I had the chance to look them over. One of the references was entitled, "Detection of Oxidases on Polyacryalamide Gels."[93] It was in the journal *Analytical Biochemistry*, dated 1973. Reading the paper was like opening up an old chest and finding a long-lost treasure. The instant I saw the first page I was certain we were going in the right direction. The article showed page after page of different oxidases stained with NBT. NADP was not required. The enzymes reacted directly with the dye. It seemed obvious that NBT was the dye we were looking for.

I called Gericke to tell him of our speculations about the use of NBT for the assay. I suggested he ask around and see if this might jog any memories about the assay. I received the following FAX back from him:

April 15, 1992

Dear David,

   Here is what I could ascertain through two unexpected sources of information and I hope that it will be of some help.

   1. The NBT reaction may indeed form the basis of the test! The unknown factor is the adaptation of this test to measure oxygenases, and not oxidases.

   2. NADP is apparently part of the assay we are interested in...

Regards,
George

Despite testing a plethora of ideas on how we might test for TDO2 in the red blood cells, nothing worked. We were unable to detect any change in the spectrum of the dye that was sensitive to the presence of tryptophan.

By the end of May 1992, things were looking very gloomy. We had not found any mutations in the *TDO2* gene that were more common in TS patients compared to controls. While mutations might be present in the three exons we had not yet tested, we were unable to clone these exons from the several DNA (genomic) libraries we had screened. We could not induce Bissbort to send us his technique to test, or even proceed with it himself, and we were unsuccessful in attempting to figure out the procedure ourselves.

The considerable effort we had invested in trying to determine if our TDO2 hypothesis was correct seemed to be petering out on all fronts. In frustration, we turned to looking for other genes that might affect the expression of Tourette syndrome.

As with many things in life, once you hit rock bottom there is no way to go but up. On May 13 we called Grey to ask about his progress. He had found some polymorphisms with the *IDO* gene, and some promising ones with both the *TGH09* and *HTO3* probes. On July 2 he FAXed a summary of his findings. With the *IDO* probe there were polymorphisms with four different enzymes. With this particular technique, some could represent the same polymorphism. There were no polymorphorphisms using expressed portions of the *TDO2* gene, but there was a nice polymorphism using the *TDO2* probe that covered the regulatory sequences. Even if none of these were mutations that affected the function of these two genes, like with the *dopamine D2 receptor* studies, these markers would at last allow us to finally do some genetic testing for the possibility that these genes might play a role in TS.

Chapter 28

The Dopamine Receptor
Studies Revisited

Our studies on the D_2A1 allele of the dopamine receptor (see Chapter 16) were finally accepted by the *Journal of the American Medical Association* (*JAMA*) in July 1991.

By the time the revised paper was accepted, we had accumulated results on nine different control groups, four of our own, and five others. This gave a total of 314 controls, of whom 24.5% carried the D_2A1 allele. Of these, there were 69 controls known to be free of alcoholism. Only 14.5% of these carried the D_2A1 allele. The significant results for different disorders were as follows:

	N	%D_2A1	p
Controls	314	24.5	
Tourette syndrome	147	**44.9**	.0001
Attention deficit disorder	104	**46.2**	.0001
Autism	33	**54.5**	.0005
Alcoholism/drug abuse	104	**42.3**	.0009
Post-traumatic stress disorder	35	**45.7**	.007

This was the first evidence, based on studies of a specific gene, to support our hypothesis that a common set of mutant genes were responsible for a spectrum of related psychiatric disorders. There was no increase in the prevalence of the D_2A1 variant in patients with depression, Parkinson's disease, or panic attacks.

A month later, I received a call from the American Medical Association. The A.M.A. was sponsoring their yearly Science Writers Conference, and this year it was to be in Atlanta, Georgia from October 1-3. The editor of *JAMA*, Dr. George Lindberg, wanted me to give a presentation on our studies of the D_2A1 variant on October 1. The paper was then scheduled to be released the next day as the lead article in the journal. After struggling for so many years to get some beginnings of acceptance of the concept that Tourette syndrome was a spectrum disorder and that the genetic factors causing TS were shared by a wide range of related disorders, this now was an opportunity to present this concept, albeit with a modifying gene rather than the *Gts* gene.

Linkage Disequilibrium

The D_2A1 was just a marker for a presumed mutation somewhere else in the *D2 receptor* gene (*DRD2*). The D_2A1 marker was located outside and 3' to the gene itself and was a considerable distance away from the presumed mutation either iin the *DRD2* gene or near it. This can be diagrammed as follows:

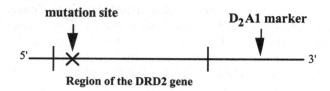

mutation site   **D₂A1 marker**

Region of the DRD2 gene

The *DRD2* gene was very large, with at least twenty thousand base pairs for the exon and introns. The mutation and the D_2A1 marker were probably very far apart. It was not at all clear how well the D_2A1 allele marked the presence of the presumed "real" *DRD2* mutation. This can be diagrammed as follows, where each line represents a chromosome in a different person, the "real" mutation that changes the function of the *DRD2* gene is shown as • and the D_2A1 marker outside of the gene is shown as ☐

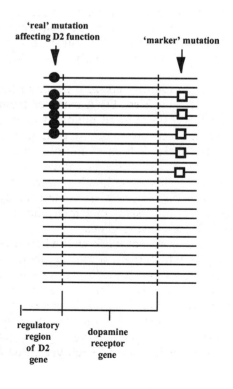

'real' mutation affecting D2 function   'marker' mutation

regulatory region of D2 gene   dopamine receptor gene

This illustrates how the D_2A1 marker is present on only some of the chromosomes carrying the "real" mutation and is present on some of the chromosomes that do not carry the "real" mutation. However, as shown in this diagram, the D_2A1 polymorphism marks the real mutation more often than the normal gene. This is called *linkage disequilibrium*, which is a term geneticists use to indicate that two mutations that are close together on the same chromosome tend to show a non-random association with each other. Now, if the "real" mutation affects the expression of a disorder such as Tourette syndrome and is in linkage disequilibrium with a marker such as D_2A1, the frequency of the D_2A1 would be greater in TS patients than controls. Studies of this type are called *association studies*, since we are studying the association between a marker, such as the D_2A1, and a disorder, such as Tourette syndrome.

The reason this technique can be so powerful is that the markers are generally fairly easy to find, since on average, they occur every three hundred base pairs; thus there should be many markers in a twenty thousand base pair gene. Some of these would affect restriction endonuclease sites and show up when cut with the right enzyme, just as the D_2A1 marker occurred in a *Taq* I site. By contrast, there may only be one or two "real" mutations that affect the function of the gene, and they take much more work to find, as so well-demonstrated by our struggles with the *TDO2* gene.

Strengths and Weaknesses of Association Studies

Just as linkage disequilibrium provides the strength of association studies, it also presents us with a weakness, since the frequency of the marker and the degree of linkage disequilibrium can be significantly different in different racial and ethnic groups. This can be easily controlled by studying different racial groups.

The other major way to identify specific genes in human hereditary disorders is through linkage studies. Here DNA samples from large families carrying a specific disorder are collected and hundreds of different markers known to be on specific chromosomes are examined. If one of those markers runs through the family in the same fashion as the disorder, the two are said to be linked. Since the location of the marker is known, the location of the disorder would also become known. This technique has been successful for many disorders, such as Huntington's disease, neurofibromatosis, cystic fibrosis, and others. In fact, it has been so successful that many have assumed it is the only valid way to look for disease-causing genes.

However, linkage studies do not work well when several genes cause a disorder, or when the way in which the disorder is inherited is unknown. In these situations, association studies can shine, since they are totally independent of the mechanism of inheritance and can pick up even minor effects of the gene being studied, thus working even if multiple genes are involved. In the past, one of the weaknesses of association studies was that you had to already have cloned the gene you suspected was causing a given disease. However, since hundreds of new genes are being cloned each year, this has become much less of a problem.

Haplotyping the *DRD2* Gene

One thing that would help the *DRD2* association studies would be to find additional markers that were either the "real" mutation or showed better linkage disequilibrium with the "real" mutations.

When I was at the Second World Congress of Psychiatric Genetics in London, I met Dr. Janet Sobell. She and her colleagues had been intensively studying the *DRD2* gene in patients with schizophrenia.[188] They were doing the same thing with this gene that we were doing with the *TDO2* gene – comparing the sequence in controls versus patients with psychiatric disorders.

In their case, the psychiatric disorder was schizophrenia. While they didn't find a mutation in the *DRD2* gene, they did find two more markers. These were a great improvement over the D_2A1 marker. First, they were probably much closer to the "real" mutation in the *DRD2* gene and second, they were quite close to each other. This meant they could both be in a single piece of DNA amplified by PCR. This allowed us to determine if they occurred together on the same chromosome,[189] a process called *haplotyping*. One of the polymorphisms, S2, involved a T ' G mutation. The other polymorphism, S3, involved a C ' T mutation; thus the four possible combinations or haplotypes were as follows:

Haplotype	S2	S3
1	T	C
2	G	C
3	T	T
4	G	T

The 3 haplotype was present almost exclusively in Orientals. The ability to identify these haplotypes provided much more information than simply knowing the two polymorphisms individually. Realizing this, we began to haplotype many of our patients.

The *JAMA* Articles

The *Journal of the American Medical Association* article came out on October 2, 1991.[67] Dr. Ken Blum thought I would be deluged by the press as he and Dr. Ernie Noble had been when their initial paper was released. I didn't think so. The story was already getting old. The result was intermediate. There was a considerable degree of interest because we, and Cloninger and colleagues, had found evidence to support an association between the D_2A1 allele and alcohol or drug abuse, after the study by Bolos and colleagues[9] suggested the association was not valid. However, the October 2 issue also contained a study from the Yale group by Dr. Joel Gelernter and Kidd.[98] They, like Bolos and co-workers, concluded that there was no association between the D_2A1 allele and alcoholism, because the frequency of the D_2A1 marker was almost as high in their controls as in their alcoholics. When I actually saw the paper in print it was apparent that many of their controls included unaffected parents of TS patients. This was a poor choice of controls, since we had found that 43% of unaffected parents of our TS patients carried the allele – hardly a random control sample.

While these studies received considerable attention, the impact was considerably diluted by the focus of the press on alcoholism and the negative report of the Yale group. For example, the headline in the *Washington Post* was, "Genetic Studies Yield Opposite Results."[13]

It was now apparent that the role of the *DRD2* gene was going to be almost as controversial as our concept that the *Gts* genes were involved in a wide range of psychiatric disorders. As with the TS controversy, the Yale group positioned themselves on the side opposite to what we believed. In a review in *Science*,[115] on the basis of the controversial results with alcoholism, they adopted the position that variants of the *DRD2* gene were *not* going to be found to play a role in any human behavior disorder.

In striking contrast to this position, based on our continuing studies of the D_2A1 polymorphism in behavioral disorders other than alcoholism, and our preliminary results, we felt we were entering an exciting new phase in the study of human behavior disorders. It was clear, however, that regardless of what we found, it was going to be controversial and difficult to get published.

All of these predictions proved to be correct.

Chapter 29

Post-Traumatic Stress Disorder

Over a period of more than two decades, Dr. LeMoal and his colleagues in France studied, in rats and mice, the effect on behavior of partially destroying the dopaminergic nerves.[p381-p384] One of the major effects was that the animals showed a poor response to stress.[p393] Because of this, I suggested to MacMurray that we should look at the frequency of the D_2A1 allele in the veterans on his ward that had post-traumatic stress disorder, or PTSD.

PTSD was a common problem among veterans returning from the Vietnam war. The diagnosis depended upon four sets of characteristics.[87] The first requirement was that the individual had to have "experienced an event that is outside the range of usual human experience and that would be markedly distressing to almost anyone (for example, serious threat to one's life...or seeing another person killed as the result of an accident or physical violence)." Second, the traumatic event must be persistently re-experienced, often in the form of flashbacks or recurrent distressing dreams. Third, there must be persistent avoidance of stimuli associated with the event, such as avoiding activities that would arouse recollections of the trauma. Finally, there must be persistent symptoms of increased arousal, such as insomnia, outbursts of anger, difficulty concentrating, exaggerated startle response, and feelings of panic. The fact that the latter included symptoms that overlapped with ADHD and Tourette syndrome, and the fact that I had several TS patients who also had PTSD, provided additional reasons to examine the frequency of the D_2A1 allele in veterans with PTSD.

As shown in the previous chapter, of the first thirty-five PTSD subjects we examined, 45.7% carried the D_2A1 allele, a significant increase (p = .007). However, because of the importance of this disorder for veterans, MacMurray and I thought we should examine this association in more detail.

MacMurray wanted to examine only those veterans who were "battle-hardened." As such, they had to have been attached to Marine or Army front line units that engaged in combat patrols leading to "firefights," have been directly exposed to hostile fire, have killed enemy troops and directly observed the enemy they killed, and have seen members of their own unit killed by the enemy. These subjects were then divided into two groups – those who had PTSD and those who did not. To eliminate any effect of racial variations in the frequency of the D_2A1 allele we studied only non-Hispanic Caucasians.

In the initial study we examined thirty-two such veterans. Of the twenty-four who had PTSD, 58.3% carried the D_2A1 allele. Of the eight who did not have PTSD, only one carried the D_2A1 allele. This difference was significant (p = .041).

We sent these results to another journal for publication. Because of the controversy about the role of the D_2A1 allele in alcoholism, the reviewers were so critical that we decided to hold off publication until we could replicate our own finding by a completely new study. This took about six months to complete. In the second group of combat-hardened veterans, of thirteen with PTSD, 61.5% carried the D_2A1 allele while of eleven without PTSD, none carried the allele (p = .002). This was even more striking than the first study. When the two were combined the results were as follows:

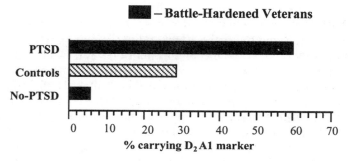

Of the battle-hardened veterans with PTSD, 59.5% carried the D_2A1 allele. Of those without PTSD, 5.3% carried the allele. These differences were highly significant (p = .0001). These results suggested that veterans who carried this allele had an increased susceptibility to PTSD. The marked decrease in prevalence of the D_2A1 allele in battle-hardened veterans without PTSD was as dramatic as the increase in those with PTSD, suggesting that veterans who did not carry this allele were protected against developing PTSD.

This was one of the most striking examples of a specific gene affecting human behavior ever reported. It was also the first demonstration of a genetic component to PTSD and the most dramatic evidence yet that variants of the DRD2 allele played an important role in specific disorders. It also supported our proposal that the D_2A1 marker was more relevant to certain personality characteristics — in this case susceptibility to stress — than to a specific diagnosis such as alcoholism. Since a poor response to stress was an important symptom in TS, ADHD, conduct disorder, autism, and other disorders, it also supported the spectrum concept that a variety of seemingly different behavioral problems may all have many genes in common.

Chapter 30

Drug Addiction

The controversy over whether the *DRD2* gene was involved in alcoholism continued to swirl. The initial reports were about evenly divided, with about four papers saying yes[6,7,25,67,79,161] and four papers saying no.[9,98,191,209] As long as all the studies found the marker in 40 − 45% of alcoholics and were reporting negative results simply because of an usually high number of D_2A1 carriers in the controls, we didn't take the negative studies too seriously. However, when two studies reported that in some groups of alcoholics, the marker was present in less than 30% of alcoholics,[191,209] we began to again wonder if some behavior other than alcoholism might not be the factor that the D_2A1 was associating with.

We were particularly influenced by the studies of Dr. Chiara and colleagues in Italy. They injected rats with various addicting drugs and measured the effect on dopamine in the brain.[23] This showed that drugs such as speed and cocaine had a much greater impact on the dopamine reward pathways than alcohol. This suggested to us that defects in the *DRD2* gene might correlate better with drug abuse than with alcoholism *per se*.

MacMurray was in a perfect position to help us test this possibility. We divided two hundred Caucasian subjects on his addiction treatment ward into those with alcohol abuse only, alcohol dependence only (had withdrawal symptoms), polysubstance abuse (multiple drugs), or drug abuse only (no alcohol use). By this time over 763 control subjects had been tested for the D_2A1 variant, providing a group that was so large that minor variations due to differences in nationality were further minimized. These results were as follows:[72]

Diagnosis	N	%D_2A1	X^2	p
Alcohol abuse	19	21.0	0.56	N.S.
Alcohol dependence	75	32.0	.30	N.S.
Polysubstance abuse	104	**42.3**	7.67	**.0056**
Drug abuse	2	50.0	.03	N.S.
Total	200	36.5	4.12	.04
Total White controls	763	**29.0**		

From this it was clear that the important variable was polysubstance abuse, not alcoholism *per se*. We also found that the more money subjects spent on different drugs the more likely they were to carry the D_2A1 variant. The subjects on the addiction ward were also more likely to carry the D_2A1 if they had ever been arrested for a violent crime. Of those who had been arrested for a violent crime and also had a history of having been expelled from school as a child for fighting, 69.2% carried the D_2A1 variant. This compared to 28% for those arrested only for drunk driving who carried the variant.

These results are easier to appreciate as a diagram:

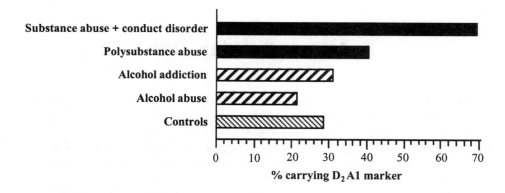

Now everything made sense. We actually now agreed with the studies concluding that the D_2A1 variant was not always related to alcoholism *per se*. We suspected that the original study of Blum et al.[7] found a very high frequency of the D_2A1 variant because they had severe alcoholism, all died of complications of alcoholism, probably had significant personality disorders, and some may have also had polysubstance abuse. If mild-to-moderately severe alcoholics with no associated drug abuse were studied, the frequency of the D_2A1 variant was no higher than in the controls. In essence, everyone appeared to have been correct — the mixture of polysubstance abusers and severity of alcoholism in their cases was just different.[72]

Chapter 31

A Gene for Obesity

Obesity is a problem for over thirty million US adults.[27] It is associated with an increased risk for diabetes mellitus, hypertension, and cardiovascular diseases. One report estimated the yearly cost of obesity to society at $39 billion.[27] Because so many are trying to lose weight, there are many clinics and programs for weight control. While genes play a major role in the cause of obesity,[p237] which genes are involved has remained a mystery.

In the process of examining the haplotyping that had been done on the V.A. addiction ward subjects and controls, MacMurray and his colleague, Dr. Pat Johnson, noticed that subjects with different *DRD2* haplotypes had different average weights and heights.

In order to combine the data on all subjects, regardless of age, height, race or sex, we obtained data from the National Institute for Health Statistics of average weights and heights for people in these different groups. This was possible by using what in statistics is called a "Z" score. Another term, called "standard deviation," is a measure of how much a person deviates from the norm. When you take your children to the pediatrician, the growth charts show the average weight and height for a given sex and age. The lines show the mean. One standard deviation includes 67% of people, and two standard deviations included 97% of people. If a person's Z score for weight is +1, then they are one standard deviation above the average for their age and sex.

The scores for the different *DRD2* haplotypes in 484 subjects were as follows:[68]

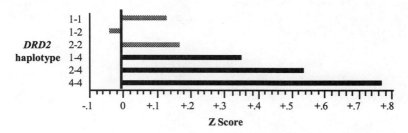

These were significantly different from each other (p = .005). It was immediately apparent that the groups that carried the 4 haplotype had higher average Z scores, i.e. weighed more, than those groups that did not carry the Z score.

When we compared those "with the 4 haplotype" to those "without the 4 haplotype," the results were as follows:[68]

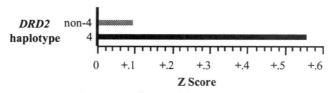

These were significantly different (p= .006).

It was clear we had found a major gene for obesity. It also made a great deal of sense. Polysubstance abuse was associated with an increase in the frequency of the A1 variant of the *DRD2* gene. This was consistent with a genetic defect in the dopamine reward pathway of the brain leading to increased susceptibility to drug abuse. Food also stimulates the dopamine reward pathway, and now another variant of the *DRD2* gene was associated with overeating.

It also made sense from the point of view of medications that are used to control weight. The vast majority of diet pills either contain dextroamphetamine or a derivative of it. Dextroamphetamine is a "dopaminergic" drug; that is, it stimulates dopamine nerves. These results suggested that a defect of the *DRD2* gene resulted in a resetting of the hunger-stat or in an alteration of activity level, either of which would have an effect on appetite or weight.

Finally, it also made sense from the observation that one of the major side effects of haloperidol and other neuroleptic drugs is weight gain.[p548] These drugs specifically inhibit the function of the *DRD2* gene.

Weight gain is one of the major causes of adult diabetes. We also had information of the blood sugars of some of his patients. The average glucose level for thirty-three non-4 haplotype subjects was 94.6, compared to 110.9 for thirty-eight carrying the 4 haplotype.

The 4 haplotype was allowing us to follow or detect a mutation that was affecting the function of the *DRD2* gene. Whatever that mutation was, it was clear it was playing an important role in a person's risk for becoming overweight and probably getting adult diabetes. This association of *DRD2* gene with obesity was subsequently confirmed in two independent studies by Noble[157] and Blum.[5] Like many of the behaviors we were studying, this was another one that was usually considered simply a defect in character, but now seemed to be, at least in part, a defect in the genes.

[Subsequent to these reports other obesity genes were reported, i.e. the *ob* gene and the *β adrenergic* gene. These are both distinct from the *DRD2* gene.]

Chapter 32

A Gene for Height

In addition to an effect on weight, the *DRD2* gene haplotypes also showed correlation with height. The results for the Z scores for height were as follows: [68]

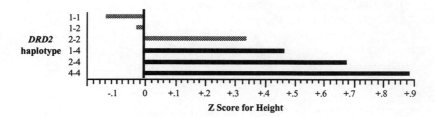

When examined on the basis of non-4 versus 4 haplotype, the results were:[68]

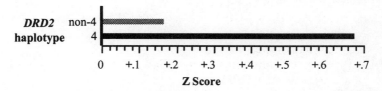

This was highly significant (p < 0.0001). This was not surprising because growth hormone and gonadotropic hormone are excreted by the pituitary and are controlled, in part, by dopamine. The gonadotrophic hormone regulates the amount of estrogen in females and testosterone in males. Growth is dependent upon both of these hormones, as well as growth hormone; thus during the period of maximum growth and during puberty, when the level of these hormones are most critical to growth, the amount of the hormones are being controlled, in part, by the *DRD2* gene. Mutations affecting the function of the *DRD2* gene would be expected to have an effect on growth, and they did.

Conventional wisdom is that height is controlled by a large number of different genes. While this is undoubtedly correct, some height genes will have a more important effect than others. The *DRD2* appears to be one of these major genes affecting height.

Department of Medical Genetics Staff - 1996

First row: Mary Ann Hernandez, Shijuan Wu, Donn Muhleman, Ying Chen, Karen Mercer, Radhika Gade, Stephani Eckert, Hsiao Chiu, Ellen Knell, Thomas Wayman, Marilyn Glasser
Second row: James MacMurray, Robert Ring, Hezekiah Blake, David Comings, George Dietz, Selene Wang

Chapter 33

The *Dopamine D3 Receptor* Gene

During all the time we were examining the role of the *dopamine D2 receptor* gene in a variety of impulsive, compulsive, and addictive behaviors, we were acutely aware of the fact that a total of five different dopamine receptor genes had been identified, cloned, and sequenced. By spending so much time on the *DRD2* gene, were we missing important effects due to mutations of the other four? We were not overly concerned about this, since no mutations of the other genes had been reported, or if they had preliminary results, no association with any behavioral disorders was suggested.

For example, in their original paper on the *DRD2*, Blum et al.[7] had examined an *EcoR* I marker of the *dopamine D1 receptor* gene and found no association with alcoholism. A tandem repeat polymorphism had been reported in the *dopamine D4* gene.[124,211] This caused a lot of excitement, because the D_4 was the site of action of the new schizophrenia drug, clozapine. However, no associations with schizophrenia had been found.[123,124,192]

In 1992, Dr. Sokoloff from France sent me information on a new marker of the *dopamine D3* receptor gene that actually involved a change in the amino acid sequence of the enzyme. In addition, the mutation site was recognized by a restriction endonuclease *Bal* I. As a result, it was easy to test for this mutation by PCR-amplifying the region of the mutation and cutting the DNA with the enzyme. This gene was of particular interest because it had D_2-like properties and was particularly active in the limbic system, the region of the brain that seemed to be very important for all the emotional problems associated with TS.[30]

TS and the *D3* Receptor Gene

After testing a number of our most severely affected TS patients for this mutation and comparing the results to controls, we noticed a relative deficiency in the frequency of 1-2 heterozygotes. Of the 139 TS patients we examined, 30.2% were 1-2 heterozygotes. By comparison, 50.5% of our controls were 1-2 heterozygotes. We were not sure what to make of this, since it was such a strange result.

In association studies there is usually a relative increase in one of the alleles; thus if the 1 allele is increased, there would be an increase in 1-1 homozygotes and 1-2 heterozygotes. If the 2 allele was increased, there would be an increase in 1-2 heterozygotes and 2-2 homozygotes. In this case, there was an increase in 1-1 and 2-2 homozygotes and a decrease in 1-2 heterozygotes. This increase in homozygosity was sufficiently strange that we decided to just sit on the results and wait for further data. Perhaps it was just a statistical error.

A few weeks later Bruce Kovacs dropped on my desk a just-published paper by Dr. Crocq and colleagues[81] entitled "Association between Schizophrenia and Homozygosity at the Dopamine D3 Receptor Gene." This was a collaborative study between French and English workers. In both countries, they observed a significant decrease in 1-2 heterozygosity at the *Bal* I marker. Together they had studied 141 schizophrenics and found that only 31.2% were 1-2 heterozygotes. In England 50.0% of their controls were 1-2 heterozygotes, and in France 57.8% were heterozygotes. They also struggled with trying to explain the results. In genetic studies in animals, it has often been noticed that heterozygotes are often more fit, a phenomena known as *hybrid vigor*. Crocq suggested the decrease in 1-2 heterozygotes was associated with less vigor at this locus.

Prolactin is a pituitary hormone. The level of prolactin in the blood is regulated, in part, by dopamine nerves which suppress prolactin release. We found that prolactin levels were higher in 1-1 homozygotes than in 2-2 homozygotes. This suggested to us that the 1 allele was relatively defective compared to the 2 allele, and this accounted for the increase in 1-1 homozygotes in TS, i.e. the severe TS subjects tended to have relatively defective dopamine D_3 receptors.

Since their results and ours were virtually identical, we decided to publish these findings in the form of a letter to *Lancet*.[74] The English TS group quickly responded that they did not find this effect in the large TS pedigree they had been using for linkage analysis.[12] They reported no decrease in 1-2 heterozygosity in nineteen subjects with TS. The problem with this study was that small numbers of subjects were examined, all the cases came from a single pedigree, and they were mildly affected. Our cases were all from different families and were severely affected; thus if the *D3* gene was acting as a modifying gene and playing a role in severity similar to our results for the *D2* gene, the effect would be absent in mild cases.

A more serious negative report came from Hebebrand and co-workers in Germany.[109] They found no decrease in 1-2 heterozygosity in 66 TS subjects who were all from different families. We had continued to examine more cases, and this report prompted us to re-examine the new totals. By this time we had results on 350 TS probands. Of these, 38.3% were 1-2 heterozygotes, compared with 49.7% heterozygotes in 358 controls. This was a significant difference. More importantly, we now had enough cases to separate them by severity. The results were as follows:

Severity	N	% 1-2
Mild	10	48.3
Moderate	119	39.5
Severe	25	31.3

There was a significant progressive decrease in 1-2 heterozygosity with increased severity of TS. These results were very similar to what we had observed with the dopamine D_2A1 marker. In addition, the decrease in 1-2 heterozygosity was even more striking in our severe pathological gamblers.

The D3 Receptor and Reproduction

In January 1994, Dr. Rick LeGro sent me a summary of the studies he had done in our laboratory on the role of the *D3* receptor gene in various aspects of reproduction. Since some of the important pituitary hormones such as prolactin, growth hormone, and ACTH, were, in part, regulated by dopamine nerves, and since the D_3 receptor was particularly prominent in the hypothalamus, which regulates the pituitary, LeGro was interested in whether variants of this gene played a role in reproduction.

Clomid is a drug used for treating women who have trouble ovulating. Rick found that the dose of clomid required to bring about ovulation was related to the frequency of 2-2 homozygotes, as follows:[145]

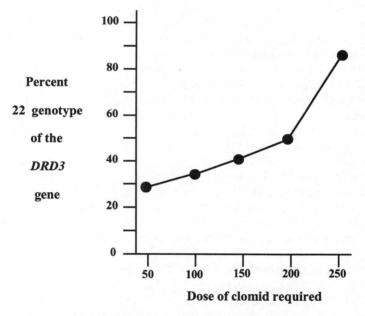

The more clomid required, the more likely the patients were 2-2 homozygotes. This provided additional evidence that the *D3* gene came in genetically different strengths.

As modest as these results were, they played a significant role in molding my opinion about the genetic basis of psychiatric disorders. It was analogous to being knocked out by a feather. There were now two genes, both very important in dopamine metabolism, that appeared to be playing a modest role in TS. This was providing support for my growing assumption that psychiatric disorders were probably due to the chance coming together of common genetic variants of a number of different genes affecting the function of dopamine, serotonin, and other neurotransmitters. It was becoming clear that psychiatric disorders involved several genes. They were polygenic.

Chapter 34

Polygenic Inheritance

When we first began to see TS patients in 1980 and were focusing mainly on the tics, the pedigrees were consistent with the presence of a single *Gts* gene running in the families. The following is a typical pedigree where squares are males and circles are females:

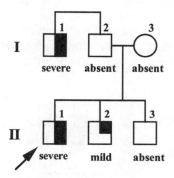

The arrow represents the proband (II-1), the first person in the family to seek medical help. Probands are usually the most severely affected member of the family. In this family, one brother (II-2), has only chronic motor tics. The other brother (II-3), the father (I-2) and the mother (I-3) have no tics, while the uncle (I-1) has full TS. Because the uncle and the son have TS, the father must carry the *Gts* gene, even though he has no symptoms. This is called incomplete penetrance. This pedigree is consistent with autosomal dominant inheritance with incomplete penetrance.[p41] This is further illustrated as follows, where the abnormal gene is marked as an X (not to be confused with the X-chromosome):

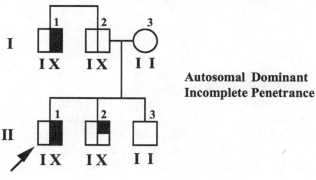

**Autosomal Dominant
Incomplete Penetrance**

In this type of inheritance, the gene is rare (less than 1%) and the best technique for identifying the gene is linkage analysis[p53] where one determines if a known genetic marker tends to occur more often in carriers (II-1, II-2) than in non-carriers (II-3).

This linkage technique has been outstandingly successful in finding the genes for many human genetic disorders, such as Huntington's disease, cystic fibrosis, neurofibromatosis, and many others. Because of this success, those who were studying the genetics of psychiatric disorders rushed to use the same technique to find the genes involved in Tourette syndrome, schizophrenia, manic-depressive disorders, panic attacks, and other behavioral disorders. Between 1985 and 1987 we were part of this rush and collected twenty-five TS families for these studies. However, by the time we thought we had excluded about 40% of the chromosome sites, I began to suspect that the linkage approach was not going to work in TS.

The reason for this skepticism was that as we gained more experience with TS and realized that a whole spectrum of behavioral disorders were involved, it became increasingly clear that the *Gts* gene was often coming from both sides of the family.[33,66] Since this had some characteristics of both dominant and recessive inheritance,[p42] we called this semidominant-semirecessive inheritance.[33,66] This is shown as follows, again with the abnormal genes marked by an X:

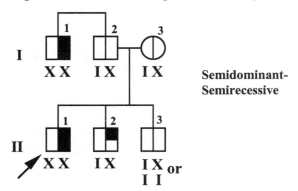

Semidominant-
Semirecessive

Here, as in recessive inheritance, the most severely affected members have a double dose of the gene. The more mildly-affected members (II-2) have a single gene, as in dominant inheritance. If one assumes the inheritance is autosomal dominant, when in fact it is semidominant-semirecessive, so many mistakes in coding for linkage studies are made that most of the power of the technique is lost. For example, in this pedigree, both I-3 and II-3 would be assumed to be non-carriers when, in fact, they might be carriers.

From about 1987 to 1992, I still thought that TS was caused by a single major *Gts* gene, probably *TDO2*, and that this gene operated in a semidominant-semirecessive fashion. However, two things began to slowly change my mind and led me to suspect it was really polygenically inherited. The first was that, despite the suggestive and seductive findings from South Africa that *TDO2* was the major gene in TS, we were unsuccessful in finding any mutations in the expressed portion of this gene. Second, and more convincing, was our finding that the *dopamine D2*, and to a lesser extent the *D3*, gene, played a role in the expression of TS.

This led me to suspect that many, and perhaps all, of the genes involved in the metabolism of the various neurotransmitters might come in different allelic forms which varied slightly in the efficiency with which they did their job of making receptors, enzymes, or transporters. Many of the mutations causing these differences might lie in the regions outside the gene itself, but which still affected the function of the gene. Because these alleles had only a modest effect on the function of the gene, they could be very common in the population (5 – 60% carrier rate). However, because they were common, people would still have a relatively high risk of inheriting two or more such genes, and the more they inherited, the more likely they were to have some form of behavioral problem.

A further aspect of polygenic inheritance was that linkage analyses would never, or rarely, be successful in finding the genes. The reason for this is shown as follows:

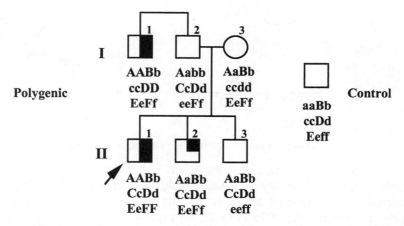

Here, we assume that in order to have symptoms, it is necessary to inherit at least five different mutant genes (genes with at least one allele that is a capital letter). Different affected members do not necessarily have the same set of mutant genes. Here the proband (arrow) is affected because he carries the B, C, D, and E genes in single dose and the A and F genes in double dose. The uncle (I-1) is affected because he carries the B, E, and F genes in single dose and the A and D genes in double dose. The brother with chronic motor tics (II-2) is mildly affected because although he has the A, B, C, D, E, and F genes in single dose, none are in double dose. All the remaining members of the pedigree are unaffected because they do not have enough mutant genes. Controls unrelated to these families have significantly fewer of the relevant mutant genes.

Simple inspection of this pedigree shows why linkage studies would fail to identify any of the mutant genes involved. For example, if the A gene was being studied and the autosomal dominant model assumed, the proband, uncle, and brother would be assumed to carry the mutant A gene, which they do. However, since the three unaffected members also carry the mutant A gene, linkage would be negative, when, in fact, the mutant A gene was involved. The same logic can be used for all six of the genes shown. The most reliable and sensitive gene-finding technique would be association studies comparing frequency of each mutant gene in severely affected probands to unrelated controls.

It should not have escaped the reader's notice that the basic pedigree was identical in all three of the above examples. However, the mechanism of inheritance was dramatically different. The problem with the field of psychiatric genetics was that most workers were assuming that autosomal dominant inheritance was the correct model and thus only linkage studies would work. Hundreds of papers were being reported that "excluded" a role of a given gene in this or that psychiatric disorder. Every time I saw one of these reports I assumed that just the opposite could very well be true.

The following diagram further illustrates the dramatic difference between single gene versus polygenic inheritance.

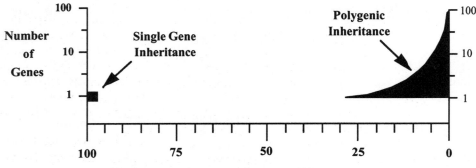

Percent of the Symptoms Accounted for by Each Gene

In single gene inheritance, that gene accounts for the vast majority of the symptoms of the disorder. By contrast, in polygenic inheritance, multiple genes are involved, each producing only a small part of the picture. A modest number of genes may contribute up to 25% of the picture, while progressively larger numbers of genes contribute to a progressively smaller part of the total picture.

Chapter 35

SIDS

SIDS, or Sudden Infant Death Syndrome, is a devastating disorder that usually affects infants in the first six months of life. It is distressingly common, occurring in up to 1 in 500 infants. Typically, a healthy child is put to bed at night and found dead in the crib the next time he is checked. The guilt engendered can be severe, and "what ifs" and "if onlys" are frequently expressed. Occasionally the child is observed to have stopped breathing, and resuscitation can be initiated in time to save the child's life. This is referred to as an Apparent Life Threatening Episode (ALTE).

One of the major theories about SIDS suggests it is due to prolonged sleep apnea, which, in turn, is associated with defective arousal mechanisms. By the late 1980s, I had encountered enough TS families in which a relative had died of SIDS to begin to wonder if perhaps there was an association between the *Gts* genes and susceptibility to SIDS. This suspicion was enhanced by the knowledge that in a sleep laboratory study of thirty-four TS patients, Jankovitch and Rohaidy[119] had reported that 23% had sleep apnea, 29% abnormal arousals, and 53% reduced REM sleep. In addition, sleep problems and disorders of arousal such as sleepwalking, night terrors, and bedwetting are common in TS patients.[p249] It was known that the risk of SIDS was higher in families where one child had already died of SIDS, suggesting that some unknown genetic factor was involved. It was also known that serotonin played a major role in regulating sleep.[p448] Was it possible that the *Gts* genes were this genetic factor?

The next figure shows one of the pedigrees we had observed. Here the proband's brother had died of SIDS at two months of age, his youngest brother almost died of SIDS, and a relative of his mother had also died of SIDS. The other members of the family showed the usual collection of problems present in TS relatives.

By the time we had accumulated seven such families, the next step was to determine what the rate of SIDS or ALTE was in a non-selected series of consecutive pedigrees. Of a total of 917 relatives, eleven, or 1 in 83, had SIDS or ALTE. This was clearly higher than in the general population. We wrote up these observations and submitted the paper to the journal *Pediatrics*. I thought, if people had problems with our suggestions that TS was associated with a wide range of behavioral disorders, they will probably really think we were crazy with this one. Sure enough, the paper was quickly rejected. I tried the other major pediatric journal, *Journal of Pediatrics*, with no better results.

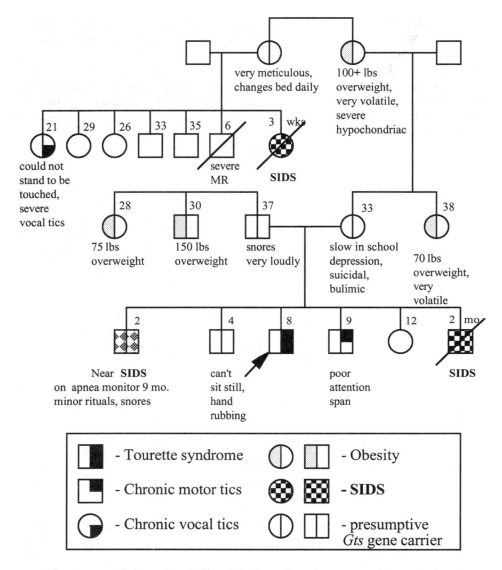

About a month later, Dr. Jeff and Barbara Sverd came to visit on their way to a family vacation in Hawaii. I joined them one morning for breakfast as we were preparing for a day's outing. I brought along a copy of our paper entitled "SIDS and Tourette Syndrome: Is There an Etiological Relationship?" Barbara's response to seeing it was, "Jeff, you were going to write that same paper." Unknown to me, he was observing the same increased frequency of SIDS in the relatives of his TS patients. I suggested he go ahead and write the paper and we would submit them together, thinking that if two independent studies showed the same result, the skeptics would have to believe the observations might have some merit.

Six months later Sverd and I submitted the pair of papers together to the *Journal of Developmental and Physical Disabilities.*[62] Although we sent them in separately, we requested that they be reviewed together, so that they would be mutually supportive. However, the editor chose to have them reviewed separately. Mine was accepted and Sverd's was not. Since both papers were very similar, we suspected the difference was simply in the reviewer — the random chance factor that influences the acceptance or non-acceptance of many papers in science. Sverd then submitted his revision to the *American Journal of Medical Genetics* where it was accepted,[204] and was actually published three months earlier than ours.

Chapter 36

The Genetic Loading Technique

Following the publication of our 1987 series of papers, we extensively updated the Human Behavior Questionnaire. The adult version now contained thirty-one pages of questions.[p699] Every person seen in the clinic was required to completely fill it out and, when available, parents and siblings were also asked to participate. When I originally conceived of this extensive database, I thought of it only in terms of allowing us to examine the effects of various genes on the different behaviors. Since initially we had no genes to examine, for several years these questionnaires simply accumulated in large piles in the lab. There was so much information in the questionnaires, it took me over a year to write a BASIC program so that a data entry person could easily enter the data into the computer. Since we had no funds to hire a data entry person, the piles just continued to grow.

One day, after an entire lab bench had been filled with questionnaires, Karen told me we had a volunteer, Cherry, with extensive experience in data entry. We eagerly took her on, and she began the slow process of entering all the questionnaires into a statistical database. As the piles began to shrink, I was eventually able to hire her part-time, using Hope Press profits. Eventually, over four thousand individuals were entered into the database.

Since we didn't have DNA samples on every person who filled out a questionnaire, for years I thought that only a portion of the total database would eventually be used. However, it gradually began to dawn on me that this data provided a unique and powerful opportunity to examine the effects of the *Gts* genes on a variety of behaviors.

The reasoning was as follows: The large number of subjects in the database allowed me to examine groups of individuals according to the degree of "genetic loading," or number of *Gts* genes they carried. TS probands would have the greatest number of *Gts* genes and thus, the greatest genetic loading. Following this would be the non-proband TS patients, i.e. brothers, sisters, mothers and fathers with TS that was not severe enough for them to seek medical care. Next came the relatives of the TS probands who had no tics themselves. Finally, the controls should have the least genetic loading. This can be summarized as follows:

Group	Genetic loading
TS probands	most *Gts* genes
Relatives with tics (**non-proband TS**)	next most *Gts* genes
Relatives without tics (**non-TS relatives**)	next least *Gts* genes
Controls	least *Gts* genes

To further examine genetic loading, the TS probands could be divided into mild or moderate (grade 1 and 2), or severe (grade 3), with non-proband TS subjects occupying a position in the middle of this subdivision. Alternately, they could be divided into TS probands with ADHD versus TS probands without ADHD.

The next aspect of this tool involved simply picking any of the behavioral aspects covered in the questionnaire and asking if they occurred with progressively greater frequency across groups with greater genetic loading for the *Gts* genes; thus the frequency across the different groups of a *behavior related to Gts genes* would look like the solid line:

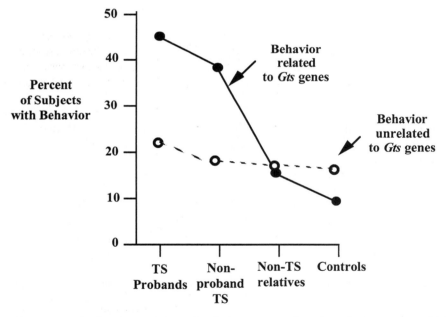

By contrast, the frequencies of a *behavior unrelated to Gts genes* would look like the dotted line. The beauty of the technique was that, like our association studies, it was totally independent of the mechanism of inheritance of TS. Since everyone agreed that TS was a genetic disorder, if a behavior showed a significant association with genetic loading for *Gts* genes, this would suggest that it was genetically controlled. The technique had a distinct advantage over twin and adoption studies in that if the results were positive, the identity of the genes involved was immediately known, i.e. the *Gts* genes. Finally, since everyone filled out the questionnaire for a wide range of symptoms before the diagnosis was made, the study was prospective, and there was no bias toward any particular set of symptoms.

Ruling Out Ascertainment Bias and Inappropriate Controls

This technique had another powerful characteristic. Pauls et al.[164,165,170] had claimed that the increase in behavioral problems we had found in TS probands was entirely due to ascertainment bias. This was the tendency for probands, or the member of the family who seeks a doctor's care, to have more problems and more severe symptoms than those who do not seek medical care. In our database, the non-proband TS subjects represented individuals who had not sought medical treatment for their TS. If various behaviors were significantly increased in frequency in this group, it would rule out the ascertainment bias objection. But significantly increased compared to who?

Pauls et al. had also objected to our choice of controls.[164] The implication was that our controls might have been from a different socioeconomic class with fewer behavioral problems than our TS subjects. This objection could be eliminated by using the non-TS relatives. Since they were from the same families as the non-probands TS individuals, all complaints about inappropriate matching of subjects to controls would be eliminated. For a behavior that is largely caused by *Gts* genes, this "ideal comparison" group would be as follows:

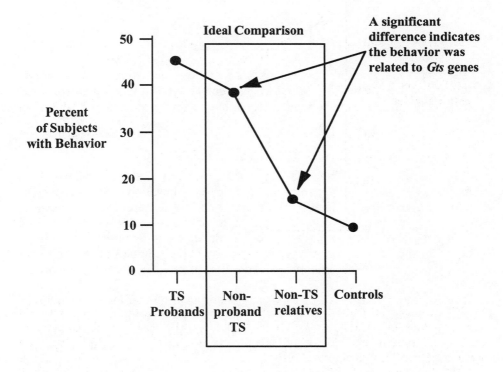

For a behavior that is increased in TS probands due to ascertainment bias but absent in non-proband TS relatives, and thus not due to *Gts* genes, the "ideal comparison" would be as follows:

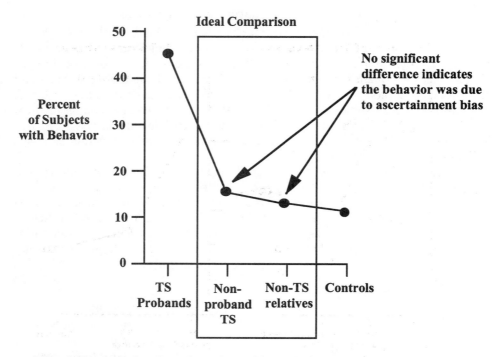

The following chapters show how this technique was used to demonstrate that the *Gts* genes played a role in irritable bowel syndrome, alcoholism, drug abuse, a wide range of sexual behaviors, conduct disorder, depression, and other behaviors.

The Effect of Examining TS Relatives As a Group

If the frequency of different behaviors is examined in the all the relatives as a group, instead of separately examining the frequency in relatives with TS versus relatives without TS, the effect of the *Gts* genes can be obscured. This is because, in general, only about one-fourth to one-third of the relatives have TS, while most do not. As a result, if the two are combined, the potentially much higher frequency in the TS relatives tends to be lost by being diluted out by the lower frequency in the relatives without TS. This is illustrated in the diagram on the next page.

It was only after I began to do these genetic loading studies that I realized that the 1988 study of Pauls et al.[164] had presented the results for the TS relatives as a whole, rather than separately examining the frequencies in relatives with TS versus relatives without TS. Was it possible that if the results were presented properly they would be similar to ours? The answer to this would have to await the publication of their detailed results.

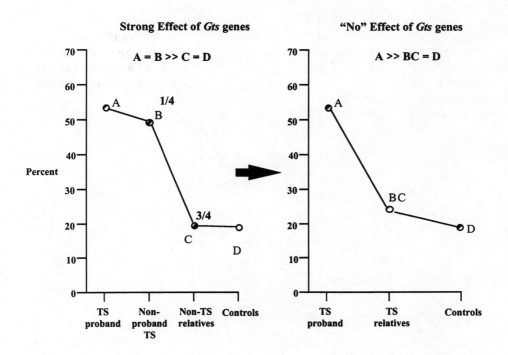

Chapter 37

Yale "Confirms" Our Findings

The Tourette Syndrome Association holds a National Conference every three years for the lay and professional members of the association. The three-day conference consists of support groups and a scientific session where researchers present their latest finding about TS. Given our philosophical conflicts with TSA, I thought it would be a long time before I was asked to speak at one of these meetings. Things changed significantly, however, after Harvey Dean was elected president and after the TSA Scientific Symposium the previous summer, where so many of our findings were verified.

When Dean visited our home on July 2, he promised that I would be a speaker at the National Meeting, and he was true to his word. The program consisted of Kurlan discussing the natural history of TS, Singer presenting the newest evidence on PET scanning and studies of TS brains, and Dr. Mark Riddle from Yale, reviewing the association between anxiety and depression and TS. Two talks on the genetics of TS were then scheduled, the first by me, to be followed by Kidd from Yale.

That seemed to have all the elements of a shoot-out at the O.K. Corral. TSA had spent about a million dollars funding five groups around the world to do linkage studies in TS, based on the assumption it was inherited as an autosomal dominant trait. They had now excluded over 80% of the genome and found nothing. I was going to stand up and say their approach was wrong, the inheritance was by a different mechanism, and the linkage approach would probably never work. I would also present our results on the association of the D_2A1 allele (Chapter 16) with TS and ADHD. Kidd would probably stand up and say the inheritance of TS really was autosomal dominant, that even though a linkage had not yet been found, it would only be a matter of time, and that our D_2A1 studies were wrong. In addition, Riddle had always adhered to the Yale line that most of the associated behaviors in TS were due to ascertainment bias. I had no idea what he would say now.

Kurlan was in the process of editing a new book on Tourette syndrome. He had asked me to write a chapter on the "Comorbid Behaviors." I promised to do so only if I could get from Pauls the details of his studies of the prevalence of behavioral disorders in TS probands compared to controls. After trying for over a year, Pauls finally sent the tables I needed for the review.

I was astounded. The figures they had on the prevalence of many different behavioral disorders in TS probands were virtually identical to what we had obtained in 1987. The comparison of these two studies is shown below.

Comparison of Behavioral Disorders in TS Probands in the Comings' versus the Pauls' Study

Behavior Problems in TS Probands	Comings and Comings (1987)[30,48]			Pauls et al. (1988)[170]		
	Probands	Controls	p	Probands	Controls	p
N	247	47		86	43	
	%	%		%	%	
ADD (%)	61.7	6.3	<0.0001	54.6	9.3	<0.0001
Alcohol (%)	—	—		7.0	0.0	0.083
Drugs (%)	—	—		7.0	0.0	0.083
Drugs &/or alcohol	15.0	4.0	0.04	—	—	
Major depression	22.9	2.1	<0.0001	40.7	16.3	0.004
Minor depression	—	—		14.0	0	0.006
Panic	15.8*	0.0	0.006	12.8	4.7	0.125
Simple phobia	—	—		18.6	7.0	0.063
Social phobia	—	—		5.8	2.3	0.345
Simple and social phobias	26.0	8.5	0.05	—	—	
Speech problems	—	—		9.3	0.0	0.035
Specific dev. disorder	26.8	4.2	0.002	30.2	4.7	<0.001
Stuttering	31.3	6.4	0.0005	15.1	4.7	0.067

* More than 3 panic attacks/week

(Bold numbers indicate comparable percentages between the two studies)

It is rare in science for two independent studies to give such similar results. In addition, if the relatives of their TS patients were divided into those with tics versus those without tics, those with tics consistently had more behavioral problems. Since these were non-proband TS subjects, this would have ruled out ascertainment bias. What was even more incredible to me was that this information was available to them at the time they wrote the letter to the editors (see Chapter 12) stating that our "assertions fall outside the mainstream of the very extensive TS literature that has developed over the past two decades."[164] I prepared a slide comparing the two studies for presentation at the TSA conference. It was going to be interesting.

The shoot-out never materialized. As the speakers were walking up to the podium, I noticed that neither Riddle nor Kidd had come. The conference went smoothly.

At It Again with DRD2

On May 14 1992, Jeffrey Sverd called to discuss some data and asked if I had heard about the abstract that the Yale group had presented at the American Psychiatric Association meeting the week before. I had not, so he FAXed me a copy. It read, "Evidence the D_2 Dopamine Receptor Alleles Do Not Influence Severity of Tourette's Syndrome."[100] It was by Gelernter, Pauls, Leckman,

Kidd, and Roger Kurlan. The authors had studied the dopamine D_2A1 allele in the Tourette syndrome families on which linkage studies were being done, to see if they could verify our claim that the prevalence of the A1 allele was more common in TS patients than controls, and more common in patients with full-blown Tourette syndrome than in mildly affected patients who only had chronic motor tics.

They reported that the frequency of the A1 allele in fifty-nine TS patients was 0.27, while in twenty-two subjects with chronic motor tics, it was 0.18. Since these two figures were not significantly different, they concluded these results did not support DRD2 alleles as a factor for severity of TS.

When I converted gene frequency to carrier frequency, or prevalence, it showed tthat 46.2% of their TS patients carried the A1 allele. This dropped to 31.8% in those with the milder chronic motor tics. Since the prevalence of the A1 allele in the normal controls was running around 26%, this looked like strong support for our hypothesis, not evidence against it. By comparing only their TS patients to patients with chronic motor tics, the numbers were too small to be significant. I felt that they were committing a type II statistical error. When I examined the data by including normal controls, the progressive increase in prevalence of the A1 allele with severity was highly significant (p = .002). When I added their results to ours, they were even more impressive.

	Comings et al.		Gelernter et al.		Total	
	N	%A1	N	%A1	N	%A1
Tourette Syndrome*	200	44.5	59	45.8	259	44.8
Mild TS**- CMT	20	35.0	22	31.8	42	33.3
Controls	394	26.1	394	26.1	394	26.1
χ^2		20.4		9.72		24.4
p		.0001		.002		<.00001

* Grade 2 and 3 cases ** Grade 1 cases   CMT = chronic motor tics χ^2 = statistical test

Our results and theirs were virtually identical. Among our full-blown TS probands 44.5% carried the D_2A1 allele, compared to 45.8% of theirs. Among our mild TS cases, 35.0% carried the D_2A1, compared to 31.8% of theirs. When compared to the controls used in the *JAMA* paper, the combined series showed a highly significant progressive increase in D_2A1 carrier prevalence with increasing severity of TS symptoms (p <.00001).

Once again, our results and theirs were virtually identical. Our white was their black.

Pauls et al. Agree ADHD is Part of the TS Spectrum

One of the points Pauls et al. had been most adamant about was that the increased frequency of ADHD in TS probands was all due to ascertainment bias.[162,165,166] To us, TS and ADHD were essentially identical entities. Virtually the only difference we could find was that one had tics and the other did not.[1,33,34,37,39,41,46,48,49,56,59,67,129,131] In September 1993, Pauls, Leckman, and Cohen published an update of their most recent results on TS and ADHD.[168]

This time they concluded that "TS and ADD may be etiologically related in some persons." They stated that, "The current findings are not completely consistent with our earlier findings that suggested TS and ADD were independent."

They had also examined learning disabilities (LD), speech disorders and stuttering, and concluded they were not genetically related to TS. Again, however, the comparisons involved TS probands to TS relatives to TS controls. The TS relatives had not been divided into those with tics versus those without tics.

I felt that these statements could not go unchallenged and was able to now turn to our TS database to examine these issues in our families. These results were put into the following letter to the editor[64] of *The Journal of the American Academy of Child and Adolescent Psychiatry*:

Tourette Syndrome, ADHD, Learning and Speech Disorders

In the study by Pauls et al.,[14] we were pleased to see that they have now concluded that some cases of ADHD are genetically related to Gilles de la Tourette syndrome (TS). This is an improvement over their prior conclusion that TS and ADHD were genetically unrelated entities.[165] However, they now claim, as they have previously,[170] that learning disorders, speech disorders, and stuttering are genetically unrelated to TS. A major problem with their analysis is that they have strongly biased the results against finding such an association by failing to distinguish between relatives with TS versus relatives without TS. If, as they claim, the associated disorders in TS are due to ascertainment bias in probands, the frequency of these problems should be no higher in non-proband TS relatives than relatives without TS. We have examined this in our TS families. Speech problems consisted of talking so fast or erratically that people had difficulty understanding them, and/or elective mutism. The results in percent were as follows:

	TS Probands	Non-Proband TS Relatives	Non-TS Relatives	Controls
N	1062	189	479	123
ADHD	71.2	55.0	8.4	5.7
LD	42.9	21.2	4.3	5.6
Speech problems	44.0	38.9	18.8	13.5
Stuttering	26.0	19.4	6.2	8.3

When analyzed for a progressive decreasing frequency across groups, all four disorders were significant at $p < 10^{-8}$. Ascertainment bias was avoided by comparing non-proband TS relatives to relatives without TS. Here the p values for all four disorders were $<.0000005$; thus when the relatives are divided into those with and without TS or chronic tics, the highly significant results suggest that TS, ADHD, LD, speech disorders and stuttering are variant expressions of TS and share genes in common.

An analysis of a separate 131 TS probands and 338 first-degree relatives [done by Ellen Knell, a graduate student in our department] also showed a major, significant association between tics and ADHD.[131] One interesting result of this study was the finding that 20% of the relatives of male TS probands without ADHD had ADHD, whereas 0% of the relatives of female TS probands without ADHD had ADHD. The usual male/female ratio of TS probands is 4:1 or more. The artificial selection by Pauls et al. of an increased proportion of female probands could account for some of their results.

Pauls et al. also suggest that ADHD alone had an earlier age of onset than ADHD + TS. We also examined this and found an average age of onset of 3.79 years for ADHD associated with TS (N = 582) versus 7.24 years for non-TS relatives with ADHD (N = 21). This trend is the opposite of what Pauls et al. found and, unlike theirs, these differences were highly significant (p = <.000001). As discussed in detail elsewhere, except for the tics, TS and ADHD are very similar disorders.[63] We interpret these age-of-onset results to indicate that ADHD with chronic tics simply represents a greater or more severe form of expression of the *Gts-ADHD* genes, with a resulting earlier age of onset than ADHD without chronic tics.

Our new database had allowed us to separately examine the frequency of these behaviors in relatives with and without chronic tics, and provided a large enough sample to avoid type II statistical errors. When finally printed,[64] the editors had removed all the numbers and substituted:

"When the relatives are divided into those with and without TS or chronic tics, the highly significant results suggest that TS, ADHD, learning disorders, speech disorders, and stuttering are variant expressions of TS and share genes in common."

In their reply, Pauls, Leckman, and Cohen ended, saying:

"Additional research, including the more precise delineation of the genetics and the localization of the gene(s) conferring risk for TS and other behaviors, will greatly clarify these differences of opinion. Imaginative and competing hypotheses, such as offered by Comings and Comings, continue to help stimulate research in this area."

It looked like the opposition was beginning to soften a bit. In fact, in the same issue, Carter, Pauls, Leckman, and Cohen[22] reported on "A Prospective Longitudinal Study of Gilles de la Tourette Syndrome." This was a study of siblings or children of probands with TS. It was called a prospective study because the children were identified at a very early age, before they had developed tics.

They were then followed for several years to see if they developed tics or other behavioral problems. This approach also eliminated the possibility of ascertainment bias. Twenty-one children were evaluated. In this preliminary study where the children had been followed from seven to ten years of age, 43% developed tics, 19% had obsessive-compulsive behaviors, 24% had ADHD, 24% speech problems, and 24% anxiety disorders. In all, despite their young age, 68% fell into an "any behavioral problem" category. The authors commented that:

> "...the increase of ADHD in these families is discordant with some of our earlier family study findings.[165] As noted, children in this sample appear to express a higher frequency of other psychiatric disorders as well...thus, the increased rates of disorder suggest that the other conditions represent a variant expression of the syndrome, as suggested by Comings and Comings."[59]

This was a well-designed study. The fact that so many of these at-risk children had psychiatric problems, despite their young age, suggested the frequency would continue to increase as they grew older. I hoped their study would continue so these children could be followed well into adolescence.

Despite these encouraging developments, I was aware of the fact that Pauls et al. were planning additional papers claiming that depression, phobias, substance abuse, and other behaviors were not genetically related to TS. This stimulated me to further utilize the database and the genetic loading technique to examine these behaviors in our own families.

Just as our theories stimulated further research by Pauls et al., their claims that these theories could be explained by ascertainment bias stimulated additional research by us. That, of course, is how science works.

Chapter 38

Irritable Bowel Syndrome
− A Genetic Disorder?

For years Dr. Abdul Badawy in England had been writing about TDO2 in rats. His studies showed that the chronic administration of alcohol, morphine, and medications used for the treatment of depression resulted in the inhibition of TDO2 and increased brain serotonin levels.[p467] This was part of the evidence that convinced me that a genetic defect in the *TDO2* gene might play an important role in the cause of TS, depression, alcoholism, drug addiction, and other parts of the TS spectrum of disorders. To show my appreciation for his work, I sent Badawy a copy of the TS book and later a copy of our work on the *D2* gene. A friendship by mail developed, and in 1991 he invited me to present a paper on the role of serotonin in alcoholism in a symposium at the International Society for Biomedical Research in Alcoholism at Bristol, England in June, 1992.

As the time for the conference approached, Brenda and I decided to take a side visit to Venice and Florence. Past experience had shown that I usually undergo withdrawal symptoms if I am away from my computer for long. To ease the separation anxiety, shortly before this trip I purchased a Macintosh PowerBook 170 and two extra batteries to keep it going on the long plane flights. Since the PowerBook had a math coprocessor, I was able to bring along the growing database containing the results of the questionnaires. I wanted to try out the genetic loading technique and chose irritable bowel syndrome as the first behavior to examine.

For years I had been impressed by the high frequency of irritable bowel syndrome and other GI problems in TS patients and their relatives. The pedigree on the following page is a typical example.

Irritable bowel syndrome is a chronic disorder characterized by cramping abdominal pains, diarrhea or constipation, and relief of the pain after a bowel movement. It is a very common disorder and by far the most frequent condition treated by gastroenterologists. Since all laboratory tests are normal, and since many people with irritable bowel syndrome have a variety of psychiatric disorders, such as depression, anxiety, ADHD, chronic fatigue, eating disorders, and obsessive-compulsive behaviors, it was usually thought of as a "functional" disorder. This is a euphemism for "without observable cause," or "psychosomatic," or "all in your head."

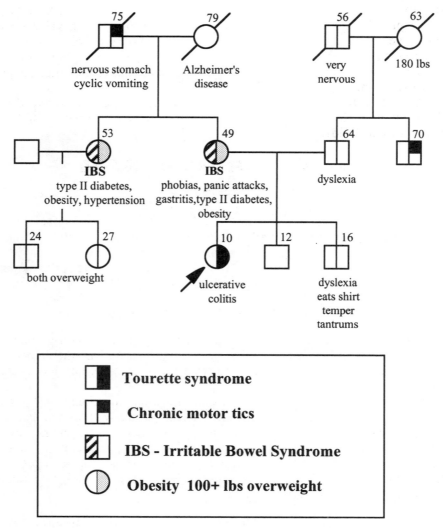

It is a sad fact that people are often not taken seriously when the diseases they have don't show up on any laboratory tests. However, since the spectrum of behavioral disorders that were present in people with irritable bowel syndrome was essentially identical to the TS spectrum of associated behaviors, and since so many of my TS patients or their relatives had irritable bowel syndrome, I wondered if the bowel problems were not just a reflection of the same serotonin deficiency that affects the function of the brain; thus I decided to both break in my new PowerBook and the Behavioral Questionnaire database by determining if the GI symptoms covered in the Behavioral Questionnaire occurred progressively more often in subjects with increased genetic loading for the *Gts* genes.

The results for the 740 adults in the database were striking; for example, the question, "Have you ever had trouble with loose stools or diarrhea, other than acute illness?" was answered "yes" by 16.2% of the controls, 13.1% of the non-

TS relatives, 24.2% of the non-proband TS subjects, 28.3% of the mild and moderate TS probands, and 40.0% of the severe TS probands. The p value for this progressive series was <0.00001, indicating a highly significant association between this symptom and the presence of the *Gts* genes. This progression with genetic loading was also significant for questions about gas or bloating, constipation, nausea, vomiting and spastic colon.

When added together to form a GI complaint score, the scores ranged from 2.20 for the grade 3 TS probands to 0.80 for the non-TS relatives (p <0.0001). This is shown as follows:

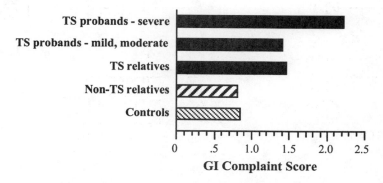

To rule out ascertainment bias, the GI complaint score in non-proband TS subjects (1.44) was compared to non-TS relatives (0.80). The difference was highly significant (p < .0001), indicating these problems were not due to ascertainment bias.

These results suggested that one of the most classic "functional" or "psychosomatic" disorders was actually a genetic disorder. It was well known that serotonin and dopamine were just as important neurotransmitters for the nerves and muscles of the intestine as for the nerves of the brain. The entire picture made the most sense by assuming that the *Gts* genes could independently result in problems with the function of either the brain or the intestine, or both.[36] This concept could be diagrammed as follows:

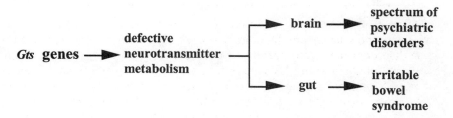

While this was the first success for the TS database, to date these results remain unpublished. Reviewers of six different journals were unconvinced that the same set of genes that caused the psychiatric symptoms could also cause the GI symptoms.

Chapter 39

The *Gts* Genes and
Drug and Alcohol Abuse

The approach used for studying the role of the *Gts* gene in functional bowel disorders worked so well, the question was, What to examine next? Because drug and alcohol abuse were so common in the relatives of TS patients,[p644] and since there was still little acceptance of the idea that the *Gts* genes, or in many circles, *any* genes, might be involved in drug and alcohol abuse, I chose that.

There was a lot of data from twin and adoption studies to indicate that genetic factors played a major role in alcoholism.[p225] Since there was much less data on genetic factors in drug abuse, I wanted to examine that first.

Many questions in our Behavioral Questionnaire were based on the National Institutes of Mental Health Diagnostic Interview Schedule. This was especially true of drug abuse. Questions were asked about the use of eight different classes of street drugs, marijuana, amphetamines (speed), barbiturates (sleeping pills), tranquilizers, cocaine, heroin, opiates, and psychedelics (LSD and others). The following diagrams show the percentage of subjects who used the drugs to get high in the four groups of subjects, with decreasing degrees of loading for the *Gts* gene. The study included a total of 595 adults.

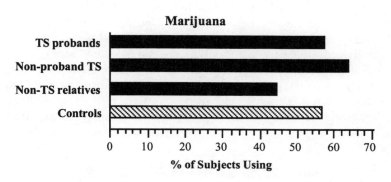

Because of the high frequency of use of marijuana by all subjects, including the controls, there were no significant differences between the four groups; however, the results were highly significant for all the other groups of drugs. For example, the results for the use of cocaine were:

173

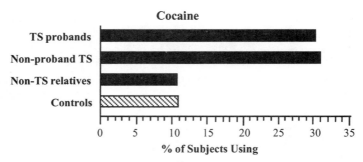

Here the progressive differences were highly significant (p = 0.00000007). It was of particular interest that the percentage of subjects using cocaine for more than two weeks was just as high in the non-proband TS subjects as the TS probands. This ruled out Pauls' ascertainment bias as an explanation of the results.

The results with other drug groups were similar, except that the use was usually higher in the non-TS relatives than in the controls. This is illustrated by the results for the use of psychedelics.

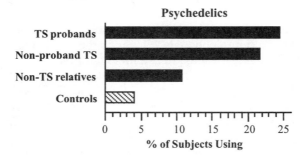

These differences were also highly significant (p= 0.000001). The higher frequency of use in the non-TS relatives was consistent with the association of the *Gts* gene with drug abuse in individuals who have no tics.

In addition to drug use, the data also made it possible to examine drug abuse. Eight different questions were asked, including illicit drug use, developing a dependence on drugs, inability to cut down, needing more and more, having withdrawal symptoms, overdose or the development of seizures, causing family problems, or causing emotional problems. All of these symptoms were highly associated with loading for the *Gts* gene, and all p values were less than 0.000001. For example, the results for the question, "Have you ever used any of the above drugs or any other illicit drug every day for two weeks or more?" were as follows:

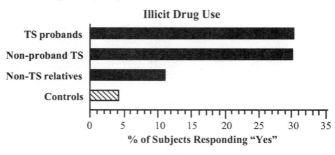

The results were similar for each of the other questions indicating a powerful role of the *Gts* gene in the susceptibility to drug abuse.

Other parts of the questionnaire allowed us to examine the role of different behaviors on the risk of having one or more of these drug abuse problems. These risks, in terms of the frequency of drug problems in subjects with the disorder versus subjects without the disorder, are called "odds ratios." An odds ratio of 1 indicates no difference between the controls and subjects, and a ratio of 2 indicates a twofold increased risk for subjects. The results for a series of behaviors were as follows:

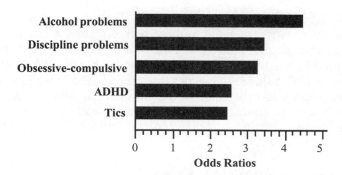

It was not surprising that those who had alcohol problems had a 4.5 times greater risk of having problems with drug abuse than those without alcohol problems. Those whose parents thought they were a discipline problem as a child had a 3.3-fold greater risk than those without discipline problems. There was a similar increased risk for those with obsessive-compulsive behaviors. The presence of childhood ADHD or tics were associated with a 2.5- and 2.3-fold increased risk. These findings were all consistent with many studies indicating that these different behaviors were all associated with an increased risk of substance abuse. Here, however, was evidence they were all caused by a common set of genes.

We also examined these questions in a group of subjects with only ADHD and no tics to determine if the *ADHD* gene had the same effect. While the numbers were smaller, the results were very similar. This was consistent with our belief that the *Gts* and the *ADHD* genes were essentially the same.

A number of questions were also asked about alcohol abuse, including whether relatives complained about the subject's drinking, whether they went on binges or benders and kept drinking for a couple of days without sobering up, whether a doctor ever told them to stop drinking, whether they had ever been arrested for drunk driving, and many others. The percent of subjects in the different groups responding "yes" to at least one of these was as follows:[37]

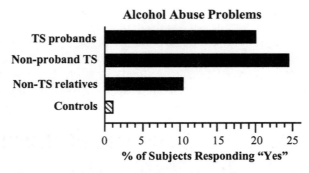

Alcohol Abuse Problems

The odds ratio results were similar to those with drug abuse except that now the risk of developing alcohol abuse problems was 5.3 times greater for those with drug abuse problems than those without such problems. While there had been doubts about whether there were genes that predisposed to both alcohol and drug abuse, these findings clearly indicated the *Gts* genes definitely did.

These observations suggested the following modification of our prior diagrams showing the interrelationship between serotonin and dopamine genes, childhood and adult disorders.[38]

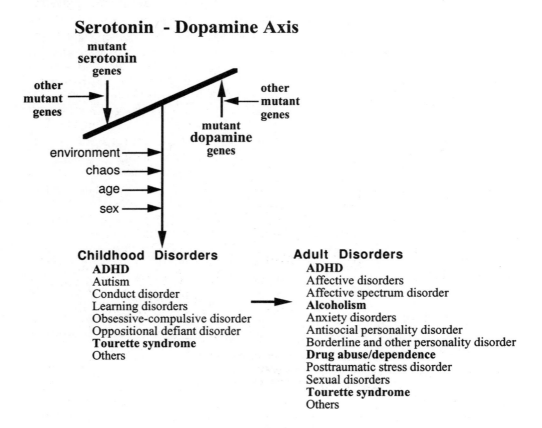

Serotonin - Dopamine Axis

Childhood Disorders
ADHD
Autism
Conduct disorder
Learning disorders
Obsessive-compulsive disorder
Oppositional defiant disorder
Tourette syndrome
Others

Adult Disorders
ADHD
Affective disorders
Affective spectrum disorder
Alcoholism
Anxiety disorders
Antisocial personality disorder
Borderline and other personality disorder
Drug abuse/dependence
Posttraumatic stress disorder
Sexual disorders
Tourette syndrome
Others

Chapter 40

The Genetics of Sexual Behavior

One of the aspects of TS that has received a great deal of attention is the compulsive swearing, or coprolalia. Contrary to popular opinion, this symptom is present in less than one-fourth of the cases. While people have often struggled to explain this unusual symptom, when TS is viewed in its broader perspective as a disorder of impulsive, compulsive, and oftentimes hypersexual behaviors, the presence of coprolalia is no longer so mysterious. One of the earliest studies to emphasize the sexual problems in TS was by Eldridge and co-workers.[91] Of the twenty-four cases of TS studied, twelve had troublesome sexual and aggressive impulses, including inappropriate sexual touching of themselves or others and varying degrees of exhibitionism. A later study of a different set of fifty TS subjects[154] showed that 32% displayed various types of inappropriate sexual behaviors. Because these were fairly severe cases, these observations tended to be ignored as unrepresentative of TS in general. While this was partly true, anyone who treats TS individuals and asks the appropriate questions is fully aware of the frequency of various forms of hypersexual behavior. I had been intrigued by this aspect of TS ever since our 1984 report of exhibitionism (see Chapter 5). Since sexual behavior in TS had never been rigorously studied, and since this was an important part of my hypothesis that the *Gts* genes were being selected for[30,55] (see Chapter 44), this was next on my list of behaviors to examine using the Gts genetic loading technique.

Our Human Behavior Questionnaire[p699] contained a number of questions about different aspects of sexual behavior. To further examine genetic loading, the TS probands were subdivided into those with and without ADHD, with the order being TS + ADHD, non-proband TS, TS-ADHD. The results of some of these questions for 881 adult subjects were as follows.

For the question, "Do you think your sex drive is: a) less than average, b) average, c) greater than average, d) much greater than average?" the results for the percent answering "much greater than average" for the five groups were:

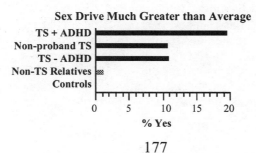

177

Of the TS probands with ADHD, 19.5% felt their sex drive was much greater than average. This dropped to 2.0% for the non-TS relatives and 0% for the controls. These differences were highly significant (p < .00000001).

For the question, "Do you think you have more recurrent thoughts about sex than others your age?" the results were:

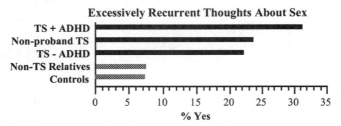

Of the TS probands with ADHD, 32% responded "yes," versus 7% for both the non-TS relatives and controls (p < .00000001).

For the question, "Did you ever exhibit yourself by removing part or all of your clothing in public?" the results for responding "yes, two to five times or more often" were:

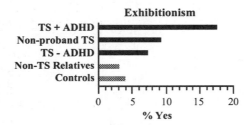

Of the TS probands with ADHD, 17% responded "yes," versus 4.1% of the controls (p < .00000001).

Other questions covering sadism, masochism, fetishism, pedophilia, and cross-dressing also showed a significant increase in the TS groups over controls.[34] When the presence of these behaviors was correlated with other TS behaviors, the highest correlation was with obsessive-compulsive behaviors. This finding suggested that many of these sexual behaviors were variant forms of an obsessive-compulsive disorder.

Homosexuality

A number of regions of the brain are larger or smaller in males than females. These are called "sexually dimorphic nuclei." One of these is located in the hypothalamus, a portion of the brain that regulates the hormones excreted by the pituitary, the master gland that regulates sexual and other behaviors. In 1991, Simon LeVay at the Salk Institute in San Diego reported in *Science*[146] that the third interstitial nuclei of the hypothalamus was twice as large in heterosexual than homosexual men, and the size in homosexual men was similar to that of heterosexual females. This created a considerable stir, since it was the first clear evidence that homosexuality might have a biological basis rather than being a matter of personal or moral choice. This was consistent with the vast majority of homosexuals who state they felt "different" from an early age and didn't actively choose to be gay.

Evidence supporting the idea that homosexuality was genetically controlled was reported in 1992.[3] This was the largest study ever reported of identical versus fraternal twins and showed that if one identical twin was homosexual, 52% of the time the other twin was also homosexual. By contrast, if one fraternal twin was homosexual, the other was homosexual only 22% of the time. Since identical twins have all the same genes, while fraternal twins share only half of their genes, this was strong support for the role of genes in homosexuality, but gave no clue to the identification of the genes involved.

An important clue to one of the genes that may be involved in male homosexuality came from the study of Dr. Dean Hamer and co-workers.[107] They observed that among the relatives of male homosexuals, if there were other male homosexuals in the family, it was much more likely they were on the mother's side than the father's side. Since one of the characteristics of X-linked inheritence is that genes on the X-chromosome can never be passed from father to son (the father always passes a Y chromosome to his sons), this implied an X-linked gene was involved. Linkage studies suggested the gene was on the long arm of the X chromosome. This, however, may represent only a portion of male homosexuality and would not account for homosexuality in females.

Our TS pedigrees often showed relatives who were homosexuals, and this seemed to be occurring at a frequency that was much higher than expected from surveys showing that 1 to 4% of the general population were homosexual.[1,120] The following are some examples of such pedigrees.

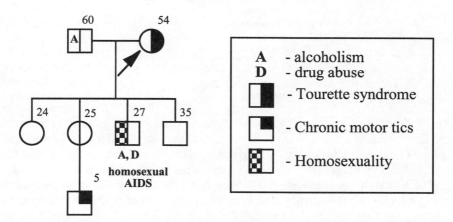

Here the 27-year-old son of a TS patient was a homosexual, alcoholic, drug addict and was dying of AIDS.

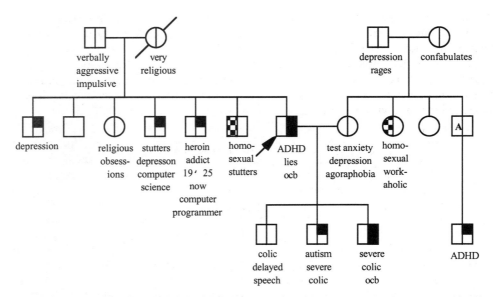

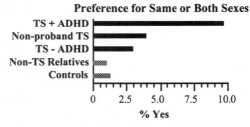

Preference for Same or Both Sexes

In this family with multiple individuals with TS, there were homosexual relatives on both sides of the family.

Our genetic loading technique provided us with a different way to look at the question of the role of genetic factors, specifically the *Gts* genes, in sexual preference. For the question, "Do you sexually prefer: a) the opposite sex, b) the same sex, or c) both?" the results for combining "the same sex" or "both" were:

These differences were significant (p = 0.0000016). This provided support to our pedigrees suggesting that the *Gts* genes could be the genetic factor involved in development of homosexuality. One of the major theories of the cause of homosexuality is that during fetal development, alterations in the level of testosterone lead to permanent changes in the sizes of several areas of the brain that regulate sexual behavior and preference.[2,214,217] Changes in brain serotonin levels can be one of the factors involved.[217] If TS is, in part, due to a serotonin deficiency, the fact that it is genetically caused means the defect would be present throughout embryonic development. As such, the outcome in some cases could be a change in sexual preference.

One of the main objections that has been raised to a genetic cause of homosexuality is that since homosexuals tend to have few or no children, such a gene or genes would be rapidly selected against and would disappear. However, if homosexuality was just one of many effects of such a gene, if multiple genes were involved, and if a specific combination of those genes led to homosexuality, while some of other combinations led to behaviors that resulted in a strong selection for those genes (see Chapter 44), this objection would not be valid.

Lest the reader think that TS subjects are all "hypersexual," (less than a third were) the problems went in both directions. The responses to the question, "Have you ever had a period of six months or more when you had an aversion to having any sexual contact with a sexual partner?" were:

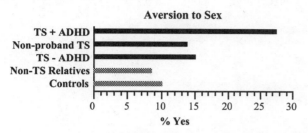

These differences were significant (p = <.00000001); thus the *Gts* genes could also have an adverse effect on sex drive.

To me, these results were very intriguing. This was the first clear evidence that many problems with variant forms of sexual behavior were genetically controlled. This idea had major implications for treatment and punishment of affected individuals. It has been my experience that when TS patients got into legal trouble with their sexual behavior, such as exhibitionism, the symptoms were usually easy to treat with one of the serotonergic antidepressants (SSRIs). This approach stood in marked contrast to the usual treatment of putting them in jail and throwing away the key.

Chapter 41

The Genetics of Conduct Disorder

Parents almost uniformly agree that the most distressing aspect of TS and ADHD is the disruptive behavior. Child psychiatrists have identified two diagnoses to encompass these behaviors – Oppositional Defiant Disorder (ODD) and conduct disorder. The characteristics of ODD include often losing one's temper, constantly arguing or talking, refusing to do chores, deliberately annoying others, blaming everyone else for one's own mistakes, swearing excessively, and being easily annoyed, angry, resentful, spiteful, or vindictive. While all children occasionally display these features some of the time, for the ODD child they are severe and present virtually every day.

Conduct disorder is characterized by the presence of antisocial acts, such as stealing, running away from home, constantly lying, starting fires, missing school, breaking into houses or cars, deliberately destroying property, being cruel to animals, forcing others into sexual activity, using weapons in fights, mugging, purse snatching, armed robbery, and being cruel to others.

These behaviors are almost universally assumed to be learned activities and the result of poor parenting, poverty, physical or sexual abuse, a broken home, or other environmental factors. TS, however, is clearly a genetic disorder, and these problems were so common in our TS children that we inherently knew that genetic factors also played a major role. It was not unusual for only the TS or ADHD child to display these problems, while other siblings were well-behaved and model students. This mitigated against a purely environment model. If the environment was normal, the parents were still married, and other children in the family were well-behaved, it made no sense to claim the presence of these behaviors in the child with TS was due to poor parenting or the environment.

Parents also inherently understood this. Oftentimes when they put their child into psychotherapy, they were told the behavioral problems were their fault because they disciplined too much, didn't discipline enough, or argued too much. Parents often knew the cause lay elsewhere.

In our 1987 series of papers, we reported that these behaviors were significantly more common in TS patients than in controls. However, those who didn't want to believe that genetic factors could play a significant role in ODD and conduct disorder were able to discount this by assuming these results were due, as Pauls suggested, to ascertainment bias. The genetic loading technique provided a way to resolve this issue.

The following show the results for three behaviors – the presence of "discipline problems," ever having "destroyed property," or "set fires."

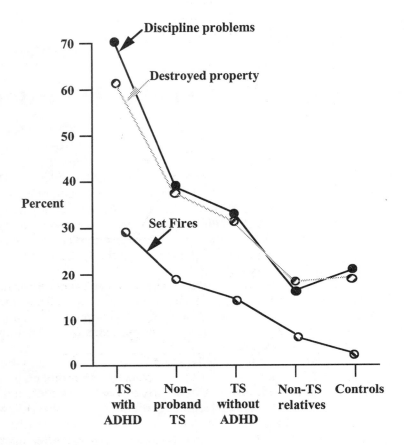

Each of these was significant at p < .00000001, and when the ideal comparison was made of non-proband TS versus non-TS relatives, each was significant at p < .00008. In fact, all nine of the behaviors comprising the diagnosis of ODD, and all twelve of the behaviors comprising the diagnosis of conduct disorder, were highly significant both for the decreasing frequency across the five groups and for the comparison of non-proband TS relatives to non-TS relatives. An additional thirteen variables related to angry and aggressive behaviors were also significant.

A diagnosis of ODD is made when five or more of the ODD variables are present for six months or more. The diagnosis of conduct disorder is made when three or more of the conduct disorder variables are present for six months or more. The following diagram shows the frequency of these two diagnoses in the different groups:

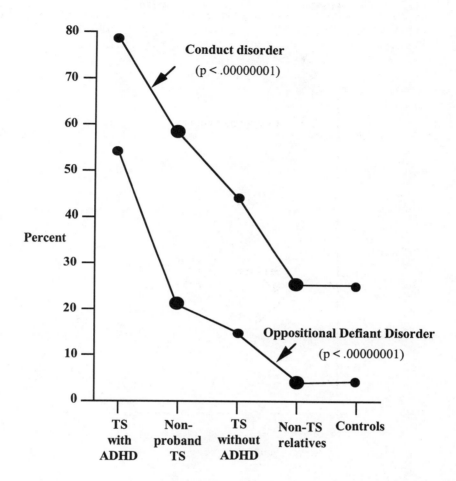

Again, there was a highly significant correlation with genetic loading for the *Gts* genes, and the ideal comparison groups (large circles) were equally significant, indicating the presence of ODD or conduct disorder was not due to ascertainment bias.

The relatives of our ADHD probands were also examined. While the numbers were smaller, the results were very similar. One particularly striking finding was that among the relatives of our ADHD probands, of those who themselves had ADHD, 31% had been arrested, while none of the relatives without ADHD had ever been arrested.

The results were clear. Genetic factors played a major role in ODD, conduct disorder, and aggressive behaviors, and the *Gts* and *ADHD* genes were involved.[41]

Chapter 42

The Genetics of Depression

Having periods of depression is a universal experience. Having severe or chronic depression is less universal, but it still constitutes the most common of the psychiatric disorders. Some subjects who suffer from repeated episodes of depression also experience periods of feeling very high or manic. This form of depression, termed manic-depressive or bipolar disorder, has been shown to have a strong genetic basis.[p191,208] Genetic factors also play a role in many cases of depression without mania, i e. unipolar depression.[208]

For many years we noticed a high frequency of significant depression in our TS patients; for example, in the 1987 study, 23% of the TS probands had major depression, compared to 2.1% of the controls.[28] In the study of Pauls et al. (Chapter 37), the corresponding figures were 41% in TS probands versus 16% of controls. Once again, we felt this was due to the chemical imbalance caused by the *Gts* genes, while Pauls and colleagues felt it was due to ascertainment bias or the stress of coping with the tics. Our experience with TS families led us to doubt this explanation, since we frequently found that one or more of the parents of TS children, usually the mother, had a history of chronic depression, even though they had no tics themselves. Moreover, the depression was often present long before the birth of their TS child.

The database again allowed this concept to be studied. All seventeen of the symptoms of depression used in the Diagnostic Interview Schedule and DSM-III-R were examined in 1,080 subjects. These symptoms showed a highly significant association with the *Gts* genes.[39] The figure on the next page diagrams the results for three of these symptoms — "depression for a period of two years or more," "wanted to die," and "attempted suicide":

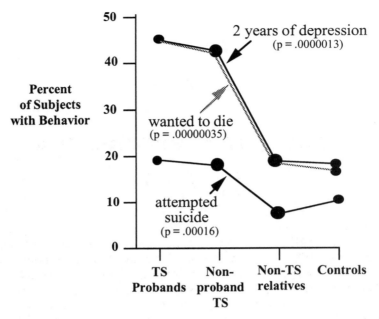

The p values represent the comparison of the non-proband TS relatives versus the non-TS relatives (large dots). All were highly significant, indicating that neither ascertainment bias nor poor selection of controls were the cause of the higher frequency of depression in the TS probands than in the controls. The one remaining possibility was that the depression was simply a result of trying to cope with the tics. Further statistical analysis showed that the severity of tics played little or no role in the severity of the depression. When a smaller number of probands with only ADHD were examined, the results were the same.[39]

These studies indicated the *Gts-ADHD* genes were capable of contributing to a genetic susceptibility to depression.

Chapter 43

Tourette Syndrome as a Spectrum Disorder

The previous chapters illustrated the role of *Gts* genes in drug abuse, alcoholism, irritable bowel syndrome, sexual behavior, conduct and oppositional defiant disorders, ADHD, learning problems, stuttering, and depression. The database also allowed an examination of the role of the *Gts* genes in a variety of other disorders. The table below shows the progressive decrease in frequency of a wide range of other behaviors with decreased loading for the *Gts* genes.[42]

Frequency of different behavioral disorders in TS probands compared to relatives with TS, relatives without TS, and controls.

Disorder	TS Pro-bands	Rel. with Tics	Rel. with out tics	Con-trols	A TS prob. vs cont.	B All 4 grps	C Rel. + tics vs - tics
N	361	113	380	68			
ADHD	61.5	50.9	7.6	7.5	10^{-9}	10^{-9}	10^{-9}
Alcohol abuse	15.0	23.0	9.2	1.5	10^{-3}	10^{-4}	10^{-5}
Depression (2 yrs)	43.9	39.3	18.8	17.6	10^{-5}	10^{-9}	10^{-6}
Discipline problems	56.9	40.0	15.1	20.6	10^{-7}	10^{-9}	10^{-8}
Drug Abuse	22.7	30.1	10.8	8.8	10^{-4}	10^{-6}	10^{-7}
Eating	32.6	27.9	34.9	25.1	10^{-1}	10^{-2}	10^{-1}
General anxiety	40.7	38.9	18.7	17.6	10^{-4}	10^{-9}	10^{-6}
Learning disorders	37.7	16.8	4.5	5.9	10^{-7}	10^{-9}	10^{-6}
Mania	51.5	47.8	10.8	4.4	10^{-9}	10^{-9}	10^{-9}
Obsessive-compulsive	57.3	47.8	12.6	10.3	10^{-9}	10^{-9}	10^{-9}
Panic attacks	55.7	5.91	30.1	31.3	10^{-4}	10^{-9}	10^{-9}
Phobias	50.1	60.2	28.9	38.2	10^{-2}	10^{-8}	10^{-9}
Reading problems	34.3	23.9	14.5	14.7	10^{-3}	10^{-9}	10^{-2}
Schizoid	45.4	40.4	14.5	13.2	10^{-7}	10^{-9}	10^{-5}
Sexual	55.1	57.5	24.7	29.4	10^{-5}	10^{-9}	10^{-9}
Sleep	38.8	38.9	11.8	17.6	10^{-4}	10^{-9}	10^{-8}
Somatization	46.1	46.6	28.2	25.0	10^{-3}	10^{-7}	10^{-3}
Stuttering	28.2	19.6	5.3	7.7	10^{-4}	10^{-9}	10^{-6}

The three columns on the right show the significance of the results as p values for TS probands versus the control (**A**), the progression of values for all four groups (**B**), and for relatives with TS versus relatives without TS (**C**). As discussed previously, when significant, the latter rules out proband ascertainment bias since non-probands are examined. A p value of less than 10^{-2} was significant, and the higher the superscript, the more significant the result. As can be seen (column **C**), all of the behaviors were significant and most were very highly significant (p 10^{-7} to 10^{-9}). For example, among the TS probands, 61.5% had ADHD, compared to 50.9% of the relatives with TS, versus 7.6% of the relatives without TS, and 7.5% of the controls (p = < .000000001).

Some of the behaviors we examined were not significant. For example, compulsive eating was not significant; however, when the analysis was restricted to those TS subjects who had obsessive-compulsive behaviors, it was highly significant. Since obsessive-compulsive behaviors themselves were highly associated with the *Gts* genes, I called this *association by association*; thus, although some behaviors seemed not to be highly associated with the *Gts* genes when all subjects were examined, the association was very dramatic when restricted to a subgroup with a disorder that itself was highly associated with the *Gts* genes. Put another way, compulsive eating was a subtype of obsessive-compulsive behavior associated with *Gts* genes.

Reading problems showed a similar *association by association*. When the whole group of TS probands was examined, reading problems were barely associated with the *Gts* genes, while learning disorders were highly associated; however, when restricted to TS probands with learning problems, the association of reading problems with the *Gts* genes was highly significant.

As I reviewed the results of dividing the relatives on the basis of whether they had tics or not, I wondered what would happen if I divided them on the basis of whether they had ADHD or not. When this was done, those with ADHD were much more likely to have the other disorders than those without ADHD. To carry this further, I also divided the relatives according to whether they did or did not have obsessive-compulsive behaviors. Again, the results were the same – all of the other behaviors were more common in the relatives with obsessive-compulsive behaviors compared to those without.

Having started down this slope, it was apparent I would have to go all the way and divide the relatives on the basis of each of the disorders being studied. Once again, those relatives who had the disorder were also most likely to have the other disorders; however, some of the disorders were more efficient at separating the relatives than others. This allowed the disorders to be ranked on the basis of this efficiency. This ranking is shown on the following page.

These results define the epitome of a spectrum disorder, in that regardless of which behavior is chosen, individuals with that behavior will tend to also have more of the other behaviors. This ranking can be used to indicate the degree to which the *Gts* genes are being expressed and suggests that mania, obsessive-compulsive, schizoid behaviors, and ADHD represent a greater degree of expression of the *Gts* genes than tics. In other words, TS is a hereditary behavioral spectrum disorder of which the tics are only one part. ADHD is the same spectrum disorder, without the tics.

Ranking of the Different Behaviors (see text)

Behavior in relative	# of other disorders significantly more common
Mania	17
Obsessive-compulsive	17
Schizoid	16
ADHD	14
Tourette syndrome-chronic tics	14
Sleep disorders	13
Panic attacks	13
Depression	13
Phobias	13
Discipline problems	13
Substance abuse	12
Somatization	12
General anxiety	11
Sexual problems	11
Stuttering	6
Reading disorders	6
Learning disorders	4

Chapter 44

Selection for the *Gts* Genes

One of the features of TS that consistently fascinated me was the probability that any gene or set of genes that could cause hypersexual, impulsive, compulsive, and aggressive behavior should be genetically selected for, in a Darwinian sense, and increase in frequency over time. If, in addition, such genes are risk factors for depression, learning disabilities, panic attacks, alcoholism, drug abuse, conduct disorder, obesity and other problems, the situation begins to take on the qualities of a serious problem for the human race.

This was such a potentially distressing possibility that even if there was only a small chance of being real, it deserved discussion. I first mentioned this in the seventh summary paper[30] of the 1987 series of papers on "A Controlled Study of Tourette Syndrome." Thus, the very last paragraph of that series of papers read,

> *"Why Are the Disinhibition Disorders So Common?*
> The limbic system has been characterized as controlling the four F's — fight, flight, feeding, and sexual activity.[173] It has not escaped my attention that the reason many of the disorders described in the present series of papers are so common is that they are (1) genetic, (2) dominant, and (3) result in disinhibition, especially of sexual activity."

At that time I still thought TS was inherited as a dominant trait. Placing this paragraph at the end of the paper and using the phrase "it has not escaped my attention," was a purposeful play on the words at the end of the famous Watson and Crick paper describing their model of the DNA helix.[216] They stated, "It has not escaped our notice that the specific pairing we have postulated immediately suggests a possible copying mechanism for the genetic material." This, of course, was the basis for all life on the planet — the ability of the genetic material to reproduce itself.

This paragraph particularly caught the wrath of Pauls et al.[164] in their 1988 letter to the editor (see Chapter 12). They complained that,

> "Aspects of this statement are unfounded, particularly his comment concerning sexual activity. In the first six reports in the series, the authors present no data to demonstrate that individuals with TS are sexually disinhibited in a way that would result in increased frequency of the disorder. Specifically, they do not pro-

vide any family data to show that TS patients have larger-than-average family sizes...To attach such a label to individuals who have already suffered tremendously because of their illness is at best insensitive; to do so without having any data to substantiate the claim is inexcusable."

In our response we pointed out that the literature had long shown the presence of disinhibited sexual behaviors in some TS patients, including coprolalia, copropraxia [excessive use of the finger sign], sexual touching of themselves and others, exhibitionism, obsessive thoughts about sex, and excessive interest in sexual matters. We also pointed out that there were numerous places in the six papers showing that TS patients reported significantly more hypersexuality, excessive thoughts about sex, and precocious interest in sex, than the controls. We then stated that,

"Similar questions about possible selective advantage have been asked about other genetic disorders associated with a high gene frequency, such as sickle cell trait, cystic fibrosis, and Tay-Sachs disease. Since in the general population the "*TS* gene" may have the highest frequency of any known hereditary disorder, the possibility of selective advantage is a very valid scientific question. Those geneticists familiar with the equation for the increase in frequency of a gene with different levels of selection know that it takes a very small increase in relative reproductive fitness to result in rather dramatic increases in gene frequency over a number of generations; thus it does not insensitively attach a label to all TS patients to suggest that the behavior of a few could result in significant selection for the "TS gene."

To further emphasize my concern, I devoted three pages to the subject in the *Tourette Syndrome and Human Behavior* book and included the figure printed on below to illustrate how one behavior related to reproductive fitness could result in an increased frequency of a gene that was also causing a whole spectrum of other disorders.

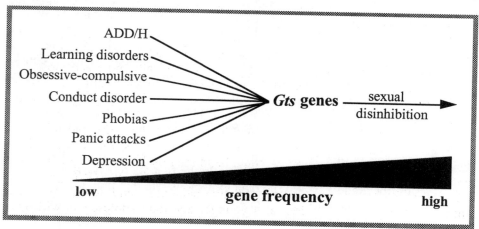

Even so, it came as no surprise to me that, as far as I could tell, this concern was shared by few other people in the world. If the concept that the *Gts* genes could cause a spectrum of disorders was a hard sell, this was even more so. Until the *Gts* genes were identified, thus allowing this hypothesis to be directly tested, it seemed hopeless to get anyone to take it seriously. Even I had trouble with some aspects of the idea; for example, even if genes are selected for, opposing factors soon come into play and the frequency of the gene quickly tends to level off at a new stable level. Since individuals with the symptoms of TS had been described as far back as Roman times, it seemed unlikely that a progressive increase in the frequency of the gene would still be taking place.

The more I thought about it, however, the more it became clear that the core of the idea was not that individuals carrying the *Gts* genes necessarily tended to have more children, but rather that they *started having children earlier*. That explained how there could be rapid selection for the gene in this century com-pared to little or no selection in previous centuries; thus in previous centuries, where lifespans were relatively short, where infant and childhood mortality was high, where most individuals received only a brief education or none at all, and where effective contraception was nonexistent, *everyone* started having children as soon as possible and had multiple pregnancies until they were no longer able to. It didn't make any difference what people's genes were like, *everyone*'s reproductive period was operating at near maximum capacity.

However, as civilization became more and more advanced, lifespans length-ened, infant and childhood mortality decreased, the duration of education signifi-cantly increased, and most importantly, effective contraception became available. Now, instead of starting families in their early teens, there was a need to put off childbearing until the parents had an education and were financially able to sup-port a family. However, those individuals carrying genes that caused learning disabilities, or impulsive, compulsive, and hypersexual behaviors, would bypass this highly-responsible route and have children earlier. Since those children who inherited these same genes would tend to behave in a similar fashion when they grew up, the effect would accumulate like compound interest; thus individuals carrying such genes might produce five generations in one hundred years, while individuals who did not carry such genes might produce only four. Even if the two groups had the same number of children per generation, the average number per unit of time would be much greater.

This effect would produce a very powerful selective advantage for the *Gts* genes. This would produce a disturbing situation in which the selection for the *Gts* genes would accelerate as societies became technologically more and more com-plex. I worried about the potential for such societies to eventually self-destruct, unless the gene or genes involved were identified in time to prevent this situation from running out of control. I thought of it as a "hidden epidemic" possibly far more serious and affecting a far wider range of individuals than the AIDS epidemic.

Short of finding the genes, was there any way to test this hypothesis? It occurred to me that one possibility would be to identify large numbers of adoles-cents with behaviors that tended to be characteristic of *Gts* or *ADHD* gene carri-ers, such as problems in school or addictive behaviors, and determine if their mothers started having children at a younger age than adolescents with good grades and no addictive behaviors. MacMurray told me of the Child Health and Development Studies of the School of Public Health at Berkeley. Starting in 1959, records were kept on over twenty thousand pregnant women in the Kaiser health system, and their children were followed for up to fifteen years. The data provided enough information to determine the age of first conception of the mothers of various groups of adolescents. Some of the results, where **MAFB** stands for the average **M**other's **A**ge at **F**irst **B**irth, and **N** represents the number of adolescents questioned, were as follows:

How often have you gotten tight from drinking?

	MAFB	N	
Never, never last year	25.03	356	
About once a year	23.60	85	
A few times a year	24.45	156	
About twice a month	23.11	114	
A few times a month	22.89	98	
About once a week	22.57	77	
A few times a week	23.61	29	
Every day	20.00	4	$p < .0001$

This showed that, for adolescents who never got drunk, the average age at which their mothers first gave birth was 25.03 years. By contrast, the average MAFB for those adolescents who got drunk once a week or more ranged from 23.61 to 20.00 years of age. These differences were highly significant ($p < .0001$).

For smoking the results were:

Do you smoke cigarettes now?

	MAFB	N	
No	24.28	794	
Yes, less than 1 a day	22.64	25	
Yes, regularly	22.70	116	$p = .003$

If they did not smoke, the average of their mother's first birth was 24.28 years. If they smoked regularly it was 22.7 years. This was also significant, $p = .003$.

For examining school performance, one of the questions concerned school work in general.

How good a student are you in general?

	MAFB	N	
Very good student	25.82	196	
Good student	23.74	492	
Fair student	23.52	192	
Poor student	22.02	15	$p < .0001$

Here the average MAFB was 25.82 years for very good students versus 22.02 years for very poor students, with the fair and good students intermediate. This was significant at p < .0001.

The results for science classes were:

How good at science?

	MAFB	N	
Above average	25.31	263	
Average	23.71	508	
Below average	23.31	124	p< .0001

Even though they may do poorly in academic subjects, individuals with ADHD, TS, or learning disorders often do well in sports. Here the results were:

How good at competitive sports?

	MAFB	N	
Above average	23.70	315	
Average	24.33	430	
Below average	24.53	146	p = N.S.

This time the results were no longer significant, and in fact, the trend was slightly in the opposite direction, with a lower average MAFB for adolescents who did well in sports versus those who were below average.

To compare all the academic subjects together – English, math, science, and social studies – for each subject, those who were above average were given a score of 2, those who were average, a score of 1, and those who were below average, a score of 0. Since there were four subjects, the maximum score was 8. The results for subjects with scores from 1 to 8 were:

Academic Score	N	MAFB	
8	77	25.85	
7	104	25.30	
6	163	24.84	
5	174	23.93	
4	208	23.73	
3	109	22.66	
2	39	22.72	
1	12	20.77	p < .001

Except for a score of 0, where the number of adolescents was too small to be accurate, there was a progressive decrease in MAFB from 25.85 years for the students who were above average in all academic subjects, to 20.77 years for those with a score of 1. This was significant (p <.001).

These combined results showed that, for adolescents who did poorly in school, smoked or drank, their mothers showed a significant tendency to start having children earlier than mothers whose adolescents did well in school and didn't smoke or drink. While environmental factors could be playing a role, the socioeconomic status of the subjects tended to be fairly uniform, since to be in the program the parents had to be making enough money to be in the Kaiser plan. To the extent that these behaviors were genetically caused, the results were consistent with the hypothesis that the genes involved would be selected for.

Although this study was completed in April 1990, I was so convinced that it would never be accepted for publication that I just put it away in the drawer and forgot about it. By December 1992, after finishing the three studies on drug and alcohol abuse and sexual behavior in TS using the genetic loading technique, I felt it was time to dust it off, since there was now convincing evidence that the *Gts* and *ADHD* genes were associated with substance abuse and hypersexuality. In addition, by that time many studies had been published showing a striking increase in the frequency, and a progressively lower age of onset, of many different psychiatric disorders. The following are some examples.

In a family study of alcoholics, Cloninger and co-workers[26] examined the risks of becoming an alcoholic by age twenty-five for the male relatives of alcoholics, by different age groups (cohorts). The dramatic results were as follows:

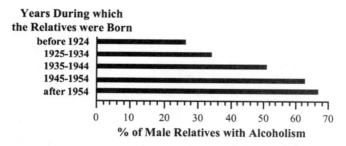

Years During which the Relatives were Born

before 1924	
1925-1934	
1935-1944	
1945-1954	
after 1954	

0   10   20   30   40   50   60   70

% of Male Relatives with Alcoholism

There was a progressive increase in the percent of male relatives with alcoholism from 26% for those born before 1924 to 67% for those born after 1954, and many of the latter had not even reached the age of twenty-five. The authors stated, "The high risks in the younger birth cohorts are especially frightening when it is realized that they have yet to pass through the full period of risk."

When the frequency of drug abuse was examined among the male alcoholic relatives of alcoholics, the risk increased from 1.8% for those forty-one years of age or greater, to 26.7% for those thirty-one to forty, to 65.4% for those seventeen to thirty years of age.[88] For female alcoholic relatives, the comparable figures were 13, 43, and 58%.

One reason these figures were so high was that relatives of alcoholics are far more likely to inherit genes for alcoholism and drug abuse than those in the general population. This, however, did not explain the strikingly increased rates of alcoholism or drug abuse in the younger relatives. This was not simply because younger people are more likely to abuse alcohol or drugs, because the responses were for a *lifetime* history of substance abuse.

Studies of individuals in the general population were giving similar trends, just of lower magnitude, and not only for alcoholism and drug abuse but depression, suicide, manic-depressive, obsessive-compulsive, and anxiety disorders as well.[8,21,82,94,102,129,141,151,181,215] Not only was the frequency increasing, but younger and younger individuals were being affected.

To determine if this was just a fluke in the United States, a worldwide study of depression in many first world countries was undertaken. Although the magnitude varied considerably with the site, the "results showed an overall trend for increasing rates of major depression over time for all sites."[82]

One concern was that limitations of memory or recall might explain these results, in that older subjects may have simply forgotten they were once severely depressed; however, careful examination of the data left the consistent conclusion that these trends were real.[80,128,130] One study was able to eliminate memory as a factor[80] in that 965 subjects who had never had an affective illness were interviewed and then re-interviewed six years later. By the time of the second interview, 11.8% had developed at least one episode of major depression. However, subjects who were younger than forty years of age were three times more likely than older subjects to develop depression. In addition, those individuals with diagnoses other than depression, such as alcoholism, drug abuse, phobias, or panic attacks, had much higher rates of developing major depression — with the frequency ranging from 27.9 to 42.9%.

A final intriguing feature of the studies was that these trends were miraculously absent in areas that were or recently had been third world countries, such as Puerto Rico, Mexico, and Korea.[20,122,144]

Taken as a whole, I felt all these observations were consistent with the hypothesis that genes responsible for "disinhibition disorders" were being selected for, and that the rate of selection increased as the standard of living and technological complexity of society increased. I was particularly concerned that higher education was the driving force behind an accelerating rate of selection for these genes. Those individuals with the highest IQs, the fewest learning disabilities, and the fewest problems in conduct disorder and substance abuse, were going on to college and graduate school. As a result, they were starting to have children when they were twenty-three to thirty years of age. By contrast, those with the lower IQs, with learning, conduct, and substance abuse disorders were more likely to drop out of school. They were starting to have children when they were sixteen to twenty-two years of age. To the degree that these behaviors were genetically controlled, the genes involved would be selected for. Since younger people were inheriting more and more of these genes, they were developing a spectrum of disorders and were having symptoms at younger and younger ages.

I discussed the manuscript with several friends. Because of the potentially controversial nature of the subject, I was advised not to send it in for publication. They were afraid it would harken back to the discredited eugenics ideas and Nazism of the 1930s. This was the same issue that Motulsky had complained about concerning our 1987 papers.

I didn't agree. I had pointed out in the manuscript that the *Gts* genes could be very desirable and advantageous. It was only when they were present in larger numbers that they caused trouble; thus eliminating the genes from the population, as the Nazis tried to do, could actually be detrimental. Since with modern medications these were very treatable disorders, the idea was to identify and treat affected individuals early so they did not have learning disorders and impulsive behaviors. That would benefit both the individuals and society. It seemed that if the hypothesis was correct, the implications for society were sufficiently important that I would be remiss in not calling attention to the potential danger. Now that the genetic loading technique had shown that drug and alcohol abuse and hyper-sexual behaviors were associated with the *Gts* genes in some people, the scientif-ic basis for the theory was strengthened. After a couple of rejections, however, I decided to once again stick the manuscript back in the drawer.

By the time the present book was complete and other genes playing a role in TS had been identified, I once again took the manuscript on gene selection out and dusted it off. By this time there was so much new data to support the concept that I decided to put it into a book called *The Gene Bomb* (see order card in the back of this book).[44]

Chapter 45

Dopamine Receptor Genes and Smoking

Nicotine is a very addicting drug. This is well-illustrated by the consequences of the 1992 strike of tobacco factory workers in Italy.

> "Once supplies were exhausted, people smoked whatever they could lay their hands on, including cigars and even cigarettes made from aromatic herbs and intended to help people to stop smoking. Some snatched lighted cigarettes from the lips of other smokers in the street. Many people crossed national borders or caught ferries to buy cigarettes in neighboring countries. On international flights, duty-free cigarette supplies were soon exhausted...There was an immediate black market. The price of a packet of tobacco rose tenfold. Social relationships were characterized by people talking about the want of cigarettes, and smokers openly showed nervousness and irritability in all social environments."[81]

In the late 1980s, California put a proposition on the ballot to raise the tax on tobacco. The proceeds were to be used to launch a statewide anti-smoking campaign and support basic research. The research grants were restricted to investigators in California. Despite heavy opposition from the tobacco companies, the proposition passed. By the time the funds were available, we had completed our initial studies showing a significant increase in the frequency of the D_2A1 variant in TS, ADHD, substance abuse, and other disorders (see Chapters 20 and 30). Given our difficulty in obtaining funds from national agencies (see Appendix) and our curiosity about whether the frequency of the D_2A1 variant might also be increased in frequency in people addicted to tobacco, we submitted a grant request to study this.

The request was turned down; however, since the objections had more to do with the selection of the subjects than the scientific validity of the study, on the next go around, we applied again. This time it was funded. Other than two small grants obtained in the mid-1980s and the small contributions from our own patients, this was the first external funding for our research that we had obtained in over twelve years.

The patients and blood samples came from Dr. Linda Ferry, head of the Department of Public Health at the Loma Linda V.A. Hospital. She ran a "stop smoking" clinic and was involved in a double-blind study of the use of bupropion, a dopamine-based antidepressant, to help people stop smoking. She reasoned that if dopamine reward pathways were involved in nicotine addiction, then augmenting these neurons with a non-addictive dopamine-based antidepressant might help people to stop smoking. The results of the study were impressive. Six months after taking medication for only twelve weeks, half of the subjects who had taken bupropion had stopped smoking, while none of those who took the placebo had stopped. Ferry sent us blood samples of those individuals who had tried in the past to stop smoking on their own but were unsuccessful, and who were not addicted to alcohol or other drugs.

With the knowledge that, like cocaine and amphetamines, nicotine also affected the dopamine reward pathways, and based on the results of Ferry's double-blind study, we were eager to determine if the D_2A1 variant was increased in frequency in people who had smoked for many years.

The new funds allowed us to add two new people in the lab – Mick Dino and Radhika Gade, Ph.D. Mick had actually joined our laboratory months earlier as a volunteer and had just finished her B.S. in psychology at Berkeley. She joined our group because she was convinced that biological factors were going to be increasingly important in understanding human behavior. I, of course, agreed. Radhika was from India and had trained with Bruce Wallace, Ph.D., head of our Division of Molecular Biology. She joined us after Bruce moved to northern California.

By the end of 1994, we had data on 312 Caucasian smokers. Of these, 48.7% carried the D_2A1 variant.[67a] By contrast, of the 714 Caucasian controls known to be free of alcohol or drug dependence and who had been typed in our lab or other labs around the country, 25.9% carried the D_2A1 variant. These were significantly different (p < .000001). We also examined several variables that seemed to measure the degree of potential addiction to nicotine. The first related to the number of packs of cigarettes smoked per day, shown as follows:

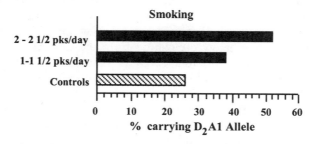

Thus, of those who smoked 1 to 1.5 packs per day, 37.5% carried the D_2A1 allele, while of those who smoked 2 or more packs per day, 52.5% carried the marker. Another measure of the degree to which a person seems to be addicted to nicotine is the maximum duration of time they are able to voluntarily stop smoking. The relationship between this and the prevalence of the D_2A1 allele is shown as follows:

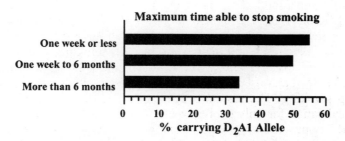

Maximum time able to stop smoking

One week or less

One week to 6 months

More than 6 months

0   10   20   30   40   50   60

% carrying D$_2$A1 Allele

Another measure of the propensity to addictive behaviors is the age at which individuals started smoking. Of those who started smoking at age twelve or younger, 62.2% carried the D$_2$A1 allele. This progressively decreased with increasing age such that for those who started smoking at age eighteen or older, 35.1% carried the marker.

In a similar study, Noble and colleagues obtained very similar results.[156] These preliminary findings suggested that in addition to a role in drug abuse, variants of the *dopamine D2 receptor* gene were also playing a role in determining why some people started smoking and then couldn't stop.

Chapter 46

Pathological Gambling

Shortly after our article came out showing that the D_2A1 variant of the *dopamine D_2 receptor* was increased in frequency in TS and related impulsive, compulsive, and addictive behaviors, Dr. Richard Rosenthal called. He specialized in the treatment of pathological gambling, a severe form of addictive behavior that probably affects close to 1% of the population. The frequency of the disorder was increasing because more and more states were legalizing some form of gambling to help balance their budgets. Because gambling is legal in many places, it is a far more respectable addiction than alcoholism or drug abuse, and fewer figures are kept on the numbers of people affected. Some have termed it "the hidden addiction." However, it can be just as destructive to people and interpersonal relationships as addiction to drugs. Because it does not involve the ingestion of drugs or smoke, it has also been referred to as a "pure addiction." I was particularly interested because many of our TS relatives had problems with pathological gambling[p239] and it appeared to be part of the TS spectrum of disorders.

Rosenthal's own clinical experience supported this relationship, since he had observed that many pathological gamblers had ADHD as children. This, plus its addictive nature and frequent association with alcohol abuse, led him to wonder if the D_2A1 allele might also be more common in this group of individuals. He and Dr. Henry Lesieur were members of the committee to re-examine the diagnostic criteria for pathological gambling for the upcoming DSM-IV, the psychiatrist's diagnostic bible. As a result, they were in the process of examining the clinical characteristics of pathological gamblers all across the country. As part of this study they had developed an extensive questionnaire to access many different aspects of pathological gambling. It would be fairly easy to also draw blood on many of these subjects for genetic studies. The third person involved in this study was Dr. Loreen Rugle, from the Addiction Recovery Center at the V.A. Hospital in Brecksville, Ohio, one of the few Pathological Gambling Treatment Centers in the V.A. system.

In addition to their questionnaire covering many aspects of gambling, I suggested that subjects also fill out our Behavioral Questionnaire. This would allow us to determine how often pathological gamblers also had other behavioral problems, such as ADHD, alcoholism, panic attacks, depression, and tics.

Over a period of two years, the blood samples and questionnaires slowly came in. By the middle of 1994, we had accumulated data on 171 Caucasian pathological gamblers. As the testing for the D_2A1 variant progressed, just as had happened with TS several years ago, I sensed from the very first gels that the frequency of this marker would be significantly increased in these individuals. By the end of the study, 50.9% of the pathological gamblers carried the D_2A1 allele.[77a] Compared to 25.9% in the 714 controls. This was highly significant at p <0.000001.

The gamblers' questionnaire we used included a number of questions that helped us to determine the severity of their compulsion to gamble. This included such things as whether they were preoccupied with reliving past gambling experiences, were unable to cut down on gambling, felt restless and irritable when they tried to stop, experienced a "craving" to gamble, committed illegal acts to support their habit, got into desperate financial problems, and others. These results were as follows:

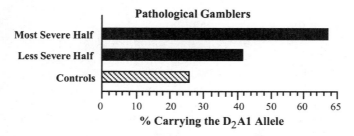

These results showed that pathological gambling was associated with the D_2A1 allele, and the more severe the problem, the higher the association. Another impulsive, compulsive, addictive behavior joined the spectrum of disorders associated with defects in the *dopamine D2 receptor* gene.

Chapter 47

Monoamine Oxidase

Monoamine oxidase should be one of those obscure enzymes that only neurochemists know about; however, for many people who have had problems with depression it is almost a household word. This is because a major group of antidepressants are called "MAO inhibitors" and the MAO part refers to monoamine oxidase. This enzyme is responsible for breaking down all three of the major neurotransmitters – dopamine, norepinephrine and serotonin.[p318,363,409,418] Since inhibition of this enzyme allows these neurotransmitters to remain in the synapse longer, MAO inhibitors help correct depression and other disorders associated with a deficiency of these compounds. The gene comes in two forms, A and B, and both are located on the short arm of the X chromosome.

In 1993 Brunner and co-workers from the Netherlands described an unusual family where many of the males had moderate mental retardation plus some troublesome behaviors.[15] The latter consisted of problems with impulsive, aggressive behavior, short temper, arson, attempted rape, and exhibitionism. Since only males in the family were affected and female carriers were normal, it was clear the genetic defect was on the X-chromosome.[p 42] Linkage studies indicated the gene involved was on the short arm of the X-chromosome, in the same region as the *MAO-A* and *-B* genes. Determination of the levels of each enzyme indicated that a deficiency of MAO-A was at fault. Further genetic studies indicated that there was a C T mutation that resulted in a change in the amino acid sequence from glutamine[296] to what is called a *termination codon*; thus instead of coding for the amino acid glutamine, the genetic code tells the cell to stop making protein at this point. This destroys the enzyme and results in a total deficiency of MAO-A activity.

Despite the presence of an identical mutation in each of eight different affected males in the same family, the severity of the aggressive behavior varied markedly in different individuals and over time in a single individual.

It is interesting that this paper was published around the time that, Peter Breggin, a psychiatrist well-known for his anti-biological psychiatry rhetoric,[11a] was claiming that it had never been proven that any gene ever had an effect on human behavior. He implied this never would be shown either. Although many recessive and dominant disorders with well-defined effects on behavior had previously been identified (phenylketonuria, Lesch-Nyhan syndrome, acute intermittent porphyria, Huntington's disease, Alzheimer's disease, and others), this was the first example of a specific genetic defect identified at the molecular level that caused predominately behavioral rather than neurological or physical problems. The pedigree is shown below.

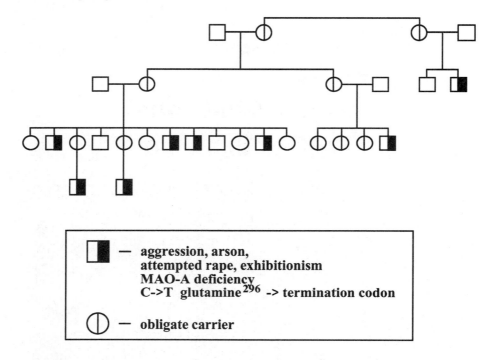

- aggression, arson,
  attempted rape, exhibitionism
  MAO-A deficiency
  C->T glutamine^{296} -> termination codon

- obligate carrier

Figure modified from Brenner et al. Science 262:578-589, 1993, *by permission, Amer. Assoc. Adv. Science*

[obligate carriers are females who carry the gene but have no symptoms]

Although the syndrome was extremely rare and possibly limited to a single family, an important philosophical barrier had been broken. Clearly a specific gene with an identified mutation could be responsible for aggressive, impulsive and hypersexual behavior. Molecular biology finally had a small, but firm, foothold in psychiatry.

Chapter 48

Cancer Genes and
Human Behavior

In 1964 Dr. Harvey from the London Hospital in England reported that, in the process of studying a leukemia virus, he discovered another virus that caused solid tumors, called sarcomas. Since tests suggested it was different from any known virus he entitled his report, "An Unidentified Virus which Causes the Rapid Production of Tumors in Mice."[108] A few years later Drs. Kirsten and Mayer described a similar virus.[127] These two viruses were subsequently named after their discoverers – the Harvey and Kirsten murine (mouse) sarcoma viruses. The protein produced by these viruses had a molecular weight of 21,000 daltons; thus it was called protein 21, or p21. Because this protein was capable of transforming normal cells into tumor cells, it was called a transforming protein. Small amounts of it were found in normal cells, suggesting that both the virus and normal cells carried the gene responsible for p21. Because it was originally identified in a <u>ra</u>t <u>s</u>arcoma it was called *ras*. The *ras* gene corresponding to Harvey virus was called *H-Ras*, and the *ras* gene corresponding to the Kirsten virus was called *K-Ras*.

It was clear that the *ras* gene was important in inhibiting cell growth, and when it became genetically mutated this inhibition was lost, resulting in uncontrolled cell growth, or cancer. Because of these properties, the *ras* genes were intensively studied.[92,194] One of its functions was to bind to a major intracellular carrier of energy called guanidine tri-phosphate, or GTP. When bound to GTP, ras was active. Ras was a GTPase, meaning it could remove one of the phosphates, converting GTP to GDP (diphosphate). When ras was bound to GDP it was inactive.

One can reasonably ask, what does this have to do with human behavior? When neurotransmitters bind to their receptors on nerve cells, in many cases they exert their effect by altering the function of proteins that bind to GTP. These proteins are called G-proteins, and ras is a G-protein. For many years there was no evidence to indicate whether ras was involved with neurotransmitters. However, in 1993, Hérault et al. reported a significant increase in the frequency of a marker of the *H-ras* gene in subjects with autism versus controls. Given our[60] and other's[16,201] observations that many children with autism develop TS, we wondered if *H-ras* might be one of the *TS* genes. We also wanted to verify its involvement in children with autism.

These studies involved examining the *Msp* I H-ras polymorphism for fragments equal to or larger than 2.1 kb. In our autistic subjects, the carrier frequency for the ≥ 2.1 kb markers was 47.9%. This was significantly higher than the 30.8% in the controls. We also examined the effect of carrying the ≥ 2.1 kb marker in single dose or double dose on different behaviors. This was of note for obsessive-compulsive and phobic symptoms.

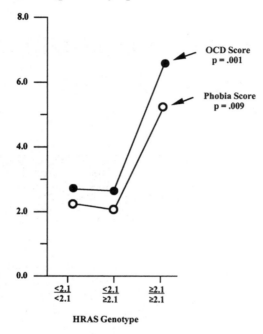

This suggested a recessive effect of the *H-ras* gene, in that when the ≥ 2.1 kb alleles were inherited from both parents, the effect was much greater than when only one gene was inherited from a single parent.

There was another intriguing aspect of these results. Patients with neurofibromatosis, a hereditary disorder characterized by skin tumors and coffee-colored skin patches, frequently have learning problems or ADHD.[198,213] When the neurofibromatosis gene was identified, it was found to have GTPase activity.[221] Children with a related disorder called tuberous sclerosis have skin lesions, learning disabilities, and a high frequency of autism. When the gene for tuberous sclerosis was identified, it was found to be GTPase-activating protein. Finally, Thelu et al.,[206] also from France, found a significantly increased frequency of the ≥ 2.1 kb markers of the *H-ras* gene in subjects with alcoholic cirrhosis.

While these effects were fairly subtle and definitely needed to be verified by others, the combination of these observations suggested that the ras family of proteins might have an effect on neurotransmitter function. As such, the *H-ras* locus might be one of the polygenic set of genes involved in TS, ADHD, autism, and possibly alcoholism.[77b]

Chapter 49

A Marker of the *TDO2* Gene

By the fall of 1992 the emphasis in our laboratory had shifted almost completely to studies of the *dopamine receptor* genes. The findings in the areas of Tourette syndrome, ADHD, drug abuse, post-traumatic stress disorder, obesity, height, and personality were so varied and rich that we hardly noticed that the *TDO2* gene was rarely mentioned anymore. This changed dramatically, however, in November after seeing a paper in a biochemistry journal by a pair of Russian scientists, Merkulov and Merkulova, from Siberia. They found a glucocorticoid response element (GRE) in intron 6 in the middle of the rat *TDO2* gene and reported the sequence of a large segment of the surrounding DNA.[149]

This was exciting to us for several reasons. First, it suggested a new mechanism by which mutations could cause an increase in the function of the human *TDO2* gene. Namely, if an intron in the middle of the gene carried a GRE mutation, it could make the gene more active. Second, this was a region we had not examined for mutations and could be the site where our presumed *Gts* mutation was hiding. Third, the sequence they published allowed us to identify one of our still-missing introns. This, in turn, allowed us to identify the appropriate oligomers necessary for amplifying the region described by the Russians.

When we did this we obtained a piece of DNA that was over one thousand base pairs long. We sequenced this piece looking for a GRE in the human gene. While we did not find anything that looked exciting, George examined the piece using a special technique called denaturing gradient gel electrophoresis (DGGE). This technique is able to pick up mutations anywhere along the whole piece of DNA. By December George had found a polymorphic marker in this region; thus after five years of working with this gene and searching everywhere, we finally had a marker of the human *TDO2* gene. We recognized that it was not *the* mutation, but it might be locked into the real *Gts* mutation by linkage disequilibrium and could thus be useful, like the D_2A1 marker was useful for the *dopamine D2 receptor* gene. We could now determine if this marker was more common in patients with TS and related disorders, than in controls.

George continued to examine our new *TDO2* marker. Since the DGGE technique was somewhat cumbersome, we immediately began to look for the sequence change involved by cloning and sequencing individuals who had the marker compared to those who did not. Fairly quickly, George had found several individuals who carried a double dose of the *TDO2* marker (homozygotes). This was especially useful in the search for the mutant base.

211

By the end of January the results were as follows, where 1-1 subjects did not carry the marker, 1-2 subjects carried a single dose, and 2-2 subjects had the marker in a double dose:

	1-1	1-2	2-2	Total	%12 or 22
Controls	26	2		28	7.1
Tourette syndrome	16	5	1	22	**27.2**
Pathological gamblers	12	4	3	19	**36.9**

If we combined the TS subjects and pathological gamblers into a single category of "impulse disorder" the results were:

Impulse disorder	28	9	4	41	**31.7**

The 31.7% figure versus 7.1% for controls was significant at $p = .015$. This finding was the first hard evidence, since hearing of Bissbort's results almost two years previously, that the *TDO2* gene might play a role in TS.

Throughout January I had been pestering Gericke and Bissbort about making the airline reservations. I sent them a set of the four papers I had written on alcoholism, drug abuse, and sexual behavior in TS, and the hypothesis that the frequency of the *TS* gene was increasing in modern society, hoping that would help to stir up a sense of urgency about these studies. It was thus satisfying on January 29, 1993, to receive the following FAX from Gericke:

> Dear David,
> I have just received your articles and this has made me very excited and very aware of the need to see what we can achieve this year.
> I spoke to Siegbert this afternoon, and we shall meet again on Monday, and regularly thereafter.
> First, the patent has been filed.
> Secondly, he first wants to repeat some work on fresh samples to see whether storage in any way affected the original samples.
> Thirdly, on Monday I shall have a first meeting with Siegbert's erstwhile postgraduate student who is now going to spend approximately half of his time on the further development of the TS assays.
> Fourthly, although Siegbert did not give me the date and hour of his proposed visit to your laboratory, he said that he is ready to supply you with a list of the requirements by next week, so that I think we can be cautiously optimistic.
> I think that we have the potential to do some really exciting work; with these assays (if they turn out be as good as we had hoped) one could utilize hybrid cell mapping to look at the other candidates of this presumed oligogenetic disorder as suggested by the early assays. This would facilitate a directed molecular approach – do you agree?

I include an abstract of our genealogical work which will be presented during our next South African Congress of Human Genetics in March.

Best regards,
George

It was beginning to look like a good year.

The same day that I got the FAX from Gericke, and the same day I finished analyzing the initial results of our *TDO2* marker, I received four of the TS papers back from the editor of a psychiatry journal. Although he said it in a nice way, the bottom line was that Tourette syndrome was not of sufficient interest to their readers to even bother having the papers reviewed.

Chapter 50

Searching for the "Real" *TDO2* Mutation

By March 1993 the results with the *TDO2* marker looked like this:

	Number of Cases	% with mutation	p
Controls	91	12.1	
Alcoholism	19	21.1	N.S.
Depression (suicide)	8	**37.5**	**.04**
Drug dependence	17	**50.0**	**.002**
Pathological gamblers	26	**38.4**	**.002**
Tourette syndrome	40	**27.5**	**.014**

The number of controls we had examined was up from 26 to 91, and the percent of 1-2 or 2-2 carriers had risen from 7.1% to 12.1%. We had more than doubled the number of TS subjects examined, and 27.5% were positive. The percentage of positives in the pathological gamblers was still high at 38.4%. We had begun to look at some of MacMurray's patients from the V.A. addiction clinic. The drug addicts showed the highest frequency of positives at 50.0%. By contrast, of the nineteen alcoholics we had examined, only 21.1% were positive. Despite the small numbers, all of these groups, except the alcoholics, were significant.

Thus, the initial results not only continued to hold up, but grew stronger, and two of the three groups we added were also showing a significant increase in the *TDO2* marker. The results with alcoholism were similar to our results with the dopamine D_2A1 marker in being much more impressive with drug abusers than just alcoholics. Like the *DRD2* gene, this was proving to be associated with a spectrum of disorders, and the correlations were even stronger.

However, what we desperately needed was to find the "real" *TDO2* mutation – the one that was producing what Bissbort said he had found. Since the time for Bissbort to arrive had come and gone, I called Gericke on February 26. He said he had met Bissbort in the hall and stated that if he didn't make a definite commitment to come, they would lose the funds for his airplane ticket. That induced Bissbort to say, "O.K. I will go in May."

May would be just slightly more than two years since I first met Bissbort in Pretoria in 1991. He said then that it would take two years to find the mutation in the DNA sequence of *TDO2*. As much as I thought that we would find it much faster, he was proving to be correct, and to date we only had a marker in linkage disequilibrium with the real mutation, not the real thing. Even if Bissbort did finally come, and even if the red blood cell studies turned out to be all we hoped they would be, we all knew that the scientific community would be far more impressed if we could actually nail down the mutation at the DNA level. It seemed to be the ultimate in bad luck if the mutation was in one of the remaining three of 11 introns – 4, 7 or 8, that we had been unable to examine. We had already tried several times to clone sections of genomic DNA that carried these introns, and failed. We had probed every human genomic library we could find, with no success. We knew that this just happens sometimes. Others had reported similar problems with other genes.

In the meantime, we were very anxious to begin examining large number of DNA samples from patients with a wide variety of disorders and it was critical that we decide quickly which marker to test for. We had four students lined up who wanted to come and work in the lab over the summer and we planned to have most of them work on the *TDO2* project. If we put them to work testing several thousand DNA samples, we needed to know what technique to use. At the rate things were going, it seemed unlikely we would find the major *TDO2* mutation by June. We could use the DGGE technique, but it was relatively slow and cumbersome. A technique called "allele-specific" PCR was faster, but to use this we had to know precisely which of the 1,200 base pairs in the DNA piece were mutant. To find out, we sequenced the DNA of the region in several 1-1 and 2-2 homozygous individuals. This showed the presence of a G->T mutation in the middle of intron 6. We could now set up the allele-specific PCR and hopefully test DNA samples much more rapidly.

Unfortunately, we quickly ran into complications. The PCR technique that Donn set up and the DGGE technique George was using should be giving identical results, but they did not. In fact, one patient that George typed as a 2-2 by his technique appeared to be an 1-1 by Donn's allele-specific PCR. Something was seriously amiss.

We knew that George's technique was capable of picking up mutations anywhere in the 1,200 bp piece of DNA. By contrast, Donn's allele-specific PCR procedure was specific for mutations at a single base pair. The most likely explanation was that there was more than one mutation present in this stretch of DNA. Since George's DGGE could detect them both, but Donn's could detect only one, this would explain the differences. To test this, we sequenced DNA from Donn's 1-1 individuals and, sure enough, there were two mutations only two base pairs apart in the center of intron 6. The second was a G->A mutation only two base pairs away; thus the sequence in this region was as follows:

$$G\text{->}A - X - X - G\text{->}T$$

We now needed two allele-specific PCR tests to match the results George was getting with his DGGE procedure. Everything would be easier if we could just find the "real" mutation.

It was no surprise that May had come and gone without Bissbort coming to California. To attempt to "prime the pump" I had sent Gericke a FAX pointing out that we were going to have four students in the lab over the summer and this would be an ideal opportunity to test the freezerful of blood samples we had accumulated and unravel many of the questions about the red blood cell procedure. On June 1, 1993, I received the following FAX:

> Dear David,
>   Siegbert hasn't been talking to me for some time and does not respond to requests for supplying information about the patent or any travel plans. My flame is burning low and I feel unhappy about not being able to respond to your exciting prospects for unraveling certain aspects if only the "technique" had been available. I shall keep the options open, however.
>
> George

I called Gericke a few days later and we had a long "strategy" talk. I told him that the students were going to work on the polymorphism we had uncovered. I also suggested he call the patent office in Johannesburg to verify that the patent had really been filed.

On June 4, I received the following FAX:

> Dear David,
>   1. PATENT OFFICE: A patent with the title "Monitoring of enzyme-catalyzed reactions" No 93/0220 has been put in under Siegbert's name on 1/13/93. I suspect that this relates to the technique which allows TDO2 measurement. We have no access to this patent before the middle of 1994 when a finalized version has to be in.
>   2. FUTURE PLANS: I managed to arrange an appointment with Siegbert and asked him to be completely honest about what the outcome of this is going to be. He said he is -
>   i) almost 99% through with the standardization,
>   ii) checking photometric and electrophoretic correlations,
>   iii) sorting out the two genetic types of TDO2 in red cells, (i.e. whether or not enzyme activity is activated by progesterone),
>   iv) not at all opposed to collaboration with yourself,
>   v) will not have the time or inclination to fly to L.A but,
>   vi) should be in a position to give you the recipe "within a month or two."
>   I have the impression that he will indeed eventually let you have the technique, but would like to pride himself that he has sorted out all the pitfalls.
>   I trust that you will feel better after having read this information.
>
> Warmest good wishes,
> George

While this was good news, and I was pleased to know for certain that the patent had been filed, I also knew that two months could easily become two years. In the meantime we would continue to vigorously pursue our own approaches.

Our Own Patent

Through all these years of no grant-funding, the City of Hope Medical Center continued to provide the salaries for Donn and George as part of the Medical Center's commitment to basic and clinical research, even if an immediate result was not apparent. Over the decade-and-a-half of TS studies, this amounted to well over a million dollars. The only way I knew to pay them back, if something came of our studies, was to ensure that the work was patented; thus back in the fall of 1987, before our series of seven articles was published, I sent in a patent application concerning the concept that genetic defects in the *TDO2* gene could be important in a wide range of psychiatric disorders. At that time, we had not even cloned the human TDO2 cDNA, and the concept was purely theoretical; Many, especially those on NIH study sections, thought the idea was crazy; however, the law required that a patent be filed before the concept of an invention is published, so it was a case of either file then or not at all. Fortunately, the patent process is almost as protracted as obtaining FDA approval of new drugs. This gave us some time to attempt to prove the concept.

After a great deal of effort, nicely orchestrated by our attorney, Ed Irons, a patent covering a portion of the work was granted and published near the end of October 1993. This publication contained all of the sequence of the *TDO2* gene that we had identified up to 1993.

Ironically, as much as the patent pleased us, it also added an element of tension to our work. Up until now, virtually no one thought this line of research was worth pursuing. We didn't want to publish the sequence of the *TDO2* gene until we had been able to check out all of the exons for mutations, and we still had exons 4, 7, and 8 to go; however, now the sequence was in the public domain. Although it had not been published in a scientific journal, and had not yet been placed in the DNA sequence data banks, anyone who regularly checked patents and had an interest in TS or psychiatric genetics had access to it. The playing field had been partially leveled. We knew that our tiny laboratory was no match for the well-funded giant laboratories that were capable of sequencing huge segments of DNA in a few weeks. We could only hope that no one noticed, or cared.

Trying to Develop an Allele-Specific Test

We had now identified two polymorphisms in intron 6 of the *TDO2* gene. However, we knew even if they are right next to each other, each of two polymorphisms could show dramatically different degrees of linkage disequilibrium to the "real" *TDO2* mutations; thus some might be good markers for the "real" mutations while the others might be very poor markers. Because of this, we could no longer use the DGGE technique, since it was too imprecise. It was necessary to be able to identify each mutation separately and determine if they were GG, GA or AA and GG, GT or TT. Testing the G->A mutation turned out to be simple since the mutation was in the recognition site for the restriction endonu-clease *Bsl* I; thus all we had to do to identify this mutation was PCR-amplify the region, and digest it with *Bsl* I. If the DNA was cut, it was the "G" allele, if it did not cut, it was the "A" allele.

By contrast, testing for the G ->T allele proved to be very difficult. We attempted to use the standard allele-specific PCR tests and found that none of them was reliable. I called Dr. Bruce Wallace at BioRad in Northern California. Wallace used to work at the City of Hope and was one of the pioneers of allele-specific PCR test. He referred me to an article he had recently published in *Genomics*[90] concerning a different approach. It had the advantage that hundreds of samples could be quickly tested. We spent several months trying to get it to work and even had one of the original authors help us out. Unfortunately, certain types of mutations give non-specific results, and a G ->T was one of those types.

We then began to explore the use of a completely different technique that had the specificity necessary to successfully identify a G ->T mutation. This was called an Oligonucleotide Ligase Assay, or OLA for short. This technique had the distinct advantage that it was much more specific for G ->T mutations than any of the allele-specific PCR techniques; however, we were having some tech-nical problems detecting the products in the electrophoretic gel.

By this time, the October 1993 American Society of Human Genetics meet-ing had rolled around. One of the thousands of posters presented at that meeting gave me the answer to our problem. It was a poster by Dr. Emily Winn-Deen of Applied Biosystems. She had been using the OLA technique and used oligomers labeled with fluorescent dyes. This allowed her to use the DNA sequencing machine made by her company to scan electrophoresed samples with different lasers. Our problem was we didn't have one of the machines, and since they cost $135,000, it was not likely we were going to get one soon.

When I got back from the meeting, I called her to see if she would be inter-ested in helping us out with our OLA assay. She was and we sent her several samples of DNA of known sequence to set up the test. By January 1994 she sent us the necessary set of oligomers and details of her technique for us to try it out in our laboratory. Since we did not have her company's machine, we attempted to identify the products of the reaction using a combination of two sensitive stains. It worked, but just barely. All too often the staining was so faint we could-n't identify the mutation.

A New Approach

After all of our struggling, the solution to the problem of testing the G ->T mutation proved to be remarkably simple. I had received a reprint of a paper by Cichon and colleagues[24] from Germany. They reported finding four polymor-phisms of the *dopamine D1 receptor* gene using PRC, followed by digestion with restriction endonucleases. I thought, "How could they be so lucky to have all four of their mutations in a restriction endonuclease site?" We were lucky if one in four mutations could be recognized by a restriction endonuclease; however, as I read the paper carefully, it was apparent they were not lucky. They had instead altered the sequence of their oligomers to generate a restriction endonuclease cut-ting site. We had the answer to our problems for the G ->T mutation; thus the sequence immediately next to the G->T mutation was GATA. This was almost close enough for the *Dpn* II restriction endonuclease to cut, since it needed a GATC sequence. All we had to do was redesign the oligomer to start with TAG so it would match the ATC part of the sequence. This is shown as follows, where the underline is the site of the G->T mutation and the bold letters show the change necessary to allow *Dpn* II to cut:

<u>G</u>AT**A**AGAATAGGGAGAAAAAGAATTA —sequence
TA**G**TCTTATCCCTCTTTTTCTTA   —redesigned oligomer

The resulting mismatch in the third position did not prevent the oligomer from working. When the G->T mutation is G, the GATC site is cut to produce 22 and 70 bp fragments. When the G->T mutation is A, only a 92 bp fragment is present. Now the test for the G->T mutation was easy.

Exons 4, 7, and 8

In the meantime, we had solved our problem of cloning exons 4, 7, and 8. George had stumbled across an ad in one of the journals for a new company advertising, with a money-back guarantee, that for $2,000 they could clone any segment of genomic human DNA that could be identified by a PCR reaction. We sent in our money and the necessary oligomers and in ten days received back two large genomic clones. Donn's PCR tests indicated that both clones indeed carried the introns we were trying to clone. We thought it would now be a simple matter to just send the DNA to our sequencing laboratory, along with the appropriate primers, and we would finally obtain the sequences around these exons; however, it was not that easy. The clones were so large that the normal sequencing procedures did not work. It took us months to cut up and individually clone the pieces that appeared to contain the exons we wanted. We got the sequences around exon 4 first and amplified exon 4 in several patients with TS and in controls. George also screened them with the SSCP electrophoresis technique. No mutations were found.

I began to worry. There were only two more exons to go. What happens if both of those are negative? Were Bissbort's findings a fantasy, or had we "excluded" an exon that actually contained the mutation?

Exon 7 was next. After the Friday clinic was over, George showed me the results of the SSCP electrophoresis technique to search for mutations in exon 7. The results were negative. But, he said, "I have to rerun it again in the cold room." This technique was sensitive to temperature and had to be done at two different temperatures to be certain the results were negative. The results of the cold run were more encouraging. Of the eleven subjects, seven showed only two bands, suggesting they were probably normal, but the other four showed three bands, suggesting a polymorphism. We had seen apparent mutations before, however, and knew that everything had to be repeated to make sure it was not an artifact. To test this, George re-amplified DNA from the same set of patients and the results were the same. This suggested we had found a mutation in exon 7. We now had to sequence the DNA to determine if the mutation was real. This process could take several weeks.

An Exon Mutation At Last

The sequencing studies showed an A ->C mutation in exon 7. The normal amino acid sequence for this region was: lysine-asparagine-isoleucine. The A ->C mutation resulted in a lysine-histidine-isoleucine sequence. This change of an amino acid sequence was potentially very exciting, because back in Africa almost three years ago, I had predicted that the mutation Bissbort seemed to have found would involve histidines. This was because oxygen binds to heme molecules, and heme molecules bind to histidines. One way to activate the TDO2 protein would be to provide an extra histidine binding site. This might give TDO2 an advantage in its competition with other liver proteins for heme, thus leaving it in a "turned on" state.

To check on whether this was real or just an artifact, George PCR-amplified and sequenced the region in two additional patients who carried the mutation in double dose. In both cases, the A ->C was present. The exon mutation was real. We had finally found a *TDO2* mutation in an exon.

A CCCCT Repeat

One of the most exciting new developments in human genetics has been the observation that the presence of highly-repeated triplet sequences in some genes could cause disease. Such repeats had been found to explain Huntington's disease, fragile X-syndrome, myotonic dystrophy, and several other more obscure diseases. We were thus excited to find a repeated sequence at the end of exon 5. This was a repeat, five base pairs long, consisting of the sequence CCCCT. Would this come in different sizes, and more importantly, would the different alleles be associated with different diseases? We found that when we amplified this region in different people, they did, in fact, come in different sized pieces.

The next critical task was to see if any of our mutations were significantly more common in subjects with TS or other disorders.

Chapter 51

The *TDO2* Mutations
in Patients

We now had identified four different polymorphisms of the *TDO2* gene — three in introns and one in an exon — and had simple tests to identify each of them. By this time another summer was coming up and we once again had an infusion of summer students to help with the critical question, "When a large number of controls and subjects with different disorders are examined, would the *TDO2* gene prove to be a gene of major importance, or would it be one more of a polygenic set of genes?" The results after testing 1,221 subjects for the G->A mutation were as follows:

Group	N	Results for the G->A Mutation % A	Odds Ratio	p
Controls	141	3.5		
ADHD	113	2.7	0.74	N.S.
Alcoholism	65	0.0	0.00	N.S.
Autism	65	6.2	1.78	N.S.
Depression	16	12.6	3.88	N.S.
Drug Addiction	71	2.8	0.79	N.S.
Gambling	166	4.8	1.38	N.S.
Schizophrenia	41	0.0	0.00	N.S.
Smokers	93	1.1	0.30	N.S.
TS	**299**	**10.4**	**3.15**	**.015**
TS carriers	**151**	**10.6**	**3.22**	**.020**
Total	1,221			

The odds ratio refers to the relative risk of getting the disorder in question, compared to the controls. This was 3.15 for TS probands and 3.22 for the TS relatives. The DNA on the subjects with depression came from brain samples of individuals who had committed suicide. While the results were not significant, the odds ratio was higher (3.88) than for any other group, suggesting that if we had been able to study more subjects, the results might have been significant. These results suggested that some mutations of the *TDO2* gene played a role in TS and severe depression. The alcoholics and schizophrenics were of interest, in that none of them carried the A mutation; however, the frequency of the A mutation in controls was so low that this could have occurred by chance.

The results for the G'T mutation in 1,297 subjects were as follows:

Results for the G->T mutation

Group	N	% G	Odds Ratio	p
Controls	197	15.7		
ADHD	**108**	**25.0**	**1.78**	**.048**
Alcoholism	65	6.1	.35	.049
Autism	65	10.8	.65	N.S.
Depression	19	15.8	1.00	N.S.
Drug Addiction	**73**	**28.7**	**2.16**	**.016**
Gamblers	165	23.0	1.60	N.S.
Schizophrenia	43	23.3	1.62	N.S.
Smokers	108	18.6	1.22	N.S.
TS	320	17.7	1.16	N.S.
TS carriers	134	11.1	0.67	N.S.
Total	1297			

The only groups with a significant increase in the T mutation were ADHD and drug addiction. The 61 individuals with alcoholism showed a barely significant decrease in the number of T mutations.

Since the DGGE technique we had originally used detected both mutations, we examined the results for either an A or a T mutation. The results for the 1,096 subjects who had both tests were as follows:

Results for either the G->A or G->T mutation

Group	N	% AorT	Odds Ratio	p
Controls	135	17.0		
ADHD	**96**	**29.1**	**2.01**	**.028**
Alcoholism	64	6.3	0.32	.038
Autism	64	17.2	1.01	N.S.
Depression	15	33.3	2.43	N.S.
Drug Addiction	**70**	**32.9**	**2.38**	**.010**
Gamblers	165	25.4	1.66	.078
Schizophrenia	34	23.5	1.50	N.S.
Smokers	84	17.9	1.06	N.S.
TS	**271**	**29.9**	**2.08**	**.005**
TS carriers	98	24.5	1.58	N.S.
Total	1096	24.1		

Of the 135 controls, 17% carried either an A or a T mutation. This was significantly increased to 29.9% for the TS subjects and 29.1% for those with ADHD. Only those with drug addiction were also significant.

We were particularly interested in whether the intron mutation was associated with any of the above psychiatric disorders. Unfortunately, it was not. The C mutation was present in 6.3% of controls, and between 3.2 and 9.1% of those with ADHD, TS, autism, and schizophrenia carried the C mutation. None of these were significant. The same unimpressive results were obtained with the CCCCT repeat. Here the most common-sized fragment was present in 70.9% of 278 controls. The prevalence in all of the same groups studied above ranged from 65.5 to 77.9, and none were significant.

A final question was whether any of the mutations were associated with changes in blood serotonin levels. This was easy to test for because we had DNA samples on many of the subjects we had studied years before (Chapter 10).[32] Only the G⁄T mutation gave significant results. The average platelet serotonin level in those 26 tested individuals who carried the T mutation was 26, compared to 13 for those 141 tested who did not carry the T mutation. This was significant (p = .03).

The results reminded me of the story of the Vermont farmer who was asked how much money he got when he sold his hogs. His cagey answer was, "Not as much as I wanted, but more than I thought I would." These results were not as dramatic as I had wanted, but they were clearly positive. They indicated that alleles of the *TDO2* gene were associated with differences in serotonin levels and played a definite, although modest role, in a number of psychiatric disorders, including TS. I felt the seven years we had invested in cloning, sequencing and searching for mutations of the *TDO2* gene were definitely worth it.

We Finally Get Bissbort's Patent

It was the ultimate irony that on November 15, 1994, just as I was writing up the results of these studies,[77] I received in the mail a copy of Bissbort's patent from the Johannesburg patent office. The dye he used turned out to be 2,6-dichlorophenolindophenol, otherwise known as DCIP, or Tillman's reagent. It was a redox dye, similar to NBT. Its advantage was that it formed a blue solution and thus, as the dye reacted and changed to a clear color, the reaction could be followed in lysates of red blood cells (which, of course, were red); however, I didn't see how it could be used to examine oxygenases. We had already convinced ourselves that oxygenase reactions do not affect redox dyes. I had George Dietz try many different permutations. He even examined mouse livers that had high levels of TDO2, to no avail. I wrote to Bissbort, hoping, now that the patent had been made public, he would share with us his exact technique. Whatever the outcome, I felt that after examining four different DNA polymorphisms it was very unlikely that a mutation of the *TDO2* gene would be found that provided the major answer to TS or other behavioral disorders. I was becoming increasingly convinced that all psychiatric disorders were polygenic in nature and that many genes would be found, each playing a modest role.

Our ongoing studies with the *dopamine β-hydroxylase* gene (Chapter 54) were lending further support to this idea.

Chapter 52

The Yale Group
Claims Depression and Anxiety
Are Not Related to *Gts* Genes

As the paper on "Tourette Syndrome: A Hereditary Neuropsychiatric Spectrum Disorder" (Chapter 43),[42] confirming that a wide range of behaviors were associated with the *Gts* genes, was winding its way through the review process, one of the reviewers mentioned the recent paper by Pauls, Leckman, and Cohen in the *British Journal of Psychiatry*, entitled "Evidence Against a Genetic Relationship Between Tourette Syndrome, Depression, Panic and Phobic Disorders."[169] I had not seen it. The reviewer suggested that since the results appeared to be diametrically opposite to what I was reporting, it needed to be addressed. A few days later Sverd called to tell me he had seen it. Since it wasn't available in our library, I had him FAX a copy to me. It was the second part of the long-awaited official report of the widely-quoted abstract refuting our studies, that they had presented at the 1988 American Society of Human Genetics meetings (page 13). They reported the frequency of these disorders in their TS probands, relatives, and controls. The results for their TS probands and controls were as follows:

Disorder	TS probands (N = 86) % affected	Controls (N = 113) % affected	p
Generalized anxiety disorder	16.7	9.0	.11
Major depressive disorder	40.7	14.2	.00002
Obsessive-compulsive disorder	36.0	1.8	<.00001
Panic disorder	12.8	2.7	.0057
Simple phobia	18.6	4.4	.0012
Social phobia	5.8	0.9	.055

Except for generalized anxiety disorder, and a borderline result for social phobia, the other behaviors were significantly more common in the TS probands than in the controls; however, to rule out ascertainment bias, the critical results would come from studies of the relatives. Rather than separately examining the results for the relatives with TS versus those without TS, they were all lumped together. As illustrated previously (Chapter 36), this tends to obscure potentially positive results. The core of the findings was presented in their table 2, as follows:

Disorder	Relatives of TS probands (N = 338) % affected	Relatives of controls (N = 113) % affected	p
Generalized anxiety disorder	17.7	10.2	.05
Major depressive disorder	38.1	20.7	.0005
Panic disorder	14.2	3.5	.0022
Simple phobia	15.0	5.9	.015
Social phobia	4.7	1.2	.05

Despite the fact that the relatives with TS and those without TS were collapsed into a single group, the frequency of all five of the disorders was significantly greater in the relatives of TS probands than in the relatives of controls. Given this, I wondered how the title of their paper could be "Evidence Against a Genetic Relationship Between Tourette Syndrome, Depression, Panic and Phobic Disorders?" This was accomplished as follows. They re-examined their data and removed any relatives who had TS, chronic tics, or obsessive-compulsive disorder. After this was done, the statistics showed that the frequencies of depression, panic and phobic disorder in the remaining relatives were no longer significantly higher than in the controls. Based on this, they then claimed there was no evidence for a genetic relationship between these disorders and the *Gts* genes.

The fallacy of this was that their own earlier studies had shown that obsessive-compulsive behaviors were one of the major manifestations of the *Gts* genes.[167] In this earlier study they reported that TS was inherited as an autosomal dominant trait with 99% penetrance in males; that is, of those males who carried the *Gts* genes, 99% had TS or chronic tics. When obsessive-compulsive behaviors were included, the penetrance was 70% in females; thus, by their own data, only 15% of relatives without TS, chronic tics or obsessive-compulsive behaviors should be carrying the *Gts* genes. As such, one would not be able to identify any of the genetic effects of the *Gts* genes in a group of subjects where only 15% carried the genes. This would be analogous to attempting to claim that the *Huntington Chorea* gene does not cause dementia, because none of the relatives *without* chorea had dementia.

A second line of reasoning they used to justify their conclusion ran as follows: They found that relatives with obsessive-compulsive behaviors were more likely to have depression, panic and phobias than relatives without obsessive-compulsive behaviors. Based on this, they claimed that depression, panic attacks, and phobias were related to obsessive-compulsive behaviors, but not to TS.

The fallacy of this is that they agreed that the *Gts* genes -> obsessive-compulsive behaviors, and that obsessive-compulsive behaviors -> depression, panic and phobias, but in a strange leap of illogic, denied that *Gts* genes -> obsessive-compulsive behaviors -> depression, panic, and phobias. In our studies of the relatives of TS patients, we had also found that obsessive-compulsive behaviors represented a higher degree of expression of the *Gts* genes than chronic tics[42] and described a similar phenomena we termed *association by association* (see Chapter 43).

Enough information was given in their paper to allow a comparison between their results for major depressive disorder and our results for ever having a major depressive episode. The latter data came from our most recent version of the TS database, and consisted of 1,340 subjects over 13 years of age. These results were as follows:

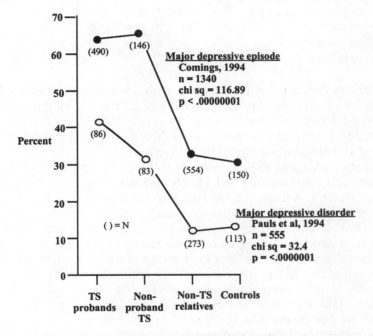

While the absolute percentages were different because the diagnosis of major depressive episode is less stringent than major depressive disorder, the trends in both were similar, and for both there was a highly significant, progressive decrease in depression with decreasing loading for the *Gts* genes.

I was astounded that once the data were available for careful analysis, they strongly supported the concept that the *Gts* genes played an important role in depression and anxiety. Were all these years of claiming we were wrong based on this? It seemed clear that, once again, the data were the same – only the interpretation of the data was different.

Chapter 53

The *Dopamine Receptor* Gene in Tourette Syndrome – Again

In the fall of 1994, Gelernter, Pauls, Leckman, Kidd, and Kurlan[101] published more results of their studies of the dopamine D_2A1 allele in TS. Similar to their previous abstract this report in the *Archives of Neurology* was entitled "D_2 dopamine receptor alleles do not influence severity of Tourette's syndrome." They found that when they used two different methods to measure severity, the tics were no worse in TS subjects who carried the D_2A1 allele than in those who did not. However, nowhere in their paper did they comment on the fact that the prevalence of the D_2A1 in the 64 TS subjects they tested was 51.6%. This level was even higher than what we had found in our own TS patients, and when compared to the prevalence of 25.9% in the 714 Caucasian controls known to be free of alcoholism or drug addiction, the p value was 0.000012; thus the difference between the two values was highly significant. I wrote a note to the editor correcting this oversight.[40]

I was, however, pleased with several other papers that Kurlan had written. As we had done earlier,[71,p617] he and his colleagues personally examined a group of school children, both in regular and special education classes.[138] We had found that 28% of children in special education classes had TS. They found a virtually identical frequency of 26%. We had found that 1 in 90 school boys had definite TS and 1 in 40 probable TS. They found a frequency of 6%, or 1 in 16 with definite or probable tics for children in regular classes. In a second paper,[134] they tested our proposal that in many TS families the *Gts* genes appeared to be coming from both the mother's and the father's side. They examined thirty-nine families with a strong family history for TS, and thirty-nine families straight from the clinic. In those with a strong family history, tics or obsessive-compulsive behaviors were present on both sides in 41%. In those from the clinic, 26% had tics or obsessive-compulsive behaviors on both sides. They concluded that their findings supported our contention that, in many cases, the *Gts* genes were coming from both parents.

When we first proposed these two ideas – that TS was a very common disorder, and that the genes often or always come from both parents – they were considered to be so radical that it took over three years and the submission of each paper to at least four different journals before we got them published. It was refreshing to see that when Kurlan did similar studies, the results were virtually identical. He even took it a step further and suggested that some cases of TS were a developmental problem.[134] By this, he meant that many children went through a normal developmental stage showing symptoms of tics, rituals and hyperactivity, and that about 3% of children simply failed to outgrow them. He termed this "developmental" TS and suggested that "full-blown" TS was the extreme end of this spectrum. My objection to this hypothesis was that when we see those milder cases, they almost always show the same type of family history as the more severe TS cases. This, plus our rapidly evolving studies on the molecular genetics of TS, convinced me that every case of TS, regardless of how mild, was a genetic rather than developmental disorder. Nonetheless, it was refreshing to have at least one person think that TS was even more common than I did.

The reason these two issues were so important is that the frequency of a disorder and whether the genes come from one or both parents determine how it is inherited. Most workers in the field assumed TS was inherited as a rare autosomal dominant disorder with the gene being inherited from one parent.[110-112,160,171,179] If it is common, and the genes come from both parents, the mechanism of inheritance is more likely to be polygenic. As such, linkage studies are unlikely to work and the association studies we were using would be the only way to identify the genes involved.[35]

Getting back to the subject of the D_2A1 allele in TS, as pointed out above- and previously (Chapter 37), Gelernter's "negative" reports were not really negative; however, a report out of Germany by Nöthen and co-workers[158] was negative. They found that the prevalence of the D_2A1 allele in 61 subjects with TS was no different than in their controls. It appeared that the difference was not because the prevalence of the allele was low in the TS individuals (37.5%), it was just unusually high in their controls. By this time we had examined 274 TS patients and found that 40.1% carried the D_2A1 allele. Others had examined 158 TS subjects and found that 41.7% carried the D_2A1 allele, an essentially identical result. Of a total of 432 TS subjects (including those of Nöthen et al), 40.7% carried the D_2A1 allele versus 25.9% for 714 controls, p = .00000016.

Combined, these results suggested that the increased prevalence of the D_2A1 allele in TS subjects might be more closely associated with behaviors or symptoms other than the tics *per se*.

Molecular Genetic Loading Technique

It occurred to me that we might develop new insights by combining the results from our behavioral questionnaires used in the genetic loading technique (Chapter 36), with the results of our molecular genetic studies of the *dopamine D2 receptor* and other genes. This would allow us to examine many individual behaviors other than just tics. By now thousands of our patients had filled out the Behavioral Questionnaire, and we had D_2A1 results on hundreds of these same individuals. This allowed us to examine the association between twenty different behaviors and the prevalence of the D_2A1 allele in the following three groups of subjects:

1. Controls who were screened to exclude those with alcoholism, drug abuse or tobacco abuse and did not have the behavior in question. We called these *controls without.*

2. TS patients or their relatives without the behavior in question. We called these *cases without.*

3. TS patients or their relatives with the behavior in question. We called these *cases with.*

The idea was that if specific alleles were related to specific behaviors, the *controls without* should show the lowest prevalence of the allele, the *cases without* should be intermediate, and the *cases with* should show the highest prevalence of the allele. Since this was using the genetic loading technique at a molecular level, we called it the *Molecular Genetic Loading Technique.*

The results for the significant behaviors, for 484 subjects, are shown below.

Prevalence (in %) of the D_2A1 Allele for Different Behaviors in Controls, TS Patients and their Relatives

Behavior	Controls without	Cases without	Cases with	p
Sexual	26.9	31.1	47.8	.0007
Stuttering	23.8	33.0	50.7	.0008
Obsessive-compulsive	26.6	32.7	49.0	.0013
Schizoid	28.6	31.9	48.4	.0016
Manic	26.6	32.8	48.5	.0017
ADHD	26.9	33.3	44.4	.0085
Tics	26.9	28.8	40.4	.0088
Conduct	25.9	32.4	41.5	.0135
Oppositional Defiant	26.9	34.3	42.2	.0274
Alcohol abuse	26.9	35.8	48.4	.037
Learning problems	25.8	34.7	40.7	.041
Sleep problems	26.2	34.9	41.0	.049

The results showed just what we expected. There were many behaviors – sexual, stuttering, obsessive-compulsive, schizoid, manic, and ADHD – that showed a greater degree of association with the D_2A1 allele than tics. The figure on the next page diagrammatically illustrates the two most significant behaviors – sexual and stuttering, and the least significant behavior – phobias.

These results showed the dramatic increase in prevalence of the D_2A1 allele across these three groups for sexual behaviors and stuttering.[73] It also illustrated how critical it was to carefully evaluate the controls. Many studies in the literature had simply drawn blood from a group of random controls without having any knowledge about whether they abused drugs or alcohol or tobacco, or had any psychiatric disorder, including childhood ADHD. Since all of these are associated with the D_2A1 allele, and probably with other genes, "controls" with these disorders must be excluded.

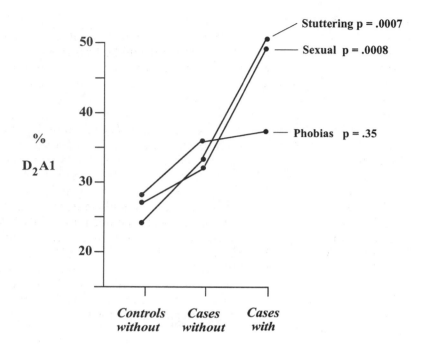

A second way to examine the data was to compare the severity of the behavior scores in those who carried the D_2A1 allele versus those who did not. The table below shows the results that were significant.

The Mean of the Different Behavior Scores for D_2A1 Carriers versus Non-carriers

Behavior Score	D_2A1 Mean	D_2A 2-2 Mean	p
Stuttering	0.23	0.12	0.002
ADHD	20.60	16.68	0.003
Mania	1.85	1.21	0.003
Conduct	2.97	2.36	0.004
Schizoid	1.63	1.11	0.007
Obsessive-compulsive	3.01	2.28	0.009
Sexual	0.75	0.48	0.017
Tics	2.78	2.12	0.042
Somatization	2.71	2.04	0.048

(N for D_2A1 = 171, for D_2A 2-2 = 313)

The results were similar to those in former table, with stuttering, ADHD, mania, conduct disorder, schizoid, obsessive-compulsive, and sexual behaviors all being more significant than the tic score. Most of these scores were still significant when the controls were excluded, indicating these results were not simply due to some unique aspect of the controls.

Once we began to use the genetic loading technique (Chapter 36), we found it was a powerful procedure for examining genetic factors in a wide range of different behaviors.[34,36-39,41,43] In a similar vein, once we saw the power of the molecular genetic loading technique, we were anxious to apply it to other genes, as well. I realized that the power of this approach would be further enhanced if a group of subjects were all tested for the same set of genes. This way it would eventually be possible to determine if the alleles were additive in their effect — one of the definitions of polygenic inheritence.

To do this, we chose a set of 319 DNA samples that we called the *polygenic set*, because we were going to use them to examine polygenic inheritance. We had two ideas about how best to use these samples. The first idea was that the power of the study would be enhanced by using the whole set, which included controls, TS probands, and TS relatives. The second idea was that we should restrict the study to controls and TS probands, since this would provide the greatest potential range in scores. The importance of this was illustrated by our above results with the D_2A1 allele. When the controls were included, the ADHD score ranged from 20.6 for the D_2A1 allele carriers to 16.7 for the non-carriers, and this was significant; however, if we only examined TS probands, the respective scores were 27.5 for the D_2A1 allele carriers versus 27.3 for the non-carriers. While the scores were higher, they were obviously not different. Our experience showed that while both approaches worked, the use of controls and TS probands was the slightly better approach. The significant results for the 176 subjects in this set are shown in table below.

The Mean of the Different Behavior Scores for D_2A1 Carriers versus Non-carriers for Controls and TS Probands in the Polygenic Set

Behavior Score	D_2A1 Mean	D_2A 2-2 Mean	p
Conduct	3.65	2.64	.006
Mania	2.31	1.40	.012
ADHD	25.57	21.23	.036
Tics	4.25	3.06	.042
Schizoid	1.91	1.20	.046
Obsessive-compulsive	3.40	2.44	.047
Oppositional Defiant	4.31	3.30	.046

We next used these techniques on another important gene for dopamine metabolism, *dopamine β-hydroxylase*.

Chapter 54

Dopamine β-Hydroxylase

The enzyme dopamine beta-hydroxylase (DβH) is very important because it converts dopamine to norepinephrine, and both are very important neurotransmitters in behavior. This pathway from the amino acid tyrosine, which comes from the diet, to norepinephrine is as follows:

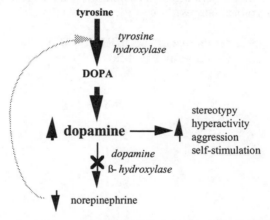

Thus, tyrosine is converted to DOPA by tyrosine hydroxylase, DOPA is converted to dopamine, and DβH converts dopamine to norepinephrine. This pathway uses what is called *feed back inhibition*; that is, when enough norepinephrine is produced, it inhibits tyrosine hydroxylase, which cuts down on the level of norepinephrine. Studies in animals have shown that when DβH is inhibited, this feed back inhibition is interrupted and dopamine levels increase.[p411] This results in hyperactivity and aggression. Low levels of norepinephrine *per se* can also play a role in these behaviors.

In studies of the blood levels, Rogeness and colleagues reported an increased frequency of the diagnosis of conduct disorder in emotionally disturbed boys with low plasma DβH levels.[159,183-186] Other studies of hospitalized patients also showed low DβH levels in children with conduct disorder.[97] A study of outpatients showed that low DβH levels were much more likely in ADHD children who also had conduct disorder than ADHD children without conduct disorder. While some studies of DβH and conduct disorder have been negative,[172] others have shown a correlation between low DβH levels and sensation-seeking behaviors.[4,210]

A potential role of DβH in learning is suggested by animal studies using DβH inhibitors. In one such study,[117] the administration of a DβH inhibitor two hours prior to training resulted in a 51% decrease in brain norepinephrine and associated decrease in learning. Other studies suggested that norepinephrine depletion impairs memory.[10,95,96]

Given these interesting reports, I wondered if studies with genetic markers of the *DβH* gene might provide a more accurate assessment of its role in ADHD, Tourette syndrome, and other behaviors, than blood levels of the enzyme. Since the human *DβH* gene has been cloned and sequenced, and two *Taq* I polymorphisms had been reported,[83] we were able to test this possibility. One of the advantages of the RFLP studies is that once the different DNA samples have been cut with a specific restriction endonuclease, electrophoresed, and the DNA transferred onto nylon filters, the same set of filters can be successively tested with a number of different gene probes. We obtained a copy of the *DβH* clone[139,140] and used it to test the same filters we had used for the dopamine D_2 studies.

We eventually examined 913 Caucasian subjects with various disorders for the *Taq* B1/B2 polymorphism, with the following results:

Prevalence of the DβH *Taq* B Alleles in Various Psychiatric Disorders

Disorder	N	%B1	Odds ratio	p
Controls	148	60.8		
TS	**352**	**70.5**	**1.54**	**.035**
TS Mild	35	54.3	0.76	.765
TS Moderate	**251**	**72.1**	**1.67**	**.020**
TS Severe	66	72.7	1.72	.093
ADHD	78	73.1	1.75	.066
Alcoholism	23	69.6	1.47	.421
Autism	40	67.5	1.34	.44
Depression	28	50.0	0.64	.644
Drug addiction	29	65.5	1.22	.634
Gamblers	111	60.4	0.98	.941
Smokers	**104**	**73.1**	**1.75**	**.043**
Total	913			

Of the 148 controls, 60.8% carried the B1 allele. This increased significantly, but modestly, to 70.5% for 352 TS probands. The only other group showing a significant increase was our group of smokers, with 73.1% carrying the B1 allele. If one thinks in terms of a single gene causing a disorder, these modest results would suggest moving on to examine another gene. However, given the success we had with examining the prevalence of the A1 allele of the *dopamine D2 receptor* gene in the three groups – controls, TS probands, and relatives with and without different behavior problems (Chapter 53) – we wanted to use the same technique on the *DβH* gene. We were also aware that for many of our 148 controls, we had no information of whether they abused alcohol or drugs. If we used the same controls as for our D_2A1 studies, where each had completed our behavioral questionnaire, we might find that the prevalence of the B1 allele was lower than 60.8%. That turned out to be the case. The following shows just the significant results:

DβH *Taq* B1 in Controls, TS Patients and Relatives

Score	Controls without		Subjects without		Subjects with		p
	N	%	N	%	N	%	
ADHD	34	47.1	163	70.6	116	81.9	.00010
Learning problems	29	48.3	190	72.6	95	81.1	.0014
Grade school/poor perf.	30	46.7	187	72.2	88	79.5	.0021
Oppositional defiant	34	47.1	206	74.8	79	77.2	.0070
Tics	34	47.1	104	75.0	181	75.7	.0074
Mania	33	48.5	216	75.0	69	76.8	.014
Alcohol	34	47.1	262	76.0	23	69.6	.018
Reading problems	18	44.4	116	73.3	169	76.9	.019
Drug abuse	34	47.1	258	76.0	27	70.4	.021
Sleep problems	28	53.6	202	74.3	83	78.3	.031
Stuttering	33	48.5	241	76.3	41	73.2	.032
Obsessive-compulsive	32	46.9	216	75.9	69	73.9	.037

The most significant behavior was ADHD; thus the prevalence of the B1 allele in controls without ADHD was 47.1%. In TS patients or relatives without ADHD (subjects without) it was 70.6%, and in the TS patients and their relatives with AHDH (subjects with), it was 81.9%. This was a highly significant progressive increase. Some of the other most significant results were for learning problems, poor performance in grade school, oppositional defiant behavior, and tics. These results can be appreciated more in diagrammatic form; thus the diagram on the following page shows the trends for the first two behaviors.

The lower prevalence of the B1 allele in these controls illustrates how important it is to have as much knowledge about the behavior of controls as about the TS patients and their relatives. The fact that ADHD, learning problems, grade school problems, and oppositional defiant behaviors showed the highest degree of association with the B1 allele is consistent with the previous correlations of plasma DβH with conduct disorder and animal studies showing the importance of norepinephrine in learning and memory.

As with the D_2A1 studies, we also compared the average of the different behavioral scores in controls and TS probands carrying the B1 allele to those not carrying it. While not as dramatic, the results were again significant for ADHD, oppositional defiant, and learning (reading) problems.

Average Behavioral Score

Behavior	B1	B 2-2	p
Oppositional defiant	4.16	3.08	.008
Sleep problems	0.63	0.36	.010
ADHD	25.17	20.86	.023
Read problems	2.14	1.57	.037

It was clear that *DβH*, another gene affecting dopamine function in the brain, was also one of a polygenic set of genes for TS and related behaviors.

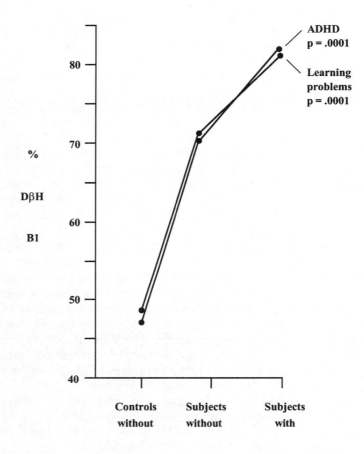

Diagram of the percentage of the DβH B1 allele in the three groups of subjects.

Chapter 55

The *Dopamine Transporter* Gene

Nerves communicate with each other by using chemicals called neurotransmitters.[p313] When a neurotransmitter such as dopamine is released into the synapse, one of the ways of removing it to get ready for another transmission is to transport it back into the nerve from which it was released. This is done by specific proteins called *transporters*. The human *dopamine transporter* gene was cloned by Drs. David Vandenberg, Tony Perisco, and George Uhl[212] of the National Institute of Drug Abuse. It is abbreviated as *DAT1*. These investigators were particularly interested in this gene because one of the mechanisms of action of cocaine is to block the dopamine transporter. This results in abnormally high levels of dopamine in the synapse and this is how cocaine causes its euphoric high.177 They suspected that people with a genetic abnormality of their *dopamine transporter* gene might be more susceptible to substance abuse. In order to be able to test this idea, it was necessary to find some genetic variants or polymorphisms at the *DAT1* gene. They were fortunate in finding two *Taq* I polymorphisms and a forty base pair repeat polymorphism at the end of the gene. The latter consisted of a forty base pair DNA sequence that was repeated between three and twelve times. When this region was amplified by PCR, simple electrophoresis showed different-sized pieces depending upon how many repeats were present. The most common number was 10, and thus it was called the 10 allele. The next most common number was 9, called the 9 allele.

As soon as these polymorphism were reported, I was excited to test them in our Tourette syndrome patients, since abnormalities in dopamine metabolism were likely to explain parts of the disorder.[p399] I contacted Uhl and obtained copies of the *DAT1* clone. It quickly became apparent that the *Taq* polymorphisms were technically difficult to use. Uhl also told me that they had been unable to find any differences in the frequency of the forty base pair repeat alleles in drug addicts, and that a colleague had already tested some Tourette syndrome patients, with negative results. This put a damper on my enthusiasm about diverting time and effort to this gene when we had so many other things to do.

Within a short time, the genes for the human serotonin[114] and norepinephrine transporter were also cloned and sequenced, and *Taq* polymorphisms had been found for each of them. I thought that some day it might be productive to go back and examine these genes.

In the summer of 1994, MacMurray told me he had met a young man at his favorite coffee shop, who was returning to school and was interested in molecular biology. MacMurray told him of our collaborative studies involving psychiatric disorders and suggested he might want to come to our laboratory for his masters research work. His name was Rob Ring. When he came for an interview, I suggested that looking at these three genes – the *dopamine, serotonin,* and *norepinephrine transporters* – in our Tourette syndrome patients would make a nice, well-defined project and an excellent thesis. I told him that the studies to date had been negative, but even if his results were also negative this would still make a good thesis. He agreed and started work in August 1994. Rob learned quickly and within a few months had the test for the forty base pair *DAT1* repeat working well and had examined over sixty subjects.

I was anxious to test the *DAT1* gene using the same techniques we had used for the *DRD2* and *DβH* genes. The initial results looked impressive. Even with the low numbers there was a significant association between the ADHD score and subjects who carried the 10/10 genotype; however, I would only feel comfortable after several hundred subjects were tested. By December Rob had tested 471 individuals. Among the 91 controls, 37.4% were of the 10/10 genotype. This percent increased to 52.3% for the 241 individuals with TS ($p = .015$). Of the 103 TS relatives, 55.3% were of the 10/10 genotype. We had also examined 36 autistic children and 58.3% of them had the 10/10 genotype ($p = .032$).

The results of examining the *controls without* specific behaviors, versus the *cases* (TS probands or relatives) *without* the behavior, versus the *cases with* the behavior, were striking. The behaviors that were significant are as follows:

Behavior	*Controls without* %10/10	*Cases without* %10/10	*Cases with* %10/10	p
Somatization	25.0	47.3	61.8	.0009
Alcohol	35.9	51.2	74.1	.0027
ADHD	35.9	49.6	62.2	.004
Major Depression	24.1	50.8	56.8	.006
Panic Attacks	30.3	50.3	57.5	.010
Obsessive-compulsive	32.4	51.1	59.3	.011
General Anxiety	29.0	51.6	59.0	.011
Mania	34.2	50.9	59.5	.012
Oppositional	35.9	50.4	59.8	.012
Sexual Disorders	32.3	50.5	58.7	.013
Reading Problems	40.9	47.2	57.0	.043

Thus, a wide range of behaviors were associated with the 10/10 genotype of the *DAT1* gene, with somatization (multiple bodily complaints that do not have a clear physical basis), alcohol abuse, and ADHD ranking on the top of the list. These three are shown diagrammatically as follows:

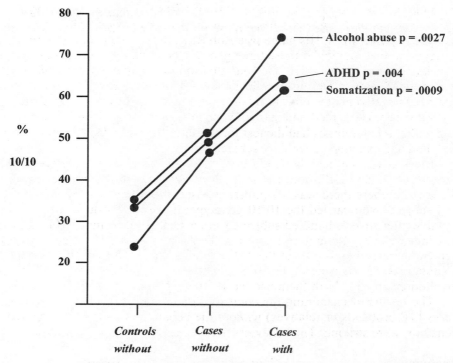

As with the *DRD2* and *DβH* studies, the prevalence of the alleles of interest was lower in controls that had been screened to exclude alcohol, drug, and tobacco abuse, as well as the behavior in question. The prevalence of the 10/10 genotype was much higher in the TS probands or their relatives (cases) that had the behavior in question.

The second method of examining the effect of the *DAT1* gene was to examine the average of the different behavioral scores in those who carried the 10/10 genotype versus those that were 10/non-10 or non-10/non-10. The significant results, when limited to controls and TS probands, were as follows:

Behavior	10/10	10/non-10 non-10/non-10	p
	Mean Score	**Mean score**	
General Anxiety	0.33	0.16	.012
Major Depression	4.00	2.87	.012
ADHD	25.44	20.42	.016
Alcohol	0.68	0.09	.037

Shortly after we submitted the results on the *DAT1* gene for publication, a paper by Cook et al.[79a] was published in the March 1994 issue of the *American Journal of Human Genetics*. The paper wasentitled "Association of Attention-Deficit Disorder and the Dopamine Transporter Gene." They also found a significant increase in the frequency of the 10 allele in children with ADHD.

Our results[176] and those of Cook et al. indicated that the *dopamine trans-porter* was another gene that played an important role in various types of human behavior.

Chapter 56

The Polygenic Inheritance
of Behavior

Once the individual studies of the three dopamine genes, *DRD2*, *DβH* and *DAT1*, were complete, all using the same DNA samples, it was possible to answer the ultimate questions needed to solve the problem of how TS, ADHD and other behaviors were inherited. They were:

- Are the alleles additive?
- Are they subtractive?
- Are they clinically significant?
- Are they specific for certain behaviors or do they contribute to a spectrum of interrelated behaviors?

If they were additive, individuals who inherited two or all three of the alleles would have higher or worse behavior scores than those who inherited one or none. If they were clinically significant, the scores would span a range where those with the lowest scores would be largely asymptomatic, while those with the highest scores would have clinically significant symptoms. If they were subtractive, individuals with none of the markers would have the lowest scores. If they contributed to a spectrum of behaviors, then the results should be positive and clinically significant for a number of different behaviors.

To test these questions, the 176 controls and TS probands in the polygenic set were divided into four groups: In group one, subjects had inherited all three alleles. In group two, they had inherited two of the three alleles. In group three, they had inherited only one of the three alleles, and in group four they had inherited none of the three alleles. The expectation was that there would be a linear decrease in scores across these four groups for a number of different behaviors. This hypothesis was tested by a statistical technique called linear analysis of variance.[89] The results are shown in table on the next page.

The results indicated that all of the above expectations were true.[78] The behaviors that showed a statistically-significant linear decrease in scores were, in order, ADHD, stuttering, oppositional defiant disorder, tics, conduct disorder, obsessive-compulsive, mania, alcohol dependence, and general anxiety. The majority of the most troublesome behavioral problems in TS were significant. All except sleep problems, depression, somatization and reading problems showed an exact, progressive, linear decrease in scores across the four groups, even if the total was not significant. For every behavior, those in group one (3 of 3 alleles) had the highest scores and except for somatization, those in group four (0 of 3 alleles) had the lowest scores. Most of the scores spanned a clinically significant range. The results were significant for nine of the twenty behaviors tested.

Comparison of the Mean Behavior Scores for the Gene Groups

Behavior	Gene Groups				
	1	2	3	4	
	3 of 3	2 of 3	1 of 3	0 of 3	p
N	24	67	70	15	
ADHD	30.0	24.7	20.4	14.1	.0002
Stuttering	1.17	1.06	0.94	0.46	.0002
Oppositional defiant	5.04	3.91	3.38	1.93	.0023
Tics	4.95	3.71	3.28	1.40	.0023
Conduct	4.08	3.05	2.87	1.93	.0038
Obsessive-compulsive	3.37	3.02	2.75	1.13	.020
Mania	2.29	2.11	1.40	0.87	.024
Alcohol dependence	1.21	0.35	0.20	0.00	.035
General anxiety	0.33	0.29	0.20	0.07	.038
Panic	3.45	3.37	2.97	2.13	.053
Schizoid	1.91	1.66	1.26	0.78	.067
Sleep problems	0.83	0.64	0.44	0.46	.149
Sexual problems	1.12	0.62	0.58	0.53	.158
Drug dependence	0.87	0.34	0.34	0.20	.168
Major depression	3.83	2.91	2.94	2.80	.173
Learning problems	0.87	0.80	0.78	0.47	.197
Phobia	2.83	2.67	2.41	2.00	.318
Grade school/poor perf.	3.33	3.09	2.97	2.80	.399
Somatization	3.09	2.68	1.69	2.69	.525
Reading problems	2.00	1.98	2.10	1.86	.893

These results indicated that all four of the above conditions were met. The results were additive, in that group one always had the highest score and the other groups were almost always intermediate. The results were subtractive in that for all but one behavior, those in group four had the lowest scores. The scores in groups one to four spanned a clinically significant range. Finally, the results provided support at a molecular level that TS is a spectrum disorder and that the individual comorbid behaviors were due to the same genes responsible for the tics. It was especially notable that the behaviors that had been at the center of so much controversy – ADHD, stuttering, conduct, substance abuse, and anxiety – were all significantly associated with these three genes. The effect of the three alleles is illustrated by the diagram on the next page.

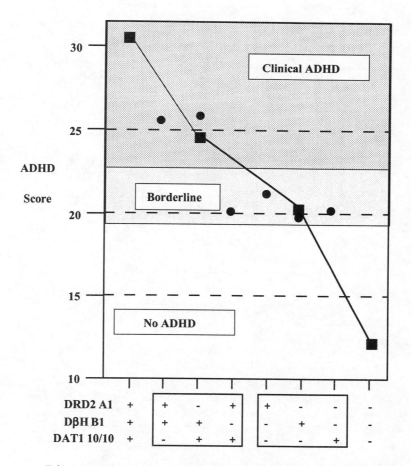

Diagram of the mean ADHD score for various combinations of the *DRD2 Taq* A1, *DβH Taq* B1, and *DAT1* 10/10 alleles. The means for the major classifications 3 of 3, 2 of 3, 1 of 3, and 0 of 3 are shown as black squares. The minor classifications, delineated at the bottom of the figure, are shown as black circles. [From *Am.J.Med.Genetics* May 1996, by permission.]

This diagram shows that, on average, those who inherited all 3 of the alleles in question had the highest ADHD scores, well into the clinical range. Those who inherited none of the 3 alleles had the lowest ADHD scores, well into the normal range. Those who inherited 2 of 3 were lower, those who inherited 1 of 3 were still lower. The effect was additive and subtractive, the results were clinically significant, and scores other than ADHD were also affected, indicating the different disorders were genetically interrelated.

The results for conduct disorder and oppositional defiant disorder were particularly important, because these conditions were so widely assumed to be due entirely to environmental causes.

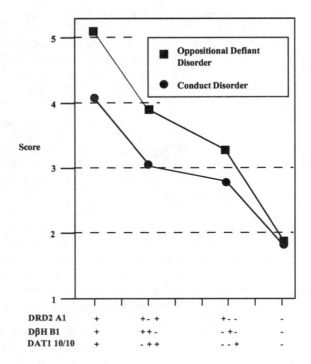

DRD2 A1	+	+- +	+- -	-
DβH B1	+	++ -	- +-	-
DAT1 10/10	+	- ++	- - +	-

Diagram of the mean conduct and oppositional defiant scores for various combinations of the *DRD2 Taq* A1, *DβH Taq* B1, and *DAT1* 10/10 alleles. The means for 3 of 3, 2 of 3, 1 of 3, and 0 of 3 alleles are shown as black squares for oppositional defiant disorder and black circles for conduct disorder.

This diagram shows that the additive and subtractive effect of the three alleles was virtually identical for oppositional defiant disorder and conduct disorder to for the ADHD score. Only the range of the scores was different, since these are unique to each score.

The results shown in the table and in the figures provided very strong support for the things we had been proposing, namely that TS, ADHD, stuttering, conduct, oppositional defiant, obsessive-compulsive, anxiety, substance abuse and other psychiaric disorders were:

- inherited in a polygenic fashion,
- part of a spectrum of related disorders,
- caused by shared genes,
- caused by alleles that were common in the population,
- caused by variants that individually had only a modest effect on gene function
- caused by genes that were additive in their effect,
- caused by genes that upset the dopamine, serotonin and other neurotransmitter balance in the brain.

I like to refer to the genes involved in polygenic inheritance as *polygenes*. When we examined the individual effect of these polygenes it was apparent that each contributed to only 0.1 to 8% of any behavioral score, suggesting that at least ten to fifty different genes were invoved. This explained why those researchers who were attempting to find genes for psychiatric disorders using linkage techniques were failing. For example, the use of over eight hundred different markers has excluded the presence of a major Tourette syndrome gene from virtually 100% of the genome. Linkage techniques require that a given gene account for at least 20% of the clinical picture, and preferably much more. Only association studies have the power to detect the more subtle effects we were seeing. There were hundreds of reports in the literature claiming to have ruled out a role of a given gene in various disorders using linkage techniques. These same genes can often be shown to play a role when association studies are used.

The fact that each genetic variant accounted for only a small portion of the clinical picture was totally consistent with the whole concept of polygenic inheritance. In order for an individual to have any reasonable chance of accumulating ten to fifty polygenes, each polygene has to have a relatively small effect on the function of the gene. This allows these variants to be very common, with 10 to 60% of the population carrying a given polygene. With such carrier frequencies, the random chance of inheriting a number of polygenes is high. As a result, polygenic disorders tend to be much more common than single gene disorders.

I also suspected that these subtle effects were due to the fact that the genetic changes were occurring in the parts of the gene that controlled gene regulation rather than the parts that had to do with gene structure. A number of studies had been published showing that there were no common structural (exon) mutations in some of the genes discussed in this book. These reports often carried the implication that if there were no exon mutations, then the gene could not be involved in the psychiatric disorder in question. This ignores the fact that there are vast streches of DNA on both sides of, and between, the exons (introns) that can effect the function of the gene. This may be where all the action is in polygenes; thus just as a failure to find linkage doesn't prove a given gene is not involved, the failure to find exon mutations also doesn't prove the gene is not involved. Some of the polymorphisms we studied had no effect on gene function. However, were were able to use them to detect an effect of the unknown mutations because the two were non-randomly associated — what we call *linkage dysequilibrium*. [I have suggested that in many cases the unknown mutations affecting gene function were the minisatellite repeat polymorphisms that are so common in the human genome.[44a]]

As dramatic and significant as the results for the three dopamine genes were for ADHD and related behaviors, it was not possible to claim that a diagnostic test for ADHD, TS, and the other comorbid behaviors was now available. This was because there were still individuals who had all three alleles and were fine, and others who had none of the three alleles and still had severe symptoms. It is also a basic truth that these disorders had some significant contributing environmental factors; however, a very important start had been made in that the concepts, tools, and techniques necessary for the journey had been identified. It was extremely likely that many other genes and alleles would be found, and each would provide an additional part of the story. In fact, between the time this book was completed and before it went to press, significant effects of many additional genes relating to five different neurotransmitters and affecting various behaviors and personality traits were identified in our laboratory. These were *MAOA* and *MAOB*, the *serotonin 1A*, dopamine *DRD1, DRD4* and *DRD5, cannabinoid* and two *GABA* receptor genes, the obesity *(OB)* gene, and the *serotonin transporter* and *norepinephrine transporter* genes. In every case each gene accounted for 1 to 8% of various behaviors, and were additive in their effect. For different genes, reproducible results were obtained in up to six completely different sets of subjects.

The fact that many genes, rather than a single gene, are involved in psychiatric disorders does not mean genetic testing is worthless. Techniques are now available to screen for many different genetic variants in a single test. Once we develop more knowledge about which genes and which genetic variants are important, the testing for a number of these polygenes may become a routine part of the assessment of patients with psychiatric problems. This will contribute not only to a more accurate diagnosis, but to more effective and precisely targeted treatment.

Chapter 57

Epilogue

One of the things that I found most irritating and disappointing about our experience with studying TS was that the professionals with the least experience with this disorder were often the most vocal in their opposition to our observations. Over a period of more than a decade, all of our thousands of patients were examined in great detail. The extensive questionnaires allowed us to check for the presence of hundreds of different behavioral symptoms in every patient and their relatives. A longitudinal history, recording behavioral problems throughout each year of their life, was taken on each patient. The pedigrees on each family were models of genetic compulsiveness and included queries about dozens of behavioral disorders in all siblings, children, parents, uncles, aunts, grandparents, cousins, nephews, and nieces.

Despite this, individuals who had never seen a TS patient, or had superficially examined only a few, or who never had the medical responsibility of caring for TS patients, had no compunctions about loudly proclaiming that our observations were mistaken. Most often these statements seemed driven by the fact they did not want our theories to be true, because it would upset their previous assumptions or previous training about the cause and treatment of behavioral disorders.

One of the statements I heard most often was that our proposals were "highly speculative." To me, they were anything *but* speculative. I had simply listened carefully to what our many thousands of patients and their families were telling us. In many ways we were simply the recorders of their collective wisdom and experience. Hundreds of my patients have told me that one of their most frustrating problems was that their doctors did not listen to, or believe, what they were telling them.

Papers and Grants

The peer review process is the backbone of science. Manuscripts reporting new findings are submitted to editors who in turn send them to experts in the field, who decide whether they appear to be scientifically valid, whether the methods are correct, and most critically, but more subtly, whether they "fit" into present scientific thinking. The latter arena is where papers that are acceptable on all other counts can run into trouble. A friend of mine once said, "If the paper represents a minute step forward in thinking about the field, no one is threatened, and it is likely to get published; however, if it represents a bigger step, watch out. You are in trouble. They are likely to find any reason they can to turn you down."

I thought at the time that this was a rather pessimistic outlook to science, a field of endeavor I had entered because I thought just the opposite was true — science was the one arena that was wide open to exciting and innovative new ideas. Soon after entering the field of the genetics of behavior, I began to see the wisdom of his outlook. I found that if the reviewers felt uncomfortable with the ideas, almost any excuse would be used to reject the paper. A pattern began to develop, in which we would first try to get a study published in the psychiatric literature. When this failed, as it usually did, we often found that the only journals that were comfortable with our genetic approach to behavior were genetics journals. Most of the papers that formed the foundations of our theory of TS as a genetic spectrum disorder caused by common genes affecting serotonin and dopamine metabolism were published in genetic rather than psychiatric journals.

Obtaining grant funds for our TS research was even more frustrating than getting the papers accepted. If a paper is turned down by one set of reviewers, it is possible to make revisions and submit it to another journal. If it has any merit, after sufficient revisions are made to satisfy the objections of the reviewers, usually it will eventually be accepted for publication. This process is more difficult with grants. The National Institutes of Health is the major granting agency, and the number of other sources of funds are severely limited.

In addition, the individuals on the study section where the grant is reviewed are part of the establishment and thus represent the established or accepted way of thinking in a field. Reviewers for a journal may feel inclined to accept a paper even it they don't completely agree, since it is only a paper. If it turns out to be wrong, the worst that happens is that no one pays attention to it or refers to it; however, if a mistake is made in approving a grant, hundreds of thousands of dollars may be wasted; thus there is much less reason to be sanguine about taking a chance on a new idea. The usual approach is "let the investigators first prove they are right, then we may fund the research." The problem with this excessively conservative approach is that if the funding to a investigator is turned off, they can do nothing — the research is usually ended.

During the period of 1984 to 1992, I attempted to obtain funds for our TS research by submitting twenty-two different grants to the National Institutes of Health (NIH), National Institute of Mental Health (NIMH), National Institute of Alcohol Abuse and Alcoholism (NIAAA), National Institute of Drug Abuse (NIDA), Alcoholic Beverage Research Foundation, and Tourette Syndrome Association. Only one of these was funded — $40,000 from the Alcoholic Beverage Research Foundation. Unfortunately, to our great frustration, we tried three additional times to obtain funds from this source, with no success.

The following are some of my favorite comments from grant reviews:

> "The hypothesis that the *tryptophan dioxygenase* gene is a candidate gene for TS is an intriguing one. However...the sequencing of the tryptophan dioxygenase DNA is not well justified and appears to have little relevance to the specific aims."

> "Although the principal investigator is a distinguished geneticist, there is no evidence that he or any of those named in

the application have training or expertise in psychiatry, psychology, statistical genetics, biostatistics, or epidemiology, all of which would be required to conduct the proposed study."

"This work is controversial and still being debated. It is noted that the work of the Yale group (Pauls and his colleagues), which is consistent with a less 'global' model for the genetics of TS and related disorders, does not feature in the proposal."

"A fishing expedition."

"Dr. Comings has no formal training in child or adult psychopathology."

"The controversial proposal that many disorders, from tics to alcoholism, are due to a single gene or genes is itself based on a chain of poorly substantiated clinical associations, a fact that does not inspire confidence on the ability of the applicant to take on even more complex studies of clinical and molecular associations." (It came as no surprise that one of our adversaries from Yale was chairman of the study section that reviewed this grant.)

In 1992 we submitted a grant entitled "Studies of the Dopamine D_2 Receptor in Nicotine Addiction" to the California Tobacco-Related Disease Research Program. It was funded and, I was told, had the second highest rating of all the grants that year. This grant turned the corner for us on funding. Within a year we had obtained additional funds from the Baker Autism Foundation, the NIH, and the National Institute of Drug Abuse.

During the lean years, there was only one single reason we were able to continue these studies, despite their total rejection by all the established research funding agencies. That was because of the continued support by the City of Hope National Medical Center. Although my salary was largely covered by patient care, they continued to supply the salaries of my two laboratory stalwarts — Donn Muhleman and George Dietz. Donn had been with me since 1978 and was the backbone of my biochemical and molecular biological research. George is a whiz with technological problems and often got the assignment of setting up new instruments and new techniques.

During the years that my research was in "safe" areas, such as chromosome structure and chromosome banding, the research money was plentiful. During this period, from 1966 to 1980, I accumulated enough of the complex instruments required for research to carry me over for many years. Other than salaries, what remained was a need for funds to cover supplies. The major source of these funds was our patients. We formed a City of Hope Tourette Syndrome Chapter that raised $5,000 to $10,000 per year. When these funds became dangerously low, I often had to dip into my own pocket and conservatively contributed over $40,000 to the effort. In later years some of this came from the profits from my publishing venture, Hope Press. This combination of resources and funds kept the research alive and progressing for over the twelve very dry years of no external funding.

I have found no more eloquent description of this frustrating situation than that given by Candice Pert, the discoverer of the opioid receptors.[p487] She wrote in *The Scientist* (April 2, 1990):

> "At the heart of this discussion are the critiques that commonly accompany reviews of manuscripts and grants – the scholarly nit-picking critique, its emotion revealed in content specifically devoid of feeling but clearly aimed at suppressing new information. It is the kind of critique that fails to recognize novelty or importance and succeeds in communication, between the lines: 'I just don't believe your work could possibly be correct (or as important as mine); therefore, I am going to stop it!' Original research is usually reviewed by so-called experts in this or that area, but both experts and areas are apt to be outmoded when new discoveries and merging disciplines are occurring at a breathtaking pace. Since experts, by definition, are products of the currently reigning paradigm, they may be particularly poorly suited for recognizing novel breakthroughs. Science is not a democratic process. Unanimity of expert opinion – no matter how powerful or highly placed the experts – is no guarantee of scientific truth."

Max Plank, the famous physicist, wrote in his *Scientific Autobiography and Other Papers* (1949):

> "A new scientific truth does not triumph by convincing its opponents and making them see the light, but rather because its opponents eventually die, and a new generation grows up that is familiar with it."

Pert put it more succinctly,

> "Science moves funerally, scientists don't change their minds, they just die off."

Type II Errors in Science

A major statistical lesson is the critical role of type II errors. There are two types of errors that are made in science. One is to say something is true when it is not. In statistics, this is called a type I error. In studying the differences between two groups of people, such as individuals with depression compared to controls, it is generally felt that the differences are real if there is only a 1 in 20 possibility the results were due to random chance, i.e. $p = .05$. If the possibility they were due to chance is only 1 in 100, the conclusions are considered even more likely to be correct. Scientists feel most comfortable publishing positive results. They feel most comfortable reporting studies where the difference between two groups are so great there is little chance of making a mistake. Take, for example, a study of twenty people with depression compared to twenty controls. If such a study showed that 50% of those with depression had attempted suicide, while none of the controls had, a statistical test shows that the possibility that this difference was due to chance is only 1 in 100. The scientist would feel comfortable with this result and would be willing to have it published.

However, what if the difference was 20% versus 5%? Now the possibility that this difference is due to chance is 1 in 5. The scientist could not conclude that there was a significant difference in these two groups in regard to having attempted suicide. The investigator has three choices: 1) forget about the study because it was negative, 2) study more cases, or 3) publish the study and claim "there is no difference between the frequency of attempted suicide in patients with depression versus controls." The last choice runs a real risk of making a type II error – of saying something is not true when in fact it may be. Type II errors are often made when too few individuals are studied. If, instead of twenty people in each group, the scientist had studied one hundred individuals in each group, the same percentages would now indicate there was a significantly higher risk that depressed people will attempt suicide than non-depressed people.

The lesson is clear. If there is a large difference between two groups of people, that difference can be detected by studying relatively small numbers of individuals; however, if the differences are more subtle, larger numbers of individuals need to be studied. In my opinion, most of the criticisms we received from the Yale Child Study Center were based on type II errors.

It is an unfortunate truism in science that if one study finds an apparent association and a second study does not, the second negative, non-confirming study is considered to be the correct one. This custom is due to the fact that this is usually the correct conclusion, but not always. The initial study is usually making a positive statement, for example, a certain behavior is more common in TS families. A refuting study is usually making a negative statement, i.e. a certain behavior is not more common in TS. To avoid making a type II error, it is often necessary to study a larger number of subjects.

I was surprised that the views espoused by the Yale Child Study Center, published as one paper,[165] one letter to the editor,[164] and one abstract,[142] had the power to turn the majority of the professional community and TSA against the idea that TS was a spectrum disorder due to a set of common genes. These three reports were accepted as fact by innumerable grant review boards (often containing individuals from Yale). This situation destroyed our ability to obtain federal or other funding for what has eventually proven to be an important line of research.

There is, however, a positive side to almost everything. The positive side of this story is that, at least for us, there was virtually no competition. Outside of some close associates, no one thought that TS or the *Gts* genes were common, no one thought our proposal that the *Gts* genes were responsible for a wide spectrum of behavioral disorders or that most psychiatric disorders were genetically interelated, was valid.

Although a consortium of labs funded by the TSA was trying to find the gene by standard linkage studies, they were totally convinced TS was inherited as an autosomal dominant trait and thought our ideas were bizarre. Of the group,

Kurlan was the first to accept that ADHD and TS were genetically related, that TS was a very common disorder,[134,138] that the genes came from both parents,[137] and that multiple genes were probably involved.[134] Others soon followed with the conclusion that the inheritance of TS was more complex than a simple autosomal dominant mechanism and that the gene or genes came from both parents.[108a]

I am certain that some will take great exception to this book, since they may feel that we have only described a number of minor modifying genes and that one or more major *TS*, or *ADHD*, or *depression* genes will still be found. By major, I mean accounting for 30 to 80% of the variability (variance) of these disorders. I would have to sympathize with such thoughts, since similar ideas served as the major driving force behind our work ever since we began our molecular genetic studies of TS in 1986. In addition, it was the thought that *TDO2* would be one of these major genes that led to our eight-year involvement in sequencing over nine thousand base pairs of DNA in and around the *TDO2* gene. For a number of years, I wrote about "major" and "minor" genes in TS. [33,67,61,61a,66] However, as outlined in this book, my own thinking slowly shifted first from the presence of a major autosomal dominant gene, to a semidominant-semirecessive gene, then to polygenic inheritance. Everything that I have learned about genes and behavior has now convinced me that most of the behavioral disorders are primarily polygenic in origin. Equally important, even though only a few of the genes have been identified, we now understand the genetic mechanisms involved and methods required to find many additional relevant genes. Knowing where and how to look is half the battle.

I should also point out that the emphasis in this book has been on our own studies simply because this is a personal account of one investigator's "adventures" in the field of the genetics of human behavior. One need only review the program of the latest World Congress of Psychiatric Genetics in *Psychiatric Genetics* to appreciate the extensive contributions of many others in the field, each of whom is free to write about their own experiences.

The overwhelmingly positive aspect of this work has been the tremendous intellectual excitement it has provided, virtually on a daily basis, for over eighteen years. Each new piece of the puzzle has fit in with the previous pieces and provided new ideas about where to go next. The finding of the role of the D_2 and D_3 receptors, and then the *dopamine β-hydroxylase* and *dopamine transporter* genes, and the association of *TDO2*, MAO, dopamine D_1 receptor and D_4 receptor variants with a number of different behaviors, dropped in different pieces of the puzzle about the polygenic inheritance of human behavioral disorders.

The Ironies

One of the reasons I was stimulated to write this book was the many ironies the story contained. These were:

• My reason for entering medicine was a fascination with both psychology and biology. The psychology part was almost lost in the many years of being involved in studies of chromosomes and DNA. Things finally came full circle, and the interest in psychology and psychiatry became a new driving force.

• I first became interested in genetics by studying the hemoglobinopathies. The *TDO2* gene, studied thirty years later, matched the *globin* gene in many intriguing ways.

• As much as I was irritated by the consistently negative response to our work by Pauls and his associates at Yale, their criticisms acted as a driving force to continue the work. If everything we did had been immediately accepted as correct, I may well have lost interest and moved onto other things. Such criticism was a definite step above a worse fate of being totally ignored. For that at least, I thank them all.

• Just before this book went to press, TSA published a booklet entitled *Problem Behaviors & Tourette Syndrome*. This listed all of the behaviors we had described in our set of papers published eight years previously, including ADHD, depression, phobias, anxiety, and obsessive-compulsive, conduct, oppositional defiant, learning, sleep, self-abusive, sexual, and other disorders. Stage three of the paradigm shift[p80] had arrived.

• When I began to study TS I assumed it was a very rare disorder. By the time I finished, it was clear my son, who I thought just had ADHD, actually had TS-ADHD, and I was a carrier. I feel that whatever *Gts* genes I carry were beneficial and probably accounted for much of my workaholic approach to life and my obsessive love of organizing complex sets of facts and writing. Other relatives in my family also had both good and bad parts of the spectrum. The *Gts* genes had come home to roost.

• Perhaps the ultimate irony is that if I did not carry some of the genes for this fascinating and complex disorder, I probably never would have been so compulsively driven to find the genes that caused it.

References

1 ACDF Investigators, (1992). AIDS and sexual behavior in France. *Nature* 360:407-409.

2 Arnold AP and Gorski RA (1984). Gonadal steroid induction of structural sex differences in the central nervous system. *Annu Rev Neurosci* 7:413-442.

3 Bailey JM and Pillard RC (1992). A genetic study of male sexual orientation. *Arch Gen Psychiatry* 48:1089-1096.

4 Ballenger JC, Post RM, Jimerson D, and et al., (1983). Biochemical correlates of personality traits in normals: An exploratory study. *Personality and Individual Differences* 4:615-625.

5 Blum K, Braverman ER, Wood RC, Gill J, Li C, Chen TJH, Taub M, Montgomery AR, and Sheridan PJ (1995). Increased prevalence of the *Taq* I A1 allele of the *dopamine D2 receptor* gene (*DRD2*) in obesity with comorbid polysubstance abuse. *Pharmacogenetics* (in press).

6 Blum K, Noble EP, Sheridan PJ, Finley O, Montgomery AR, Ritchie T, Ozkaragoz T, Fitch RJ, Sadlack F, Sheffield D, Dahlmann T, Halbardier S, and Nogami H. (1991). Association of the A1 allele of the *D2 dopamine receptor* gene with severe alcoholism. *Alcohol* 8:409-416.

7 Blum K, Noble EP, Sheridan PJ, Montgomery A, Ritchie T, Jadadeeswaran P, Nogami H, Briggs AH, and Cohn JB (1990). Allelic association of human *dopamine D2 receptor* gene in alcoholism. *J Am Med Assn* 263:2055-2059.

8 Bode JCh 1987. Die internistischen Folgeerkrankungen des Alkoholismus. In: *Psychiatrie der Gegenwart 3*, edited by Kisker KP, Lauter H, Meyer J-E, Müller C, and Strömgen, E Springer Verlag, Berlin. pp. 205-242.

9 Bolos AM, Dean M, Lucas-Derse S, Ramsburg M, Brown GL, and Goldman D (1990). Population and pedigree studies reveal a lack of association between the *dopamine D2 receptor* gene and alcoholism. *J Am Med Assn* 26:3156-3160.

10 Botwinick CY, Quartermain D, Freedman LS, and Hallock MF (1977). Some characteristics of amnesia induced by FLA-63, an inhibitor of dopamine beta hydroxylase. *Pharmacol Biochem Behav* 6:487-491.

11 Bowden CL, Deutsch CK, and Swanson JM (1988). Plasma dopamine-beta-hydroxylase and platelet monoamine oxidase in attention deficit disorder and conduct disorder. *J Am Acad Child Adolesc Psychiatry* 27:171-174.

11a. Breggin PR (1991) *Toxic Psychiatry*. St. Martin's Press. New York, N.Y.

12 Brett P, Robertson M, Gurling H, and Curtis D (1993). Failure to find linkage and increased homozygosity for the *dopamine D3 receptor gene* in Tourette syndrome. *Lancet* 341:1225.

13 Brown D (1991). Genetic studies yield opposite results. *The Washington Post* October 2:A3.

14 Brunner HG, Helen M, Breakfiled XO, Ropers HH, and van Oost BA (1993). Abnormal behavior linked to a point mutation in the structural gene for monamine oxi-

dase. *A Psychiat Genet* 3:122.

15 Brunner HG, Nelen MR, van Zandvoort P, Abeling NGGM, van Gennip AH, Wolters EC, Kuiper MA, Ropers HH, and van Oost BA (1993). X-linked borderline mental retardation with prominent behavioral disturbance: Phenotype, genotic localization and evidence for disturbed monoamine metabolism. *Am J Hum Genet*. 52:1032-1039.

16 Burd L, Fisher WW, Kerbeshian J, and Arnold ME (1987). Is development of Tourette disorder a marker for improvement in patients with autism and other pervasive developmental disorders. *J Am Acad Child Adolesc Psychiatry* 26:162-165.

17 Burd L and Kerbeshian J (1988). Familial pervasive development disorder, Tourette disorder and hyperlexia. *Neurosci Biobehav Rev* 12:233-234.

18 Cai N (1985). [Regulation of receptor sensitivity and psychiatry]. *Chung Hua Shen Ching Ching Shen Ko Tsa Chih* 18:124-127.

19 Caine ED, McBride MC, Chiverton P, Bamford KA, Rediess S, and Shiao J (1988). Tourette's syndrome in Monroe County school children. *Neurology* 38:472-475.

19a Campbell M, Fish B, Shapiro T, and Floyd A (1971). Study of molindone in disturbed preschool children. *Current Therapeutic Research* 13:28-33.

20 Canino GJ, Bird HR, Shrout PE, Rubio-Stipec M, Bravo M, Martinez R, Sesman M, and Guevara LM (1987). The prevalence of specific psychiatric disorders in Puerto Rico. *Arch Gen Psychiatry* 44:727-735.

21 Carlson GA, Rich CL, Grayson P, and Fowler RC (1991). Secular trends in psychiatric diagnoses of suicide victims. *J Affective Disord* 21:127-132.

22 Carter AS, Pauls DL, Leckman JF, and Cohen DJ (1994). A prospective longitudinal study of Gilles de la Tourette's syndrome. *J Am Acad Child Adolesc Psychiatry* 33:377-385.

23 Chiara GD, Imperato A, and Mulas A (1987). Preferential stimulation of dopamine release in the mesolimbic system: A common feature of drugs of abuse. In: *Neurotransmitter Interactions in the Basal Ganglia*, edited by Sandler M. and et al., Raven Press, New York. pp 171-182.

24 Cichon S, Nöthen MM, Erdman J, and Propping P (1994). Detection of four polymorphic sites in the human *dopamine D1 receptor* gene (*DRD1*). *Hum Molec Genet* 3:209.

25 Cloninger CR (1991). *D2 dopamine receptor* gene is associated but not linked with alcoholism. *J Am Med Assn* 266:1833-1834.

26 Cloninger CR, Reich T, Sigvardsson S, von Knorring, AL and Bohman M (1988). Effects of changes in alcohol use between generations on the inheritance of alcohol abuse. In: *Alcoholism: Origins and Outcome*, edited by Rose RM and Barrett JE. Raven Press, New York. pp. 49-74.

27 Colditz GA (1992). Economic costs of obesity. *Am J Nutr* 55:503S-507S.

28 Comings BG and Comings DE (1987). A controlled study of Tourette syndrome. V. Depression and mania. *Am J Hum Genet* 41:804-821.

29 Comings DE (1979). Pc 1 Duarte, a common polymorphism of a human brain proteins, and its relationship to depressive disease and multiple sclerosis. *Nature* 277:28-32.

30 Comings DE (1987). A controlled study of Tourette syndrome. VII. Summary: a common genetic disorder causing disinhibition of the limbic system. *Am J Hum Genet* 41:839-866.

31 Comings DE (1989). The genetics of human behavior: Lessons for two societies. *Am J Hum Genet* 44:452-460.

32 Comings DE (1990). Blood serotonin and tryptophan in Tourette syndrome. *Am J Med Genet* 36:418-430.

33 Comings DE (1990). *Tourette Syndrome and Human Behavior*. Hope Press, Duarte, CA. pp. 1-828.

34 Comings DE (1994). The role of genetic factors in human sexual behavior based on studies of Tourette syndrome and ADHD probands and their relatives. *Am J Med Gen (Neuropsych Genet)* 54:227-241.

35 Comings DE (1994). Candidate genes and association studies in psychiatry. Letter to the editor. *Am J Med Gen (Neuropsych Genet)* 54:324.

36 Comings DE (1994). Gastrointestinal disorders in Tourette Syndrome: Are "Functional" Disorders Genetic? *(submitted)*.

37 Comings DE (1994). Genetic factors in substance abuse based on studies of Tourette syndrome and ADHD probands and relatives. II. Alcohol abuse. *Drug and Alcohol Dependence* 35:17-24.

38 Comings DE (1994). Genetic factors in substance abuse based on studies of Tourette syndrome and ADHD probands and relatives. I. Drug abuse. *Drug and Alcohol Dependence* 35:1-16.

39 Comings DE (1995). Genetic factors in depression based on studies of Tourette syndrome and Attention Deficit Hyperactivity Disorder probands and relatives. *A J Med. Gen (Neuropsych Genet)* 60:111-121.

40 Comings DE (1995). Dopamine D_2 receptor and Tourette syndrome. *Arch Neurol (in press)*

41 Comings DE (1995). The role of genetic factors in conduct disorder based on studies of Tourette syndrome and ADHD probands and their relatives. *J Dev Behav Pediatr (in press)*

42 Comings DE (1995). Tourette syndrome: A hereditary neuropsychiatric spectrum disorder. *Ann Clin Psychiatry* 6:235-247.

43 Comings DE (1995). Tourette Syndrome: A Behavioral Spectrum Disorder. In: *Behavioral Neurology of Movement Disorders*, edited by Weiner J and Lang, AE. Raven Press, New York. pp. 293-303.

44 Comings DE (1996). *The Gene Bomb. Do Technologically Advanced Societies Accelerate the Selection of Genes for Addictive and Disruptive Behaviors?* Hope Press, Duarte, CA.

44a. Comings, D.E. Minisatellites and polygenic inheritance. A new paradigm for the inheritiance of complex traits. (submitted).

45 Comings DE and Comings BG (1982). A case of familial exhibitionism in Tourette's syndrome successfully treated with haloperidol. *Am J Psychiatry* 139:913-915.

46 Comings DE and Comings BG (1984). Tourette's syndrome and attention deficit disorder with hyperactivity: are they genetically related. *J Am Acad Child Psychiatry* 23:138-146.

47 Comings DE and Comings BG (1985). Tourette syndrome: clinical and psychological aspects of 250 cases. *Am J Hum Genet* 37:435-450.

48 Comings DE and Comings BG (1987). A controlled study of Tourette syndrome. I. Attention-deficit disorder, learning disorders, and school problems. *Am J Hum Genet* 41:701-741.

49 Comings DE and Comings BG (1987). Tourette's syndrome and attention deficit disorder with hyperactivity. [letter]. *Arch Gen Psychiatry* 44:1023-1026.

50 Comings DE and Comings BG (1987). Hereditary agoraphobia and obsessive-compulsive behaviour in relatives of patients with Gilles de la Tourette's syndrome. *Br J Psychiatry* 151:195-199.

51 Comings DE and Comings BG (1987). A controlled study of Tourette syndrome. IV. Obsessions, compulsions, and schizoid behaviors. *Am J Hum Genet* 41:782-803.

52 Comings DE and Comings BG (1987). A controlled study of Tourette syndrome. VI. Early development, sleep problems, allergies, and handedness. *Am J Hum Genet* 41:822-838.

53 Comings DE and Comings BG (1987). A controlled study of Tourette syndrome. II. Conduct. *Am J Hum Genet* 41:742-760.

54 Comings DE and Comings BG (1987). A controlled study of Tourette syndrome. III. Phobias and panic attacks. *Am J Hum Genet* 41:761-781.

55 Comings DE and Comings BG (1988). A controlled study of Tourette syndrome-Revisited. *Am J Hum Genetics* 42:209-216.

56 Comings DE and Comings BG (1988). Tourette's syndrome and attention deficit disorder. In: *Tourette's Syndrome and Tic Disorders: Clinical Understanding and Treatment*, edited by Cohen DJ, Bruun RD, and Leckman JF. John Wiley & Sons, New York. pp. 120-135.

57 Comings DE and Comings BG (1990). A controlled family history study of Tourette syndrome. III. Other Psychiatric Disorders. *J Clin Psychiat* 51:288-291.

58 Comings DE and Comings BG (1990). A controlled family history study of Tourette syndrome. II. Alcoholism, drug abuse and obesity. *J Clin Psychiat* 51:281-287.

59 Comings DE and Comings BG (1990). A controlled family history study of Tourette syndrome. I. Attention deficit hyperactivity disorder, learning disorders and dyslexia. *J Clin Psychiat* 51:275-280.

60 Comings DE and Comings BG (1991). Clinical and genetic relationships between autism-PDD and Tourette syndrome: A study of 19 cases. *Am J Med Genet* 39:180-191.

61 Comings DE and Comings BG (1991). Common genes for spectrum disorders: Implications for psychiatric genetics. *Psychiat Genet* 2:5-6.

61a Comings DE and Comings BG (1992). Alternative hypotheses on the inheritance of Tourette syndrome. In Chase TN, Friedhoff AJ and Cohen DJ (editors) Tourette Syndrome Genetics, Neurobiology, and Treatment. *Advances in Neurology* 58:189-199.

62 Comings DE and Comings BG (1993). SIDS and Tourette syndrome: Is there an etiologic relationship? *J Dev Physical Disabil* 5:265-279.

63 Comings DE and Comings BG (1993). Comorbid Behavioral Disorders. In: *Tourette Syndrome and Related Disorders*, edited by Kurlan R, Marcel-Decker, New York. pp. 111-147.

64 Comings DE and Comings BG (1994). TS, learning, and speech problems. *J Am Acad Child Adolesc Psychiatr* 33:429-430.

65 Comings DE, Comings BG, Devor EJ, and Cloninger CR (1984). Detection of major gene for Gilles de la Tourette syndrome. *Am J Hum Genet* 36:586-600.

66 Comings DE, Comings BG, and Knell E. (1989). Hypothesis: Homozygosity in Tourette syndrome. *Am J Med Genet* 34:413-421.

67 Comings DE, Comings BG, Muhleman D, Dietz G, Shahbahrami B, Tast D, Knell E, Kocsis P, Baumgarten R, Kovacs BW, Levy DL, Smith M, Kane JM, Lieberman JA, Klein DN, MacMurray J, Tosk J, Sverd J, Gysin R, and Flanagan S (1991). The dopamine D_2 receptor locus as a modifying gene in neuropsychiatric disorders. *J Am Med Assn* 266:1793-1800.

67a. Comings DE, Ferry L, Bradshaw-Robinson S, Burchette R, Chiu C, and Muhleman D (1995), The *dopamine D2 receptor (DRD2)* gene: A genetic risk factor in smoking. *Pharmacogenetics (in press)*.

68 Comings DE, Flanagan SD, Dietz G, Muhleman D, Knell E, and Gysin R (1993). The *dopamine D2 receptor* (*DRD2*) as a major gene in obesity and height. *Biochem Med Metabolic Biol* 50:176-185.

69 Comings DE, Gursey BT, Avelino E, Kopp U, and Hanin I (1982). Red blood cell choline in Tourette syndrome. *Adv Neurol* 35:255-258.

70 Comings DE, Gursey BT, Hecht T, and Blume K (1982). HLA typing in Tourette syndrome. *Adv Neurol* 35:251-253.

71 Comings DE, Himes JA, and Comings BG (1990). An epidemiological study of Tourette syndrome in a single school district. *J Clin Psychiat* 51:463-469.

72 Comings DE, Muhleman D, Ahn C, Gysin R, and Flanagan SD (1994). The *dopamine D2 receptor* gene: A genetic risk factor in substance abuse. *Drug and Alcohol Dependence* 34:175-180.

73 Comings DE, Muhleman D, Chiu C, Dietz G, and Gade R (1995). *Dopamine D2 receptor* gene in Tourette syndrome (TS). *Psychiatric Genetics* 5:S

74 Comings DE, Muhleman D, Dietz G, Dino M, Legro R, and Gade R (1993). Association between Tourette's syndrome and homozygosity at the *dopamine D3 receptor* gene. *Lancet* 341:906.

75 Comings DE, Muhleman D, Dietz G, Shahbahrami B, Tast D, and Kovacs BW (1990). The *dopamine D2 receptor* gene is a modifier of the expression of the Tourette syndrome (*Gts*) and *ADHD* gene. *Am J Hum Genet* 46:(Abstract)

76 Comings DE, Muhleman D, Dietz GW, and Donlon T (1991). Human tryptophan oxygenase localized to 4q31: Possible implications for human behavioral disorders. *Genomics* 9:301-308.

77 Comings DE, Muhleman D, Gade R, Chiu C, Wu H, Dietz G, Winn-Dean E, Ferry L, Rosenthal RJ, Lesieur HR, Rugle L, Sverd J, Johnson P, and MacMurray JP (1995). Exon and intron mutations in the human *tryptophan 2,3-dioxygenase* gene and their potential association with Tourette syndrome, substance abuse and other psychiatric disorders. *(submitted)*.

77a. Comings DE, Rosenthal RJ, Lesieur HR, Rugle L, Muhleman D, Chiu C, Dietz G, and Gade R (1994). The molecular genetics of pathological gambling: The *DRD2* gene. *Pharmacogenetics (in press)*.

77b Comings DE, Wu J, Chiu C, Muhelman D, and Sverd J (1994). Studies of the *HRAS* gene in psychiatric disorders. *(submitted)*.

78 Comings DE, Wu H, Chiu C, Ring RH, Dietz G, and Muhleman D (1995). Polygenic inheritance of Tourette syndrome, stuttering, ADHD, conduct and oppositional defiant disorder: The additive and subtractive effect of three dopaminergic genes — *DRD2*, *DβH* and *DAT1* genes. *Am J Med Genetics (Neuropsych Genetics) (in press)*.

79 Cook CCH, Holmes D, Brett P, Curtis D, and Gurling HMD (1992). The D_2 dopamine receptor locus in heavy drinking and alcoholism: A study of 11 British families. *Alcoholism: Clinical & Experimental Research* 16:806-809.

79a Cook EHJr, Stein MA, Krasowski MD, Cox NJ, Olkon DM, Kieffer JE, and Leventhal BL (1995). Association of attention-deficit disorder and the *dopamine transporter gene*. *Am J Hum Genet* 56:993-998.

80 Coryell W, Endicott J, and Keller M (1992). Major depression in a nonclinical sample: demographic and clinical risk factors for first onset. *Arch Gen Psychiatry* 49:117-125.

81 Crocq M-A, Mant R, Asherson P, Williams J, Hode, Mayerova A, Collier D, Lannfelt L, Sokoloff P, Schwartz J-C, Gil M, Macher J-P, Mcguffin P, and Owen MJ (1992). Association between schizophrenia and homozygosity at the *dopamine D3 recep-*

tor gene. *J Med Genet* 29:858-860.

82 Cross-National Collaborative Group, (1992). The Changing Rate of Major Depression. *J Am Med Assn* 268:3098-3105.

83 d'Amato T, Leboyer M, Malafosse A, Samolyk D, Lamouroux A, Junien C, and Mallet J (1989). Two *Taq* I dimorphic sites at the human β-hydroxylase locus. *Nucleic Acids Res* 17:5871.

84 Devor EJ (1990). Untying the Gordian Knot - The Genetics of Tourette Syndrome. *J Nerv Ment Dis* 178:669-679.

85 Devor EJ, Grandy DK, Civelli O, Litt M, Burgess AK, Isenberg KE, van de Wetering BJM, and Oostra B (1990). Genetic linkage is excluded for the D_2 dopamine receptor lambda-Hd2G1 and flanking loci on chromosome 11Q22-Q23 in Tourette syndrome. *Human Heredity* 40:105-108.

86 *Diagnostic and Statistical Manual of Mental Disorders. Third Edition.* (1980). American Psychiatric Association, Washington D.C.

87 *Diagnostic and Statistical Manual of Mental Disorders. Third Edition-Revised.* (1987). American Psychiatric Association, Washington, D.C.

88 Dinwiddie SH and Reich T (1991). Epidemiological perspectives on children of alcoholics. *Recent Dev Alcohol* 9:287-299.

89 Dunn O and Clark V (1995). *Applied Statistics: Analysis of variance and regression. 2nd. Edition.* Wiley, New York.

90 Ehsani A, Low J, Wallace RB, and Wu AM (1993). Characterization of a new allele of the human *ERBB2* gene by allele-specific competition hybridization. *Genomics* 15:426-439.

91 Eldridge R, Sweet R, Lake R, Ziegler M, and Shapiro AK (1977). Gilles de la Tourette's syndrome: clinical, genetic, psychologic, and biochemical aspects in 21 selected families. *Neurology* 27:115-124.

92 Ellis R, DeFeo D, Shih TY, Gonda MA, Young HA, Tsuchida N, Lowy DR, and Scolnick EM (1981). The p21 *src* genes of Harvey and Kirsten sarcoma viruses originate from divergent members of a family of normal vertegrate genes. *Nature* 292:506-511.

93 Feinstein RN and Lindahl R (1973). Detection of oxidases on polyacrylamide gels. *Anal Biochem* 56:353-360.

94 Fishburne PM, Abelson H, and Cisin I (1979). National Survey on Drug Abuse. Main Findings, National Institute on Drug Abuse. *U. S. Dept. of Health, Educat Welfare Publication ADM 80-976.*

95 Flexner JB and Flexner LB (1976). Effect of two inhibitors of dopamine β-hydroxylase on maturation of memory in mice. *Pharmacol Biochem Behav* 5:117-121.

96 Flexner JB, Flexner LB, and Church AC (1983). Studies on memory: The cerebral spread of an engram in mice as affected by inhibitors of dopamine β-hydroxylase. *Pharmacol Biochem Behav* 18:519-523.

97 Galvin M, Shekhar A, Simon J, Stilwell B, TanEyck R, Laite G, Karwisch G, and Blix S (1991). Low dopamine-beta-hydroxylase: A biological sequelae of abuse and neglect? *Psychiatry Res* 39:1-11.

98 Gelernter J, O'Malley SO, Risch N, Kranzler HR, Krystal J, Merikangas K, Kennedy JL, and Kidd KK (1991). No association between an allele at the *D2 dopamine receptor* gene (*DRD2*) and alcoholism. *J Am Med Assn* 266:1801-1807.

99 Gelernter J, Pakstis AJ, Pauls DL, Kurlan R, Gancher ST, Civelli O, Grandy D, and Kidd KK (1990). Gilles de la Tourette Syndrome Is Not Linked to D_2 Dopamine Receptor. *Arch Gen Psychiatry* 47:1073-1077.

100 Gelernter J, Pauls D, Leckman J, and Kurlan R. (1992). Evidence that D_2 dopamine receptor alleles do not influence severity of Tourette's syndrome. *Am J Psychiatry* (abstracts):127-128.

101 Gelernter J, Pauls DL, Leckman J, Kidd KK and Kurlan R (1994). D_2 dopamine receptor alleles do not influence severity of Tourette's syndrome. *Arch Neurol* 51:397-400.

102 Gershon ES, Hamovit JH, and Guroff JJ (1987). Birth-cohort changes in manic and depressive disorders in relatives of bipolar and schizoaffective patients. *Arch Gen Psychiatry* 44:314-319.

103 Gleick J (1988). *Chaos Making a New Science.* Viking, New York. pp. 1-352.

104 Golden GS (1990). Tourette Syndrome: Recent Advances. *Neurol Clin* 8:705-713.

104a Greenhill LL, Barmack JE, Spalten D, Anderson M, and Halpern F (1981) Molindone hydrochloride in the treatment of aggressive, hospitalized children. *Psyhopharmacology Bull* 17:125-126.

105 Gupta SL and Dai W (1990). Molecular cloning, sequencing and expression of human interferon-gamma-inducible indoleamine 2,3-dioxygenase cDNA. *Biochem Biophys Res Comm* 168:1-8.

106 Gusella JF, Wexler NS, Conneally PM, Naylor SL, Anderson MA, Tanzi RE, Watkins PC, Ottina K, Wallace MR, Sakaguchi AY, Young AB, Shoulson I, Bonilla E, and Martin JB (1983). A polymorphic DNA marker genetically linked to Huntington's disease. *Nature* 306:234-238.

107 Hamer DH, Hu S, Magnuson VL, Hu N, and Pattatucci AML (1993). A linkage between DNA markers on the X chromosome and male sexual orientation. *Science* 261:321-327.

108 Harvey JJ (1964). An unidentified virus which causes the rapid production of tumors in mice. *Nature* 204:1104-1105.

108a Hasstedt SJ, Leppert M, Filloux F, van de Wetering B, and McMahon WM (1995). Intermediate inheritance of Tourette syndrome, assuming assortative mating. *Am J Hum Genet* 37:682-689.

109 Hebebrand J, Nöthen MM, Lehmkuhl G, Poustka F, Schmidt M, Propping P, and Remschmidt H (1993). Tourette's syndrome and homozygosity for the *dopamine D3 receptor* gene. *Lancet* 341:1483.

110 Heutink P, Sandkuyl LA, van de Wetering BJM, Oostra BA, Weber J, Wilkie P, Devor EJ, Pakstis AJ, Pauls D, and Kidd KK (1991). Linkage and Tourette syndrome. *Lancet* 337:122-123.

111 Heutink P, van de Wetering BJM, Breedveld GJ, and Oostra BA (1992). Genetic study on Tourette syndrome in the Netherlands. *Adv Neurol* 58:167-172.

112 Heutink P, van de Wetering BJM, Breedveld GJ, Weber J, Sandkuyl LA, Devor EJ, Heiberg A, Niermeijer MF, and Oostra BA (1990). No evidence for genetic linkage of Gilles de la Tourette syndrome on chromosomes 7 and 18. *J Med Genet* 27:433-436.

113 Hill SY, Aston C, and Rabin B (1988). Suggestive evidence of genetic linkage between alcoholism and the MNS blood groups. *Alcoholism: Clinical & Experimental Research* 12:811-814.

114 Hoffman BJ, Mezey E, and Brownstein MJ (1991). Cloning of a serotonin transporter affected by antidepressants. *Science* 254:579-580.

115 Holden C (1991). *Alcoholism* gene: Coming or going? *Science* 254:200.

116 Hudson JI and Pope HGJr (1990). Affective spectrum disorder: Does antidepressant response identify a family of disorders with a common pathophysiology? *Am J Psy-*

References

chiatry 147:552-564.

117 Isquierdo I, Beamish D, and Anisman H (1979). Effect of an inhibitor of dopamine-beta-hydroxylase on the acquisition and retention of four different avoidance tasks in mice. *Psychopharmacology* (Berlin) 63:173-178.

118 Jacobs P (1965). Aggressive behavior, mental subnormality and the XYY male. *Nature* 208:1351.

119 Jankovic J and Rohaidy H (1987). Motor, behavioral, and pharmacologic findings in Tourette's syndrome. *Can J Neurol Sci* 14:541-546.

120 Johnson AM, Wadsworth J, Wellings K, Bradshaw S, and Field J (1992). Sexual lifestyles and HIV risk. *Nature* 360:410-412.

121 Kano Y, Ohta M, Nagai Y, Yokota K, and Shimizu (1988). Tourette's disorder coupled with infantile autism: A prospective study of two boys. *Japn J Psychiatr* 42:49-57.

122 Karno M, Hough RL, Burmam A, Escobar JI, Timbers DM, Santana F, and Boyd JH (1987). Lifetime prevalence of specific psychiatric disorder among Mexican Americans and Non-Hispanic Whites in Los Angeles. *Arch Gen Psychiatry* 44:695-701.

123 Kennedy JL, Sidenberg DG, Macciardi FM, and Joffert RT (1993). Genetic association study of tyrosine hydroxylase and D_4 dopamine receptor variants in bipolar I patients. *Psychiat Genet* 3:120-121.

124 Kennedy JL, Vantol HHM, Petronis A, Sidenberg DG, Macciardi F, and Bassett AS (1992). Dopamine D_4 receptor variants and schizophrenia. *Am J Hum Genet* 51:365.

125 Kerbeshian J and Burd L (1988). Differential responsiveness to lithium in patients with Tourette syndrome. *Neuroscience and Biobehavioral Reviews* 12:247-250.

126 Kerbeshian J and Burd L (1989). Tourette disorder and bipolar symptomatology in children and adolescents. *Can J Psychiatry* 34:230-233. *(in press)*

127 Kirsten WH and Mayer LA (1967). Morphologic responses to a murine erythroblastosis virus. *J Natl Cancer Inst* 39:311-335.

128 Klerman GL (1988). The current age of youthful melancholia. Evidence for increase in depression among adolescents and young adults. *Br J Psychiatry* 152:4-14.

129 Klerman GL, Lavori PW, Rice J, and et al., (1985). Birth-cohort trends in rates of major depressive disorder among relatives of patients with affective disorder. *Arch Gen Psychiatry* 42:689-693.

130 Klerman GL and Weissman MM (1989). Increasing rates of depression. *J Am Med Assn* 261:2229-2235.

131 Knell E and Comings DE (1993). Tourette syndrome and attention deficit hyperactivity disorder: Evidence for a genetic relationship. *J Clin Psychiat* 54:331-337.

132 Kuhn TS (1970). *The Structure of Scientific Revolutions. Ed. 2nd* University of Chicago Press, Chicago. pp. 1-210.

133 Kurlan R (1989). Tourette's syndrome: Current concepts. *Neurology* 39:1625-1630.

134 Kurlan R (1994). Hypothesis II: Tourette syndrome is part of a clinical spectrum that includes normal brain development. *Arch Neurol* 51:1145-1150.

135 Kurlan R, Behr J, Medved L, Shoulson I, Pauls D, Kidd JR, and Kidd KK (1986). Familial Tourette's syndrome: report of a large pedigree and potential for linkage analysis. *Neurology* 36:772-776.

136 Kurlan R, Behr J, Medved L, Shoulson I, Pauls D, and Kidd KK (1987). Severity of Tourette's syndrome in one large kindred. Implication for determination of disease prevalence rate. *Arch Neurol* 44:268-269.

137 Kurlan R, Eapen V, Stern J, McDermott MP, and Robertson MM (1994). Bilineal transmission in Tourette's syndrome families. *Neurology* 44:2336-2342.

138 Kurlan R, Whitemore D, Irvine C, McDermott MP, and Como PG (1994). Tourette's syndrome in a special education population: A pilot study involving a single school district. *Neurology* 44:699-702.

139 Lamouroux A, Houhou L, Biguet NF, Serck-Hanssen G, Guibert B, Icard-Liepkalns C, and Mallet J (1993). Analysis of the human dopamine β-hydroxylase promoter: Transcriptional induction by cyclic AMP. *J Neurochemistry* 60:364-367.

140 Lamouroux A, Vigny A, Faucon Biguet N, Darmon MC, Frank R, and Henry JP (1987). The primary structure of dopamine-beta-hydoxyalse: insights into the relationship between the soluble and the membrane-bound forms of the enzyme. *EMBO J* 6:3931-3937.

141 Lavori PW, Klerman GL, Keller MB, Reich T, Rice J, and Endicott J (1987). Age-period-cohort analysis of secular trends in onset of major depression: Findings in siblings of patients with major affective disorder. *J Psychiatr Res* 21:23-35.

142 Leboyer M, Malafosse S, Boularand S, Campion D, Gheysen F, Samolyk D, Henriksson B, Denise E, Des Lauriers A, Lepine J-P, Zarifian E, Clerget-Darpoux F, and Mallet J (1990). Tyrosine hydroxylase polymorphisms associated with manic-depressive illness. *Lancet* 335:1219.

143 Leckman JF and Cohen DJ 1988. Descriptive and diagnostic classification of tic disorders. In: *Tourette's Syndrome & Tic Disorders*, edited by Cohen DJ, Bruun RD, and Leckman JF. John Wiley & Sons, New York. pp. 4-19.

144 Lee KC, Kowak YS, and Rhee H (1987). The national epidemiological study of mental disorders in Korea. *J Korean Med Sic* 2:19-34.

145 Legro RS, Muhleman D, Comings DE, Lobo RA, and Kovacs BW (1994). A dopamine D₃ receptor genotype is associated with hyperandrogenic chronic anovulation and resistance to ovulation induction with clomiphene citrate. *Fertility and Sterility (submitted)*.

146 LeVay S (1991). A difference in hypothalamic structure between heterosexual and homosexual men. *Science* 253:1034-1037.

147 Matteo S (1988). The risk of multiple addictions. Guidelines for assessing a woman's alcohol and drug use. *West J Med* 149:741-745.

148 McMahon WM (1990). Utah Tourette Family Study. *Am Psychiat Assoc 143rd Ann Meeting Abstracts* 128.

149 Merkulov VM and Merkulova TI (1992). Nucleotide sequence of a fragment of the rat *tryptophan oxygenase* gene showing high affinity to glucocorticoid receptor in vitro. *Biochim Biophys Acta* 1132:100-102.

150 Minderaa RB, van Gemert TM, and van de Wetering BJM (1988). Onverwachte presentatiewijzen van het syndroom van Gilles de lat Tourette. *Tijdschrift voor Psychiatrie* 30:246-254.

151 Murphy GE and Wetzel RD (1980). Suicide risk by birth cohort in the United States, 1949 to 1974. *Arch Gen Psychiatry* 37:519-523.

152 Myers RM, Tilly K, and Maniatis T (1986). Fine structure genetic analysis of a β-globin promoter. *Science* 232:613-618.

153 Najfeld V, Menniger J, Muhleman D, Comings DE, and Gupta SL (1993). Localization of *indoleamine 2,3-dioxygenase* gene to chromosome 8p12-p11 by fluorescent in situ hybridization. *Cytogenetics Cell Genetics* 64:231-232.

154 Nee LE, Caine ED, Polinsky RJ, Eldridge R, and Ebert MH (1980). Gilles de la Tourette syndrome: clinical and family study of 50 cases. *Ann Neurol* 7:41-49.

155 Noble EP, Blum K, Ritchie T, Montgomery A, and Sheridan PJ (1991). Allelic association of the *D2 dopamine receptor* gene with receptor-binding characteristics in alcoholism. *Arch Gen Psychiatry* 48:648-654.

156 Noble EP, Jeor ST, Ritchie T, Syndulko K, Jeor SC, Fitch RJ, Brunner RL, and Sparkes RS (1994). *D2 dopamine receptor* gene and cigarette smoking: A reward gene? *Medical Hypothesis* 42:257-260.

157 Noble EP, Noble RE, Ritchie T, Grandy DK, and Sparkes RS (1994). *D2 Receptor* gene and obesity. *Internat J Eating Disorders* 15:205-217.

158 Nöthen MM, Hebebrand J, Knapp M, Hebebrand K, Camps A, von Gontard A, Wettke-Schäfer R, Cichon S, Poustka F, Schmidt M, Lehmkuhl G, Remschmidt H, and Propping P (1994). Association analysis of the *dopamine D2 receptor* gene in Tourette's syndrome using the haplotype relative risk method. *Am J Med Gen (Neuropsych Genet)* 54:249-252.

159 O'Connell P, Cawthon R, Xu GF, Li Y, Viskochil D, and White R (1992). The *neurofibromatosis type 1 (NF1)* gene: identification and partial characterization of a *putative tumor supressor* gene. *J Dermatology* 19:881-884.

160 Pakstis AJ, Heutink P, Pauls DL, Kurlan R, van de Wetering BJM, Leckman JF, Sandkuyl LA, Kidd JR, Breedveld GJ, Castiglione CM, Weber J, Sparkes RS, Cohen DJ, Kidd KK, and Oostra BA (1991). Progress in the search for genetic linkage with Tourette syndrome – An exclusion map covering more than 50% of the autosomal genome. *Am J Hum Genet* 48:281-294.

161 Parsian A, Todd D, Devor EJ, O'Malley KL, Suarez BK, Reich T, and Cloninger CR (1991). Alcoholism and alleles of the human dopamine D_2 receptor locus. Studies of association and linkage. *Arch Gen Psychiatry* 48:655-663.

162 Pauls D, Hurst C, Kruger S, Leckman J, Cohen D, and Kidd K (1984). Evidence against a genetic relationship between Tourette syndrome and attention deficit disorder. *Am J Hum Genet* 36:68S.

163 Pauls DL, Bucher KD, Crowe RR, and Noyes RJr (1980). A genetic study of panic disorder pedigrees. *Am J Hum Genet* 32:639-644.

164 Pauls DL, Cohen DJ, Kidd KK, and Leckman JF (1988). Tourette syndrome and neuropsychiatric disorders: Is there a genetic relationship? *Am J Hum Genetics* 42:206-209.

165 Pauls DL, Hurst CR, Kruger SD, Leckman JF, Kidd KK, and Cohen DJ (1986). Gilles de la Tourette's syndrome and attention deficit disorder with hyperactivity. Evidence against a genetic relationship. *Arch Gen Psychiatry* 43:1177-1179.

166 Pauls DL, Hurst CR, Leckman JF, Cohen DJ, Kruger SD, and Kidd KK (1987). Tourette's syndrome and attention deficit disorder with hyperactivity. In reply. *Arch Gen Psychiatry* 44:1025-1026.

167 Pauls DL and Leckman JF (1986). The inheritance of Gilles de la Tourette's syndrome and associated behaviors. Evidence for autosomal dominant transmission. N Engl J Med 315:993-997.

168 Pauls DL, Leckman JF, and Cohen DJ (1993). Familial relationship between Gilles de la Tourette syndrome, attention deficit disorder, learning disabilities, speech disorders, and stuttering. *J Am Acad Child Psychiatry* 32:1044-1050.

169 Pauls DL, Leckman JF, and Cohen DJ (1994). Evidence against a genetic relationship between Tourette's syndorme and anxiety, depression, panic, and phobic disorders. *Br J Psychiatry* 164:215-221.

170 Pauls DL, Leckman JF, Raymond CL, Hurst CR, and Stevenson JM (1988). A family study of Tourette's syndrome: Evidence against the hypothesis of association with a wide range of psychiatric phenotypes. *Am J Hum Genet* 43:A64.

171 Pauls DL, Pakstis A, Kurlan R, Kidd KK, Leckman JF, Cohen DJ, Kidd JR, Como P, and Sparkes R (1990). Segregation and linkage analyses of Tourette syndrome and related disorders. *J Am Acad Child Psychiatry* 29:195-203.

172 Pliszka SR, Rogeness GA, and Medrano MA (1988). DBH, MHPG and MAO in children with depressive, anxiety and conduct disorders: Relationship to diagnosis and symptoms ratings. *Psychiatry Res* 24:35-44.

173 Pribram KH (1971). *Languages of the brain – experimental paradoxes and principles in neuropsychology.* Prentice-Hall, Englewood Cliffs, NJ.

174 Rappoport JL (1989). *The Boy Who Couldn't Stop Washing.* E.P. Dutton, New York. pp. 1-260.

175 Riddle MA, Hardin MT, Ort SO, Leckman JF, and Cohen DJ (1988). Behavioral symptoms in Tourette's syndrome. In: *Tourette's syndrome & Tic disorders,* edited by Cohen DJ, Bruun RD, and Leckman JF. John Wiley & Sons, New York. pp. 152-162.

176 Ring RH and Comings DE (1995). Association of *dopamine transporter* gene (*DAT1*) repeat alleles with comorbid behaviors in Tourette syndrome probands, their relatives and controls. *(submitted)*

177 Ritz MC, Lamb RJ, Goldberg SR, and Kuhar MJ (1992). Cocaine receptors on dopamine transporters are related to self-administration of cocaine. *Science* 237:1219-1223.

178 Robertson MM (1989). The Gilles de la Tourette syndrome: the current status. *Br J Psychiatr* 154:147-169.

179 Robertson MM and Gourdie A (1990). Familial Tourette's syndrome in a large British pedigree associated with psychopathology, severity, and potential for linkage analysis. *Br J Psychiatry* 156:515-521.

180 Robertson MM, Trimble MR, and Lees AJ (1988). The psychopathology of the Gilles de la Tourette syndrome. *Br J Psychiatry* 152:383-390.

181 Robins LN (1986). Changes in conduct disorder over time. In: *Risk in Intellectual and Psychosocial Development,* edited by Farran DC and McKinney JD. Academic Press, Orlando.

182 Robins LN, Helzer J, Croughan J, and Ratclif KS (1981). National Institutes of Health diagnostic interview schedule. *Arch Gen Psychiatry* 38:381-389.

183 Rogeness GA, Hernandez JM, Macedo CA, Amrung SA, and Hoppe SK (1986). Near-zero plasma dopamine-β-hydroxylase and conduct disorder in emotionally disturbed boys. *J Amer Acad Child Psychiat* 25:521-527.

184 Rogeness GA, Hernandez JM, Macedo CA, Mitchell EL, Amrung SA, and Harris WR (1984). Clinical characteristics of emotionally disturbed boys with very low activities of dopamine β-hydroxylase. *J Am Acad Child Adolesc Psychiatry* 23:203-208.

185 Rogeness GA, Javors MA, Maas JW, Macedo CA, and Fisher C (1987). Plasma dopamine-beta-hydroxylase, HVA, MHPG and conduct disorder in emotionally disturbed boys. *Biol Psychiatry* 22:1155-1158.

186 Rogeness GA, Maas JW, Javors MA, Macedo CA, Harris WR, and Hoppe SK (1988). Diagnoses, catecholamine metabolism, and plasma dopamine-β-hydroxylase. *J Am Acad Child Adolesc Psychiatry* 27:121-125.

187 Sandyk R and Bamford CR (1988). Fluctuations of symptoms during manic-depressive mood changes in Tourette's syndrome [letter]. *J Clin Psychopharmacol* 8:149|.

188 Sarkar G, Kapelner S, Grandy DK, Marchionni M, Civelli O, Sobell J, Heston L, and Sommer SS (1991). Direct sequencing of the *dopamine D2 receptor* (*DRD2*) in schizophrenics reveals three polymorphisms but no structural change in the receptor. *Genomics* 11:8-14.

189 Sarkar G and Sommer SS (1991). Haplotyping by double PCR amplification of specific alleles. *BioTechniques* 10:436-440.

190 Schmid W, Scherer G, Danesch U, Zentgraf H, Matthias P, Strange CM,

Rowekamp W, and Schutz G (1982). Isolation and characterization of the rat *tryptophan oxygenase* gene. *EMBO J* 1:1287-1293.

191 Schwab S, Soyka M, Niederecker N, Ackenheil M, Scherer J, and Widenauer DB (1991). Allelic association of human dopamine D_2-receptor DNA polymorphism ruled out in 45 alcoholics. *Am J Hum Genet 49 (suppl)*:203A.

192 Shaikh S, Collier D, Kerwin RW, Pilowsky LS, Gill M, Xu W-M, and Thornton A (1993). Dopamine D_4 receptor subtypes and response to clozapine. *Lancet* 341:116.

193 Shapiro AK, Shapiro ES, Young JG, and Feinberg TE (1988). *Gilles de la Tourette Syndrome. Ed. 2nd* Raven Press, New York. pp. 1-558.

194 Shih C, Padhy LC, Murray M, and Weinberg RA (1981). Transforming genes of carcinomas and neuroblastomas introduced into mouse fibroblasts. *Nature* 290:261-264.

195 Singer HS, Allen R, Brown J, Salam M, and Hahn I-H (1990). Sleep disorders in Tourette syndrome: A primary or unrelated problem? (abstract). *Ann Neurol* 28:424.

196 Singer HS and Rosenberg LA (1989). Development of behavioral and emotional problems in Tourette syndrome. *Pediatr Neurol* 5:41-44.

197 Singer HS and Walkup JT (1991). Tourette syndrome and other tic disorders. Diagnosis, pathophysiology, and treatment. *Medicine* 70:15-32.

198 Stine SB and Adams WV (1989). Learning problems in neurofibromatosis. *Clin Orthop* 254:43-48.

199 Sverd J (1988). Imipramine treatment of panic disorder in a boy with Tourette's syndrome. *J Clin Psychiatry* 49:31-32.

200 Sverd J (1989). Clinical presentations of the Tourette syndrome diathesis. *J Multihandicapped Person* 2:311-326.

201 Sverd J (1991). Tourette syndrome and autistic disorder: A significant relationship. *Am J Med Genet* 39:173-179.

202 Sverd J, Gadow KD, and Nolan EF (1991). Psychiatric symptoms and Tourette syndrome: A study of their relationship. *Presentation Annual Meeting of the American Academy of Child and Adolescent Psychiatry, San Francisco, CA.*

203 Sverd J, Curley L, Jandorf L, and Volkersz L (1988). Behavior disorder and attention deficit in boys with Tourette syndrome. *J Amer Acad Child Adolescent Psychiat* 27:413-417.

204 Sverd J and Montero G (1993). Is Tourette syndrome a cause of sudden infant death syndrome and childhood obstructive sleep apnea? *Am J Med Genet* 46:494-496.

205 Sverd J and Nolan E (1989). Gilles de la Tourette syndrome, autistic disorder, neuropsychiatric disturbance: Is there an etiological relationship? *1st World Congress Psychiatric Genetics 85. (Abstract)*

206 Thelu M-A, Zarski J-P, Froissart B, Rachail M, and Seigneurin J-M (1993). c-Ha-ras polymorphism in patients with hepatocellular carcinoma. *Gastroenterol Clin Biol* 17:903-907.

207 Tone S, Takikawa O, Habara-Ohkubo A, Kadoya A, Yoshida R, and Kido R (1990). Primary structure of human *indoleamine 2,3-dioxygenase* deduced from the nucleotide sequence of its cDNA. *Nucleic Acids Research* 18:367.

208 Tsuang MT and Faraone SV (1990). *The Genetics of Mood Disorders*. Johns Hopkins University Press, Baltimore. pp. 1-220.

209 Turner E, Ewing J, Smith TL, Irwin M, Schuckit M, and Kelsoe J (1992). Lack of association between an RFLP near the D_2 dopamine receptor and alcoholism. *Biol Psychiatry* 31:285-290.

210 Umberkoman-Wita B, Vogel WH, and Wita PJ (1981). Some biochemical and

behavioral (sensation-seeking) correlates in healthy adults. *Res Commun Psychol Psychiat Behav* 6:303-316.

211 Van Tol HHM, Wu CM, Guan H-C, Ohara K, Bunzow JR, Civelli O, Kennedy J, Seeman P, Niznik HB, and Javanovic V (1992). Multiple dopamine D_4 receptor variants in human population. *Nature* 358:149-152.

212 Vandenberg DJ, Persico AM, and Uhl GR (1992). A human dopamine transporter cDNA predicts reduced glycosylation, displays a novel repetitive element and provides racially-dimorphic *Taq* I RFLPs. *Molec Brain Res* 15:161-166.

213 Wadsby M, Lindehammar H, and Eeg-Olofsson O (1989). Neurofibromatosis in childhood: Neuropsychological aspects. *Neurofibromatosis* 2:251-260.

214 Ward IL and Ward OB (1985). Sexual behavior differentiation: Effects of prenatal manipulations in rats. In: *Handbook of behavioral neurobiology*, edited by Adler N, Pfaff D, and Goy R. Plenum Press, New York. pp. 77-98.

215 Warshaw MG, Klerman GL, and Lavori PW (1991). Are secular trends in major depression an artifact of recall? *J Psychiatr Res* 25:141-151.

216 Watson JD and Crick FHC (1953). Molecular structure of nucleic acids. A structure for deoxyribose nucleic acid. *Nature* 171:737-738.

217 Wilson CA, Gonzalez I, and Farabollini F (1991). Behavioral effects in adulthood of neonatal manipulation of brain serotonin levels in normal and androgenized females. *Pharmacol Biochem Behav* 41:91-98.

218 Wilson JR (1988). Individual differences in drug response. In: *Biological Vulnerability to Drug Abuse. NIDA Research Monograph 89*, edited by Pickens RW and Svikis DS. U.S. Dept. Health and Human Services, Rockville, MD. pp. 93-107.

219 Wilson RS, Garron DC, Tanner CM, and Klawans HL (1982). Behavior disturbance in children with Tourette syndrome. *Adv Neurol* 35:329-333.

220 Wingerson L (1990). *Mapping our genes*. Dutton, New York. pp. 1-338.

221 Xu GF, O'Connell P, Viskochil D, Cawthon R, Robertson M, Culver M, Dunn D, Stevens J, Gesteland R, White R, and et al., (1990). The neurofibromatosis type 1 gene encodes a protein related to GAP. *Cell* 62:599-608.

222 The XYY controversy: Researching violence and genetics. (1980). *Hastings Center Report Special Supplement*:1-32.

Appendix

An Update on New Medications

As mentioned in the note on page 5, other than the newer studies on the genetics of TS covered in this book, the major other area necessary to bring the *Tourette Syndrome and Human Behavior* book up to date is a review of some of the newer medications that have become available since the book was published. In this appendix, I will review my experience with the newer selective serotonin reuptake inhibitors (SSRIs) – Zoloft, Paxil and Luvox; drugs similar to the SSRIs that also affect other neurotransmitters – Effexor and Serzone; newer neuroleptics – Risperdal and Moban; anticonvulsants – Depakote; other miscellaneous potentially useful medications – Tenex, Soma, Melatonin; and some newer uses of the previous medications, such as the use of oral clonidine for insomnia.

I. Newer SSRIs

Zoloft® (sertraline) – Zoloft was the first new SSRI to be released since the original book was published. I have used Zoloft in over three hundred children and adults with TS. Like Prozac, it has proven to be very effective in treating many of the disorders in the TS spectrum, including depression, obsessive-compulsive disorder, panic attacks, phobias, general anxiety, compulsive sexual behaviors, short temper, irritability, conduct and oppositional defiant disorder. Zoloft has a shorter half life than Prozac. As result, its effects are gone much sooner after the medication is stopped.

In children I usually start with 25 mg per day. Since Zoloft can cause insomnia, it is better if given in the morning. Since it can cause nausea it helps to be given after breakfast. Many children with TS also have ADHD. Parents need to know that Zoloft and the other SSRIs can cause hypomania or mania; thus if a child seems much more hyperactive after a recent increase in the dose of Zoloft, the dose should be decreased.

Zoloft can be very helpful in treating oppositional defiant and conduct disorder. TS and depression is often associated with irritability, short temper, and rage episodes. After treatment with an SSRI these symptoms may disappear. I have found a combination of the clonidine patch for the treatment of tics, ADHD and conduct disorder plus an SSRI, such as Zoloft – for the treatment of obsessive-compulsive behaviors, depression, mood swings, irritability, temper tantrums, phobias, panic attacks, and anxiety – to be a particularly effective combination of medications for treatment of the TS spectrum of disorders.

sertraline (Zoloft)	
Action:	selective serotonin reuptake inhibitor
Starting dose:	25 - 50 mg/day
Usual Dose:	50 - 150 mg/ day
Side effects:	nausea, tiredness, dizziness, sweating, sexual dysfunction, dry mouth, constipation, mania, insomnia.
Effectiveness:	depression, phobias, panic attacks; obsessive-compulsive, conduct and oppositional defiant disorder
Availability:	50 (light blue), 100 (light yellow)

Paxil® (paroxetine) — Paxil is the fourth SSRI to be released. Like its predecessors, it received FDA approval to treat depression, but is also effective for other aspects of the TS spectrum of disorders. The specificity for selective inhibition of serotonin reuptake is even greater than its predecessors, and the half-life of the compound and its active breakdown products is the shortest (1 day) of all the SSRIs. This means the blood level of the drug drops very quickly after Paxil is discontinued.

paroxetine (Paxil)	
Action:	selective serotonin reuptake inhibitor
Starting dose:	20 mg/day
Usual Dose:	20-40 mg/ day
Side effects:	nausea, tiredness, dizziness, sweating, sexual dysfunction, dry mouth, constipation
Effectiveness:	depression, phobias, panic attacks; obsessive-compulsive, conduct and oppositional defiant disorder
Availability:	20 mg (pink), 30 mg (blue)

Luvox® (fluvoxamine) — Unlike the other SSRIs, in the United States Luvox was approved for treatment of obsessive-compulsive disorder[6,7,12] rather than depression; however, it is also effective in the treatment of depression.[16] The initial dose is 50 mg per day, with maintenance doses of 50 to 300 mg/day. Its half-life is 1 to 2 days.

Despite the emphasis on obsessive-compulsive disorder, double-blind comparative studies indicate a higher percentage of patients respond to Anafranil (clomipramine) than any of the other SSRIs.[8] This, however, is modulated by the fact that Anafranil also has a higher incidence of side effects.

fluvoxamine (Luvox)	
Action:	selective serotonin reuptake inhibitor
Starting dose:	50 mg/day
Usual Dose:	50-300 mg/ day
Side effects:	nausea, tiredness, insomnia, sexual dysfunction, constipation
Effectiveness:	obsessive-compulsive, conduct and oppositional defiant disorder; depression, phobias, panic attacks
Availability:	50 mg, 100 mg

II. Other New Antidepressants.

Effexor® (venlafaxine) — Effexor is an SSRI-like medication that also causes the selective reuptake inhibition of norepinephrine. There is also weak inhibition of dopamine reuptake. Despite their high degree of effectiveness, for some people the pure SSRIs do not work for depression. I have found that in some of these cases an SSRI-like medication that also inhibits the reuptake of norepinephrine, such as Effexor, may be effective without significant side effects. In addition, while the SSRIs are effective in the treatment of depression and other symptoms, some patients prefer Effexor; thus these new antidepressants that inhibit the reuptake of both serotonin and norepinephrine are a significant addition to the armamentarium of medications for the treatment of depression, obsessive-compulsive disorder, anxiety and other aspects of the TS spectrum of behaviors.

venlafaxine (Effexor)	
Action:	selective serotonin and norepinephrine reuptake inhibitor
Starting dose:	25 - 37.5 mg twice a day
Usual Dose:	37.5 to 50 twice a day
Side effects:	tiredness, nausea, sweating, dry mouth, decreased appetite, dizziness, sexual dysfunction
Effectiveness:	depression, phobias, panic attacks; obsessive-compulsive, conduct and oppositional defiant disorder
Availability:	25, 37.5, 50, 75, and 100 marked on tablet

Serzone® (nefazodone) — Serzone is one of the newer antidepressants, which, like Effexor, has an effect on more than one neurotransmitter. While its primary action is that of a selective serotonin reuptake inhibitor, it also inhibits norepinephrine uptake and interacts with both serotonin-2 and α1-adrenergic receptors. Serzone has been primarily studied in depression.[4,5,13] Its broader range of action appears to have several advantages, including improvement of anxiety associated with depression and fewer problems with agitation, insomnia, weight gain, and sexual dysfunction. Like the SSRIs, it will probably be effective in the treatment of obsessive-compulsive disorder, although there have been few studies of this.

The starting dose is usually 100 mg twice a day for the first week, and 150 mg twice a day for the second week, with further adjustment as necessary. TS patients may be more sensitive and require lower than average doses. As with other SSRIs, Serzone is safe; patients have ingested overdoses of 1,000 to 11,200 mg without a fatality. It has a half-life of 2 to 4 hours. When switching from SSRIs it is usually best to discontinue other drugs with a short half-life for 1 to 2 days before starting Serzone. If switching from Prozac, which has a 6-7+ day half-life, it is best to wait a week before starting Serzone.

nefazodone (Serzone)	
Action:	selective serotonin and norepinephrine reuptake inhibitor, antagonist of serotonin-2 and α1-adrenergic receptors
Starting dose:	100 mg twice a day
Usual Dose:	150-200 mg twice a day
Side effects:	tiredness, dry mouth, nausea, constipation
Effectiveness:	depression, agitated depression, depression with anxiety, irritability
Availability:	100 mg (white), 150 mg (peach), 200 mg (yellow), 250 mg (white)

III. New Neuroleptics

Risperdal® (risperidone) – Risperdal is a new neuroleptic that interacts not only with dopamine D_2 receptors, but also with serotonin-2 (5-HT2) receptors. It is an antagonist (inhibitor) at both receptors. Risperdal was approved for the treatment of schizophrenia. Unlike Haldol, which treats only the positive symptoms of schizophrenia (delusions, hallucinations, hostility, excitement, and thoughts of persecution and grandeur), it is effective for both positive and negative symptoms (apathy, social withdrawal, emotionlessness, and lack of spontaneity).[1,2,18] The effectiveness on negative symptoms is thought to be related to its interaction with 5-HT2 receptors.

Because of its broader range of action, there was hope that Risperdal would also be as or more effective in the treatment of TS than Haldol, but with fewer side effects. In many cases this appears to be true. I have treated over 60 TS patients with Risperdal and have found it to be quite effective. In about 20% of the patients it is either ineffective or there are too many side effects. While these figures are similar to those for Haldol and Orap, the important feature is that that Risperdal can be effective in some cases that have not responded well to either Haldol or Orap.[13,15] The additional feature of antagonism of serotonin-2 receptors is felt to play a major role in the increased effectiveness of Risperdal.[15] As with Haldol, I have found that low starting doses of .5 to 1 mg decrease the incidence of side effects. The dose can the be adjusted daily or weekly according to the clinical response.

While the most common side effect is tiredness,[15] all of the other side effects seen with Haldol and Orap can occur. The first patient I ever treated with risperidone developed such prominent akathisia (motor restlessness) that the medication had to be discontinued; however, as reported by others[13,15] I have had numerous patients respond to risperidone after failing to respond to Haldol. Several parents have commented on an improvement in social interactions after their TS child was placed on risperidone. They felt their conversation was more normal and spontaneous. Those interested in how remarkable risperidone can be for some TS individuals should read Susan Hughes' new book, *What Makes Ryan Tick*? (See insert)

risperidone (Risperdal)	
Action:	dopamine D_2 receptor and serotonin-2 (5-HT) receptor antagonist, some affinity for α2-adrenergic receptors
Starting dose:	0.5 to 1.0 mg/day
Usual Dose:	1 - 12 mg/day
Side effects:	tiredness, headache, stomachache, akathisia, weight gain, Parkinsonian symptoms, sexual dysfunction
Effectiveness:	70 -80% of TS patients
Availability:	1 mg (white), 2 mg (orange), 3 mg (yellow), 4 mg (green)

Moban® (molindone) – One of the most difficult aspects of the treatment of some cases of TS are those individuals whose tics, ADHD, and obsessive-compulsive behaviors may have responded well to clonidine and other medications, but who continue to have rage episodes, aggression, and such severe oppositional defiant behavior that they are extremely difficult to live with, both at home and at school. I have found Moban to be very helpful in such cases.

The starting dose is 5 mg (1/2 of a 10 mg tablet) twice a day, with subsequent changes according to response. When it works, these behaviors often virtually disappear without any significant side effects. While not structurally similar to the other neuroleptics, Moban has a mode of action and side effect profile similar to other neuroleptics (Haldol, Orap, Prolixin); however, in my experience, while it is not very effective in the treatment of tics, it can be quite effective in the treatment of explosive and aggressive behavior.[19a,104a] Although it can be given in conjunction with the other neuroleptics such as Haldol or Orap, I generally attempt to decrease the dose of these medications to help decrease the risk of side effects. As with the other neuroleptics, one of the most disturbing side effects can be akathisia, or an intense feeling of restlessness. This responds well to Benadryl 12.5 to 25 mg by mouth.

molindone (Moban)	
Action:	Calming of the ascending reticular activating system
Starting dose:	2.5 to 5.0 mg 1 to 2 times a day
Usual Dose:	5 to 10 mg 2 - 3 times a day
Side effects:	tiredness, akathisia, dystonia, rapid pulse, depression, Parkinsonian symptoms
Effectiveness:	explosive rage episodes, oppositional defiant disorder, conduct disorder, aggression
Availability:	5 mg (orange), 10 mg (lavender), 25 mg(light green), 50 (blue), 100 (tan), liquid 20mg/ml

IV Anticonvulsants

Depakene® (valproic acid) – In the previous book I discussed the use of Tegretal in the treatment of rage attacks and aggression. Tegretal is an anticonvulsant; another anticonvulsant that can also be effective is valproic acid, available as Depakene (valproic acid) and Depakote (valproic acid + sodium valproate). One of the proposed modes of action of valproic acid is through an increase in brain GABA, a major inhibitor of nerve activity.[p481] Part of the side effects are G.I. in nature (nausea, diarrhea, constipation, loss of appetite). These may be decreased by the use of Depakote, a more slowly-released form of the medication. Other side effects include tiredness, tremor, ataxia, and incoordination. A rare but serious side effect is liver failure. This usually occurs in the first six months of use. Liver functions tests during this time can warn of such problems.

Some of you may have read Susan Hughes' book, *RYAN – A Mother's Story of Her Hyperactive/Tourette Syndrome Child*. As outlined in her companion book, *What Makes Ryan Tick?* updating her experiences with Ryan's rage attacks, she reports that he responded so well to a combination of Depakote, Risperdal, and Ritalin that he was able leave a residential treatment facility, return home and attend public high school.

valproic acid (Depakene, Depakote)	
Action:	Anticonvulsant possibly related to increased brain GABA
Starting dose:	250 - 500 mg/day
Usual Dose:	250 - 1,250 mg/day
Side effects:	nausea, vomiting, diarrhea, tremor, incoordination, liver failure
Effectiveness:	explosive rage episodes, oppositional defiant disorder, conduct disorder, aggression
Availability:	Depakene 250 (orange);
	Depakote 125 mg (pink), 250 (peach), 500 (lavender);
	Depakote sprinkle 125 capsule

V. Other Medications

Tenex (guanfacine) – Tenex is an α2-adrenergeric agonist, just like clonidine. Its advantage over clonidine is its longer duration of action; thus while clonidine may require doses every 2 to 4 hours, Tenex is usually needed at 4 to 6 hour intervals. Because of this, it is my drug of choice when clonidine patches have to be stopped either because they are causing severe contact dermatitis (welts) or because summer is approaching and the child will be spending too many hours in the swimming pool.

Like clonidine, Tenex is marketed for the treatment of hypertension in adults; however, when the blood pressure is normal, there is usually little effect on blood pressure.

guanfacine (Tenex)	
Action:	α2-adrenergic receptor agonist
Starting dose:	0.5 mg, 1 to 2 times a day
Usual Dose:	0.5 to 1 mg, 1 to 3 times a day
Side effects:	tiredness, dry mouth, dizziness
Effectiveness:	Effective for tics, ADHD, and conduct in 60-70% of TS patients
Availability:	1 mg (light pink diamond), 2 mg (yellow diamond)

Soma® (carisoprodol) – Soma is a muscle relaxant that works by blocking activity between neurons in the spinal cord and the reticular formation in the brain. It has a rapid onset of action and lasts four to six hours. It is used to treat acutely painful musculoskeletal conditions. To my knowledge, it has never before been considered as a mode of treatment of TS. I had a patient with severe TS whose tics had been only partially responsive to all the usual medications for TS. She had some muscle pain which I treated with Soma. The next day she called to say her tics were 50% better. We stopped the 6 mg of Orap she was taking and she now prefers to treat her TS with Soma. Since then I have treated over thirty TS patients with Soma. In about three out of four cases it has been effective in decreasing the tics by about 50%. Soma comes in 350 mg tablets. The usual dose is 1 to 3 per day.

carisoprodol (Soma)	
Action:	inhibition of internerve activity in the spinal cord and reticular apparatus
Starting dose:	350 mg 1 to 3 per day
Usual Dose:	350 mg 1 to 3 per day
Side effects:	tiredness, dizziness, headache
Effectiveness:	About 75% of TS patients
Availability:	350 mg (white)

Melatonin — Melatonin is a natural hormone produced from serotonin in the pineal gland. It plays an important role in regulating the daily rhythms of the body, including sleep. The oral administration of melatonin at bedtime, in doses of 2 to 10 gm, has been reported to be useful in the treatment of a range of sleep disorders, including insomnia, frequent night-wakenings, and day-night reversals.[9] It works best when combined with strict environmental sleep structuring, such as insisting on a regular and reasonable bedtime. After several months of treatment the sleep structure alone may be adequate. In a study of ninety children with a wide range of disorders there were no side effects and no development of tolerance.[9] Melatonin is available at most health food stores without a prescription.

DDAVP® Nasal Spray (desmopressin acetate) — Enuresis or bedwetting, is a common problem in children with TS and ADHD.[p245] Imipramine given at bedtime (10 to 75 mg) is a common and usually effective method of treatment of enuresis; however, occasionally imipramine either does not work, or is contraindicated. In such cases, if the bedwetting is severe enough to justify treatment, DDAVP Nasal Spray is an effective alternative treatment.[11,14]

Desmopressin is a synthetic form of a natural hormone, vasopressin, also known as anti-diuretic hormone. It acts directly on the kidneys to inhibit diuresis, or the excretion of water. When administered by nasal spray and adsorbed through the nasal mucosa, desmopressin has an effect that is one-tenth as potent as when the medication is given by injection. The usual initial dose is one spray, followed by adjustment for each individual. Each spray delivers 10 mcg, and the recommended dose is 10 to 40 mcg. Occasional side effects at higher doses include headache, nausea, nasal congestion and mild abdominal cramps. Adequately controlled studies beyond 4 to 8 weeks have not been conducted.

Adderall — Adderall from Richwood Pharmaceutical Company, Inc, is a combination of equal parts of four admphetamine compounds: dextroamphetamine saccharate, amphetamine aspartate, dextroamphetamine sulfate and amphetamine sulfate. It comes in 10 mg and 20 mg sizes and is used for the treatment of childhood and adult ADHD. It was off the market for several years for the completion of FDA required testing and is now back on the market. In my experience it is often superior to both Ritalin and regular Dexedrine. Like Dexedrine it tends to have a longer duration of action than Ritalin and as a result there is less rebound and noontime doses in school can be avoided. The side effects are the same as the other stimulant medications and include decreased appetite, insomnia and the potential of increasing tics in individuals with Tourette syndrome. The latter is not inevitable and I have used it in many individuals with Tourette syndrome and ADHD.

VI. New uses of older medications.

Clonidine — The use of clonidine was discussed extensively in the previous book. One aspect of its use that has gained wide acceptance is in the treatment of insomnia in children with ADHD[17] and TS. For those who have trouble getting to sleep at night, often because of racing thoughts, .1 to .2 mg of clonidine at bedtime can be very helpful. If the individual is already using a clonidine patch, but is still having trouble sleeping, the patch can be supplemented with oral clonidine at bedtime. For those already taking oral clonidine, a regular or moderately-increased dose can be given at bedtime.

Many patients have told me that not all generic forms of clonidine are effective; for example, one mother found that clonidine from Schein worked much better for her child than clonidine from Puret.

Nicotine patches – In the previous book I discussed the use of nicotine gum in the treatment of TS. Since then there have been occasional reports of the utility of nicotine patches in TS treatment.[3,10] In one report,[3] patients with or without prior Haldol treatment responded to treatment with the nicotine patch with an average 50% decrease in tic severity. I have used nicotine gum or patches in eight TS patients and to date, none have shown a significant decrease in symptoms. This could be due to that fact that I have used nicotine in only the cases that did not respond to the usual medications, or there may be a tendency for only a few successfully treated cases to end up being reported.

References

1 Chouinard G, Jones B, Remington G, et al. (1993). A Canadian multicenter placebo-controlled study of fixed doses of risperidone and haloperidol in the treatment of chronic schizophrenic patients. *J Clin Psychopharmacol* 13:25-40.

2 Claus A, Bollen J, De Cuyper H, and et al. (1992). Risperidone versus haloperidol in the treatment of chronic schizophrenic inpatients: A multicentre double-blind comparative study. *Acta Psychiatr Scand* 85:295-305.

3 Dursun SM, Reveley MA, and Bird R (1994). Longlasting improvement of Tourette's syndrome with transdermal nicotine. *Lancet* 344:1577-1570.

4 Elson AS, Elso, MS, Torrente JR, Wright RN, and Yocca FD (1990). Nefazodone: preclinical pharmacology of a new antidepressant. *Psychopharmacol Bull* 26:311-315.

5 Fontaine R, Ontiveros A, Elie R, Kensler TT, Roberts DL, Kaplita S, Ecker JA, and Faludi G (1994). A double-blind comparison of nefazodone, imipramine, and placebo in major depression. *J Clin Psychiat* 55:234-241.

6 Freeman CPL, Trimble MR, Deakin JF, Stokes TM, and Ashford JJ (1994). Fluvoxamine versus clomipramine in the treatment of obsessive-compulsive disorder: A multicenter, randomized, double-blind, parallel group comparison. *J Clin Psychiat* 55:1-5.

7 Goodman WK, Price LH, Rasmussen SA, Delgad, PL, Heninger GR, and Cherney DS (1989). Efficacy of fluvoxamine in obsessive-compulsive disorder. *Arch Gen Psychiatry* 46:36-44.

8 Greist JH, Jefferson JW, Kobak KA, Katzelnick DJ, and Serlin RC (1995). Efficacy and tolerability of serotonin transport inhibitors in obsessive-compulsive disorder. *Arch Gen Psychiatry* 52:53-60.

9 Jan JE and Espezel H (1995). Melatonin treatment of chronic sleep disorders. *Dev*

Med Child Neurol 37:279-281.

10 McConville B, Sanberg PR, Fogelson MH, et al. (1992). The effect of nicotine plus haloperidol compared to nicotine only and placebo only in reducing tic severity and frequency in Tourette's disorder. *Biol Psychiatry* 31:832-840.

11 Miller K and Klaluber GT (1990). Desmopressin acetate in children with severe primary nocturnal enuresis. *Clin Ther* 12:357-366.

12 Perse TL, Greist JH, Jefferson JW, Rosenfeld R, and Dar R (1987). Fluvoxamine treatment of obsessive-compulsive disorder. *Arch Gen Psychiatry* 144:1543-1548.

13 Rickels K, Schweizer E, Clary C, Fox I, and Weise C (1944). Nefazodone and imipramine in major depression: a placebo-controlled trial. *Br J Psychiatry* 164:802-805.

14 Rittig S, Knudsen UB, Sorensen S, et al. (1988). Long-term double-blind crossover study of desmopressin intranasal spray in the management of nocturnal enuresis. In: *Desmopressin in Nocturnal Enuresis: Proceeding of an International Symposium*, edited by Meadow SR. Horus Medical Publications, London. pp. 43-55.

15 van der Linden C, Bruggeman R, and van Woerkom CAM (1994). Serotonin-dopamine antagonist and Gilles de la Tourette syndrome: An open pilot dose-titration study with Risperidone. *Movement Disorders* 9:687-688.

16 Wilde MI, Plosker GL, and Benfield P (1993). Fluvoxamine — An updated review of its pharmacology, and therapeutic use in depressive illness. *Drugs* 46:895-924.

17 Wilens TE, Biederman J, and Spencer T (1994). Clonidine for sleep disturbances with attention deficit hyperactivity disorder. *J Am Acad Child Adolesc Psychiatry* 33:424-426.

18 Zinner HJ, Fuger J, Kasper S, et al. (1992). Changes of positive and negative syndromes: A double-blind clinical trial with risperidone versus haloperidol in chronic schizophrenia. *Pharmacopsychiatry* 25:118-110.

Abbreviations, Definitions, Glossary

<   Less than. For example p <.001 means the value was less than 0.001.

A   Adenine. One of the four bases in DNA. It pairs with thymine, **T**.

ADHD Attention Deficit Hyperactivity Disorder, previously called hyperactivity or minimal brain damage (MBD). ADHD is the most common behavioral disorder of childhood.

agonist A chemical compound that stimulates a given receptor; for example, dopamine is an agonist for dopamine receptors.

allele Genes come in two copies – one from the mother and one from the father. The individual genes, maternal or paternal, are called alleles. If there are different forms of the gene due to mutations, each of these different forms is also called allele.

allele-specific PCR This is a technique that can identify the specific mutations in different alleles.

ALTE Apparent Life Threatening Event, or near sudden death in an infant.

amino acids Building blocks of protein. Tryptophan and phenylalanine are the names of two of the more than twenty amino acids.

antagonist A chemical compound that inhibits or blocks a given receptor; for example, haloperidol is an antagonist of dopamine D_2 receptors.

ascertainment The process of finding cases or individuals with a given disorder.

ascertainment bias The tendency to have more severe cases of a given disorder, or individuals with two separate disorders, come to medical attention instead of milder cases.

ASHG American Society of Human Genetics, the society of human geneticists in North America.

base The individual building block of DNA. There are four bases: adenine, cytosine, guanine, and thymine.

base pairs The bases align themselves into specific pairs. Guanine pairs with cytosine, and adenine pairs with thymine.

Behavioral Questionnaire The thirty-one-page questionnaire, covering many different aspects of human behavior, that all new patients to the City of Hope Clinic must complete. A copy is included in the book *Tourette Syndrome and Human Behavior*.

bipolar depression Manic-depressive disorder. A form of depression with wide mood swings.

Blue Script The name of a special cloning vector that under specific conditions of growth produces blue colonies when no foreign DNA is inserted, and white colonies when foreign DNA is inserted.

borderline A psychiatric disorder intermediate in severity between neurosis and psychosis.

Brenda Dr. Brenda Comings.

C Cytosine. One of the four bases in DNA. It pairs with guanine, **G**.

case(s) Individual(s) in a study.

cDNA DNA representing the messenger RNA sequence of a gene (produced by an enzyme called reverse transcriptase).

chi square A statistical test especially useful in determining if the percentage of persons affected in a test group is significantly different from those in the control group.

chromosome Unit of a giant piece of DNA containing many genes. Chromosomes and their associated proteins are most easily seen during cell division (mitosis) when they are stained (*chromo*-colored, *some*-body).

clone *Noun*. A segment of DNA that is "grown up" into many copies by being inserted into primitive organism or "vector." When the vector reproduces to make many copies, the segment of DNA is also grown up or "cloned" into many copies.

  Verb. To clone. To grow up a segment of DNA by growing it in a vector.

consanguineous When the parents are related to each other before marriage.

coprolalia Involuntary, compulsive swearing.

cytogenetics The study of chromosomes.

D$_1$ The dopamine D$_1$ receptor.

D$_2$ The dopamine D$_2$ receptor.

D$_3$ The dopamine D$_3$ receptor.

D$_4$ The dopamine D$_4$ receptor.

D$_5$ The dopamine D$_5$ receptor.

DAT1 The human *dopamine transporter* gene.

DβH Dopamine beta-hydroxylase, an enzyme that converts dopamine to norepinephrine.

DβH The *dopamine β-hydroxylase* gene (italicized).

denature In DNA studies this refers to separating the double-stranded DNA into individual single strands.

DGGE **D**enaturing **G**radient **G**el **E**lectrophoresis. A special type of electrophoresis of DNA that allows one to detect the presence of mutations anywhere along the DNA fragment.

Diagnostic Interview Schedule A structured interview used to make a diagnosis of the DSM psychiatric disorders.

Dietz Ph.D., George One of the essential members of the research team in the Department of Medical Genetics, City of Hope Medical Center.

dimorphic Of two different sizes. Often used to refer to different sizes of parts of the brain in males and females. See **sexually dimorphic**.

DIS   See **Diagnostic Interview Schedule**

disinhibition   Poorly inhibited. Removing influences that inhibit nerve cell activity. Inability to refrain from inappropriate behaviors.

DNA   DeoxyriboNucleic Acid, the genetic material of the cell.

dominant   A trait caused by a gene in which only a single abnormal gene is required to produce the disorder. In strictly dominant conditions, the disorder produced by one abnormal gene is the same as when two abnormal genes are present.

Donn   See Muhleman, Donn

dopamine   A chemical that acts as a neurotransmitter in the brain. Dopamine neurons are especially involved in the control of muscle movements and have been implicated in schizophrenia, Tourette syndrome and Parkinson's disease.

dopamine β-hydroxylase   An enzyme that converts dopamine to norepinephrine.

dopamine transporter   A protein that directs the re-uptake of dopamine into the neuron from which it was released.

DRD1   The *Dopamine Receptor D1* gene.

DRD2   The *Dopamine Receptor D2* gene.

DRD3   The *Dopamine Receptor D3* gene.

DRD4   The *Dopamine Receptor D4* gene.

DRD5   The *Dopamine Receptor D5* gene.

DSM-III   The **D**iagnostic and **S**tatistical **M**anual of the American Psychiatric Association, 1980 edition. A manual listing the diagnostic criteria for all psychiatric diagnoses in the United States.

DSM-III-R   Diagnostic and Statistical Manual of the American Psychiatric Association, Third Edition, Revised 1987.

DSM-IV   Diagnostic and Statistical Manual of the American Psychiatric Association, Fourth Edition 1994.

***Eco*RI**   A restriction endonuclease enzyme.

electrophoresis   A technique by which chemicals are separated in an electrical field.

endonuclease   An enzyme that cuts DNA fragments in the center regions, i.e. not at the ends, as in exonuclease.

enzyme   A protein that serves as a catalyst for a specific chemical reaction.

epiphenomena   Events that are secondary to a more basic (genetic) defect.

et al.   Refers to co-workers in the citation of a paper.

etiology   Cause.

etiological   Causal.

exon   A segment of DNA within the gene that is read into the nuclear RNA, remains in the messenger RNA and is translated into protein.

expression   Refers to manner in which different symptoms of a genetic disorder may be present in an individual carrying the gene(s). In mild expression there are few or mild symptoms; in severe expression there are many or severe symptoms.

5' Refers to the other end of a segment of DNA. Specifically, it refers to the position on the sugar molecule (5') that the phosphate group is attached to.

familial Occurring in two or more members of a family. May or may not be genetic.

filter A piece of nylon on which DNA fragments are bound for genetic testing by hybridization.

frontal lobes Major lobes of the brain located behind the forehead.

G Guanine. One of the four bases in DNA. It pairs with cytosine, **C**.

gene The portion of DNA that carries the code for a specific protein or RNA.

G->A A mutation involving a change from a guanine to an adenine in DNA.

G->T A mutation involving a change from a guanine to a thymine in DNA.

genetics The study of hereditary disorders or mechanisms.

genome All the genes and DNA between the genes in an organism.

genomic Pertaining to the DNA of the genome.

genotype The results of a specific genetic test on both chromosomes, i. e. from the mother and the father. For example, for blood groups A, B, and O, if a person was type AB, that would be his genotype for that gene.

George see Dietz Ph.D., George

Gericke M.D., George Director of the Department of Human Genetics, Pretoria, South Africa.

G.I. Gastrointestinal.

globin The protein part of hemoglobin.

gonadotrophic hormone A pituitary hormone that regulates the secretion of gonadal hormones such as testosterone.

***Gts* gene** The mutant *Gilles de la Tourette Syndrome* gene. Gene names are always italicized.

***gts* gene** The normal counterpart to the *Gts* gene.

haplotype The results of two or more genetic tests for genes close to each other on one chromosome. For example, if a mutation occurred at point A, resulting in a mutant A' on one chromosome and a normal A on the other, and if another mutation occurred close by at point B, resulting in chromosomes B' or B, and if we knew that A and B' were on the same chromosome and A' and B were on the other chromosome, AB' and A'B would be the haplotypes for that pair of mutations.

heme A compound containing iron. Heme is the part of hemoglobin that allows it to bind oxygen.

hemoglobin The protein in red blood cells that carries oxygen from the lungs to the tissues.

hemoglobinopathy An abnormal hemoglobin due to a mutation that changes the amino acid sequence of the globin molecule.

hereditary Inherited by genetic mechanisms.

heterozygote An individual in whom a specific gene from the mother and the father are different. For example, an individual who has the AB blood type is a heterozygote for the ABO genes.

heterozygous The state of having different genes at a given site.

5-HIAA 5-hydroxyindole acetic acid. A breakdown product of serotonin. Measurement of 5-HIAA in the spinal fluid gives an estimate of the serotonin activity of the brain.

histidine An amino acid. The heme molecule of hemoglobin binds to histidines in the globin protein.

homozygote An individual in whom a specific gene from the mother and the father are the same; for example, an individual with the AA blood type, usually referred to as A, is a homozygote for the ABO genes.

homozygous The state of having the same gene at a given site.

HTO3 The **H**uman **T**ryptophan **O**xygenase cDNA clone #3.

hybridization A technique to anneal or zip together a DNA sequence, usually made radioactive, to non-radioactive matching sequence.

hypothalamus A portion of the brain just above the pituitary gland that plays a major role in regulating many bodily functions.

IBS Irritable Bowel Syndrome. A chronic disorder of the colon characterized by cramping, mucus, diarrhea or constipation.

IDO Indoleamine **Di**Oxygenase, an enzyme that breaks down tryptophan.

IDO **gene** The gene that makes IDO.

in situ hybridization A technique for hybridizing DNA to human chromosomes. Often used to determine on which chromosome the DNA sequences are located.

indoleamine 2,3 dioxygenase An enzyme that breaks down tryptophan. It is found in most tissues, including the brain, intestines, and macrophages.

intron A segment of DNA inside the gene that codes for a portion of nuclear RNA that is read from the gene, but is excised (cut out) from the messenger RNA. As a result, intron sequences are not seen in the expressed part of the gene (protein).

IRB Internal Review Board. An institutional board that reviews research proposals to assure the protection of the patient's rights and safety.

JAMA The *Journal of the American Medical Association.*

Karen Mercer My secretary.

Kovacs M.D., Bruce An obstetrician-gynecologist on the staff of the University of Southern California and associated with the Department of Medical Genetics for many years.

LA/TSA Los Angeles Tourette Syndrome Association.

library In molecular genetics this refers to a collection of clones. For example, a collection of clones of DNA fragment from human DNA is termed a human genomic library.

ligase An enzyme that seals two pieces of DNA together, end to end.

limbic Pertains to the limbic system, the part of the brain controlling emotions. It is called limbic because it bends around the central part of the brain like a limb.

linkage disequilibrium A situation in which two different mutations or markers are so close to each other that there is little opportunity for rearrangement over time. As a result, these two markers tend to appear together in different people.

linkage When two traits or genetic markers travel together in families, they are said to be linked.

log linear analysis A specific statistical procedure that allows one to determine which of a set of variables are most highly associated with another (dependent) variable.

MacMurray M.D., Jim Director of the Addiction Treatment Unit at the Jerry L. Pettis V.A. Hospital, Loma Linda, CA.

messenger RNA See mRNA.

motor Pertaining to muscle. A motor movement is a muscle movement.

mRNA Messenger RNA. The RNA produced by the genes that passes from the nucleus to the cytoplasm where it is translated into a specific protein or enzyme.

Msp A restriction endonuclease.

Muhleman, Donn A critical member of the research team in the Department of Medical Genetics, City of Hope National Medical Center.

multifactorial A form of inheritance in which more than one type of gene and environmental factors are involved.

mutation A change in the structure of DNA that can be inherited.

N Number. Often refers to the number of cases or patients in a study.

N.S. Not Significant. A term used when statistical comparison shows no differences between two or more groups.

neopterin A compound that is excreted in increased amounts during infections and immune disorders.

neurons Nerve cells.

neurotransmitters Chemicals that are involved in the communication between one nerve and another.

NIAAA National Institute of Alcohol Abuse and Alcoholism

NIDA National Institute of Drug Abuse

NIH National Institutes of Health

NIMH National Institute of Mental Health

non-proband A member of the family other than the individual who first sought medical care for a specific disorder.

norepinephrine A chemical that acts as a neurotransmitter in the brain. It is formed from dopamine.

NTB NitroTetrazolium Blue A dye used in certain staining reactions.

nucleotide See **base**.

OCB Obsessive-Compulsive Behavior. Less severe than disorder.

OCD Obsessive-Compulsive Disorder. A disorder characterized by obsessive thoughts and compulsive motor actions or behaviors.

OLA   Oligonucleotide Ligase Assay. A technique for identifying a specific mutation in a segment of DNA.

oligomers Short synthetic pieces of DNA used in the amplification of DNA by the PCR technique.

oligos Abbreviation for oligomers.

oxidase An enzyme which uses ionic oxygen (0-) as a substrate

oxygenase An enzyme which uses molecular oxygen (O_2) as a substrate.

p   Probability. In statistical comparisons, if $p = 0.05$, it is usually considered that there are significant differences between the groups being compared. This p indicates there is a 1 in 20 possibility that the differences were simply due to random chance. If $p = 0.01$, it is more significant, with a 1 in 100 possibility of being due to chance. If $p = 0.001$, it is highly significant. If $p = 0.0001$ or less, it is very highly significant.

paradigm A model. In science, the accepted paradigm refers to the prevailing and accepted model in a given field.

paradigm shift A change in the accepted model. A paradigm shift takes place when the accumulated scientific evidence becomes so strong that most scientists feel compelled to accept the new model.

PDD   Pervasive **D**evelopmental **D**isorder. An autism-like disorder.

PCR   Polymerase **C**hain **R**eaction. Refers to a technique used to amplify small pieces of DNA millions of times. An extremely powerful technique widely used in molecular genetics.

pedigree A recorded family history often diagrammed for easy interpretation.

penetrance Refers to whether an abnormal gene has produced any symptoms. If the gene is non-penetrant, there are no symptoms. If it is penetrant, there are some symptoms, and the number is described by the degree of expression.

polygenes Our term for the genes involved in polygenic inheritance.

polygenic Caused by multiple genes.

polymerase An enzyme used in the synthesis or replication of nucleic acids. For DNA – DNA polymerase. For RNA – RNA polymerase.

polymerase chain reaction See **PCR**.

polymorphism A genetic variation present in some people but not others; for example, ABO blood groups are polymorphisms. Some people are AA, some AB, and some OO.

porphyria A hereditary disorder affecting the precursors to the heme part of hemoglobin. One form of porphyria is very common in South Africa.

primer A short piece of DNA (oligomer) used to start the synthesis of DNA. Primers are especially used in PCR reactions.

proband The first individual in a family who comes to see the doctor.

prospective Done before a diagnosis is made. For example, if a type of data is collected before a diagnosis is made, or before the patient is placed in a specific group, several types of bias are prevented. Such a study is called a prospective study.

PTSD Post-Traumatic Stress Disorder.

psychopathology Psychological abnormalities or disorders.

quinolinic acid A breakdown product of tryptophan that causes nerve cell death.

receptors Structures on the surface of nerve cells that tightly bind neurotransmitters. They define which nerve cells will respond to which neurotransmitters and whether the effect will be to stimulate or inhibit the nerve.

recessive A trait caused by a gene in which two abnormal alleles are required to produce the disorder. Individuals who carry a single abnormal allele have no symptoms.

redox Reduction-oxidation. A term that refers to a compound, often a dye, that facilitates oxidation or reduction of other chemicals.

renature In DNA studies, this refers to allowing individual single strands of DNA to go back to the double-stranded form.

restriction endonuclease An enzyme that cuts DNA at specific sites.

RFLP Restriction Fragment Length Polymorphism. A polymorphism due to variations between people in the distance between two sites on a DNA molecule cut by a restriction enzyme

RNA RiboNucleic Acid. Consists of several types, such as messenger RNA, transfer RNA, ribosomal RNA, and heterogeneous nuclear RNA.

segregation analysis A mathematical analysis of how disorders are inherited based on studies of many families.

sequence The sequence of bases, A, T , G, C in a given segment of DNA.

sequenced Indicates that the sequence of a gene or segment of DNA is known.

serotonin A chemical that acts as a neurotransmitter in the brain. It functions as an inhibiting neurotransmitter. The limbic system and frontal lobes are particularly rich in serotonin.

sexually dimorphic Different size in males and females. Usually refers to the size of portions of the brain.

single strand DNA is composed of two strands of nucleotides. The individual strands are termed single strands.

SIDS Sudden Infant Death Syndrome.

somatiform *Soma* refers to body. Somatiform disorder or complaints are complaints about the body. This term is synonomous with the older term "psychosomatic," implying the bodily pain or dysfunction is largely psychological in origin.

spectrophotometer An instrument used to determine the amount of various compounds present in a solution by passing light through it at specific wavelengths.

SSCP Single Strand Conformation Polymorphism. A specific procedure that involves denaturation of a short segment of DNA, followed by electrophoresis, allowing the detection of mutations or polymorphisms in the DNA. These are called SSCP polymorphisms. The technique is called SSCP electrophoresis.

SSRI Selective Serotonin Reuptake Inhibitor. Antidepressant medications that work by inhibiting the re-uptake or clearance of serotonin from the nerve synapse. This allows the brain to use serotonin more effectively.

stains all A stain from Eastman Kodak that can detect small amounts of DNA.

substrate A chemical that is changed by an enzyme into another chemical. For example, alcohol is the substrate for alcohol dehydrogenase, the enzyme that breaks down alcohol.

synapse The space between two nerves. Nerves communicate with each other by releasing neurotransmitters into this space.

syndrome A group of symptoms or signs that identifies a specific disorder, such as Tourette syndrome.

3' Refers to one end of a segment of DNA. Specifically, it refers to the position on the sugar molecule (3') that the phosphate group is attached to.

T Thymine. One of the four bases in DNA. It pairs with adenina, **A**.

tandem repeat A tandem repeat refers to a series of identical sets of the same DNA sequence aligned end to end; for example, CAT CAT CAT would be a three base pair tandem repeat.

tandem repeat polymorphism A situation where different people have different numbers of repeats in a tandem repeat; for example, CAT CAT in some people and CAT CAT CAT in others would represent a 2 versus a 3 tandem repeat polymorphism.

Taq **I** A restriction endonuclease enzyme.

TDO2 **gene** The gene that makes TDO2, or tryptophan dioxygenase, or tryptophan 2,3-dioxygenase.

TDO2 Tryptophan **DiO**xygenase. An enzyme that breaks down tryptophan. The 2 refers to the presence of two oxygen molecules.

tic An involuntary, sudden, rapid muscle movement or vocal noise.

Tourette syndrome A common, hereditary syndrome consisting of chronic motor (muscle) and vocal tics and associated with a wide range of other behaviors.

transporters Proteins that direct the re-uptake into the neuron of various neurotransmitters. There are dopamine, serotonin, norepinephrine, and other transporters.

tryptophan 2,3-dioxygenase The same as tryptophan oxygenase, tryptophan dioxygenase, or TDO2.

tryptophan An amino acid required to make serotonin.

TS Tourette syndrome or Gilles de la Tourette syndrome.

TSA Tourette Syndrome Association.

type I error A statistical error resulting from stating something is true when in fact it is not true.

type II error A statistical error resulting from stating something is not true when in fact it is true. This error often results from not studying enough subjects.

vector A primitive form of DNA, often circular, that reproduces in bacteria or other organisms. When a piece of foreign DNA is inserted into such a vector, it can be cloned

Index

A

A.M.A. – see *American Medical Association*
Abbuzahab, Dr.19-20
Ackenbach Child Behavior Checklist 102
ACTH 147
acute intermittent porphyria 206
Adam and the Magic Marble 81-2
addicting 139, 201
ADHD iii, 39-43, 47, 53-4, 59, 63, 71, 74, 77, 86-7, 89-95, 98, 101, 118, 137-8, 158, 163,
        165-9, 175, 177-8, 183-5, 188-191, 195, 197-8, 201, 205, 210-1, 223-5, 233-5,
        237-9, 242-3, 245-9, 256-7, 273, 277, 280, 282-3 (also see *attention deficit disor-
        der* and *attention deficit hyperactivity disorder*)
adoption studies 158, 173
Advances in Human Genetics 77
Affective Spectrum Disorder 85-6, 94
aggressive 13-4, 19, 25, 33, 49, 91, 93, 95, 103, 177, 184-5, 193, 207-8, 277
agoraphobia 70, 118,
AIDS 179, 195
alcohol abuse 139, 173, 175-6, 189, 198, 200, 205, 233, 242
alcohol dependence 139, 245-6,
Alcoholic Beverage Research Foundation 252
alcoholic cirrhosis 210
alcoholism 54, 61, 66, 70, 73-6, 86-7, 89, 92, 94-6, 98, 116, 122, 131,134-5, 138-140, 144,
        160, 169, 173, 189, 193, 198-9, 205, 210, 212, 215, 223-4, 231, 233, 238, 253, 258
alcoholism gene 73-5, 89, 98, 116
ALTE 153, 282
alternative hypothesis 118
alternative start site 127
Alzheimer's disease 18, 207
American Academy of Child and Adolescent Psychiatry 74, 125
American Journal of Human Genetics 12, 29, 47, 57, 81 243
American Journal of Psychiatry 26, 85
American Medical Association 131
American Psychiatric Association 85, 164, 285
American Society of Human Genetics 42, 59, 61, 66, 74, 86, 91, 219, 227, 283
Amish linkage study 75
amphetamines 173, 202
Anafranil 274
Analytical Biochemistry 129
angry 19, 25, 36, 48, 66, 182, 184
annoying others 183
anorexia nervosa 86
anti-biological psychiatry 207

antisocial acts 183
anxiety 17, 21, 59, 70, 86-7, 93-4, 102, 118, 125, 163, 168-9, 189, 191, 198, 227-9, 245-246, 248, 257, 273, 275
any behavioral disorder 63, 86, 145
Archives of General Psychiatry 42, 47, 58, 71
Archives of Neurology 231
arguing 183
Arno Episode, the 65
arrested 140, 175, 185
arson 49, 207
ascertainment bias 13-4, 42-3, 63, 69, 71, 99-101, 119, 159, 163-6, 168, 171, 174, 183, 185, 187-8, 190, 227, 283
Associated Press 66
association by association 190, 229
association studies 133-4, 145, 151, 158, 232, 249
attention deficit disorder 41-2, 62, 78, 86-7, 125, 131 (also see *ADHD* and *attention deficit hyperactivity disorder*)
attention deficit hyperactivity disorder 21-2, 39, 85, 100-1, 283 (also see *ADHD* and *attention deficit disorder*)
autism i, iii, 91-2, 94, 98, 130, 138, 209-10, 223-5, 238-9, 289
autosomal dominant 5, 17-8, 29-31, 88, 90, 101, 118, 149-152, 163, 228, 232, 255-26

B

β adrenergic gene 142
Badawy, Abdul 169
Baker Autism Foundation 253
barbiturates 173
BASIC 47, 157
Behavior Problem Checklist 47
behavioral disinhibition 59
Behavioral Questionnaire 170, 173, 205, 232, 282
behavioral spectrum disorder 37, 99, 118, 190
Berkeley 53-4, 196, 202
Beuhrens, Adam 81
Beuhrens, Carol 81
Beutler, Ernest 114
Bible 82
biochemical defect 25
BioRad 219
bipolar disorder 75, 187, 283
Bissbort, Siegbert, 109-14, 116-19, 122-28, 212, 215-16, 221, 225
blood sugars 142
Blum, Ken 89, 90, 92-3, 95, 134, 140, 142, 145
Bolos 95, 134
Book 77
Bower, Bruce, 87
breaking into houses or cars 183
Breggin, Peter 207
British Journal of Psychiatry 227
broken home 183
Brunner 207

Bruun, Ruth 59, 85
bulimia 85
bupropion 202
Burd, Larry 92

C

CAAT box 104
California Tobacco-Related Disease Research Program 253
cancer 19, 45, 209
carisoprodol 279
Carter 167
cases with 233, 242
cases without 233, 242
cataplexy 85
catechol-o-methyl-transferase 123
CCCCT repeat mutation 221, 225
cDNA 73, 218, 284, 287
chaos theory 62, 76
Cherry 157
Chiara 139
child abuse 35
Child Health and Development Studies 196
choline 22
chromosome 10-5, 18, 21, 26, 29-30, 51, 73, 75, 77, 88, 91, 93, 97, 104, 118, 123, 132-4,
        149-50, 179, 207, 253, 256, 284, 286-7
chromosome 4q31 51, 73-4, 97, 118
chronic fatigue 169
Ciba-Giegy 41-2
Cichon 219
cigarettes 196, 201-2
City of Hope 10-1, 18-20, 22, 36, 46, 80, 117-8, 120, 218-9, 253, 283-4, 288
Civilli, Oliver 90
clomid 147
clomipramine 274
clonidine 273, 279-80
Cloninger, Robert 29, 134, 198
cocaine 139, 173-4, 202, 240-1
Cohen, Donald 40-2, 57-9, 165, 167, 227
college 9-10, 198
colossal mistake 66
Comings, Brenda 20-2, 25, 31, 33, 35-6, 45-6, 53-4, 57, 63, 65-6, 73-4, 81, 87, 100, 107,
        109, 113-4, 121, 169, 284
comorbid behaviors 76, 100-1, 163, 246, 249
competitive sports 197
complex systems 62
compulsive eating 61, 86, 91, 190
compulsive swearing 7, 17, 177, 284
COMT (see *catechol-o-methyl-transferase*)
conduct disorder 14, 19, 21, 45, 47, 62, 76, 91, 93, 98, 102, 118, 125, 138, 140, 160, 183-5,
        189, 193, 199, 223, 234, 237, 239, 245, 247-8, 273
conduct problems 33, 39, 45, 93, 100

contraception 195
Controlled Family History Studies 69-71, 86-7, 92, 101
Controlled Study of Tourette Syndrome 57, 193
controls without 233, 242
Cook 243-4
Cook County Hospital 10
coprolalia 17, 177, 194, 284
copropraxia 194
Cornell 15
Crocq 146
cross-dressing 178
Crowe, Ray 92-3
cruel to animals 183
cruel to others 183
Cylert 90
cystic fibrosis 7, 91, 133, 150, 194

D

D1 receptor 145, 219, 256, 284-5
D2 receptor 89-96, 98, 117, 123, 130, 132, 145-6, 150, 164, 169, 205-6, 211, 232, 238, 253, 256, 283-4
D_2A1 90-6, 131-4, 137-40, 146, 163, 165, 201-3, 205-6, 211, 215, 231, 233-5, 238-9
D_2A 2-2 234-5
D3 receptor 145-7, 150, 256, 284-5
D4 receptor 145, 256, 284-5
Darwin 50, 58, 193
DβH 237-40, 242-3, 245, 247-8 (see *Dopamine β-Hydroxylase*)
DCIP 225
DDAVP nasal spray 280
Dean, Harvey 87, 163
DeKlerk 109
dementia 18, 228
denaturing gradient gel electrophoresis 128, 211, 284 (also see *DGGE*)
Depakene 278
Depakote 273, 278
depression 17, 47, 49, 66, 70, 73, 75-6, 85-6, 91, 94, 100, 102, 123, 131, 160, 163-4, 168-9, 187-190, 192, 198-9, 205-7, 215, 223-4, 227-9, 238, 242, 245-6, 254-7, 273-5, 283
desmopressin acetate 280
destroyed property 183, 184
Devor, Eric 29, 101
Dexedrine 40, 90
DGGE 128, 211, 216, 218, 224, 284 (also see *denaturing gradient gel electrophoresis*)
Dia 97
diabetes 142
Diagnostic Interview Schedule 46, 63, 69, 173, 187
Dietz, George 113, 115, 128, 211, 216, 220, 221, 225, 253
dimorphic nuclei 178
Dino, Mick 202
discipline 45, 183, 184, 189, 191
dioxygenase 50, 97, 252, 287, 291
disinhibition disorders 199

DNA 11, 30, 50-1, 83-4, 90-4, 97, 105-6, 114, 120-2, 124, 127-8, 133-4, 145, 157, 211, 216, 218-20, 223, 225, 235, 238, 241, 245, 249, 252, 256, 283-91
DNA helix 193
DNA insert 105-6, 127
DNA library 130
DNA mutation 112, 126, 286, 288
DNA polymerase 84, 289
DNA polymorphism 225
DNA sequencer 124
Don't Think About Monkeys 82
Donalan, Tim 51, 74
DOPA 236
dopamine 89-91, 93, 95, 118, 123, 139, 142-3, 146-7, 150, 165, 171, 176, 202, 207, 215, 231, 235, 237, 240-2, 245, 248-9, 275, 282, 284-5, 288, 291
dopamine β-hydroxylase 225, 235, 237-8, 256, 284-5
dopamine D1 receptor 145, 219, 256, 285
dopamine D2 receptor 89-91, 123, 130 145, 164, 203, 205-6, 211, 231-2, 238, 253, 276, 283-5
dopamine D3 receptor 145-6, 238, 284-5
dopamine D4 receptor 145, 256, 284-5
dopamine receptor 86, 89-91, 131, 145, 201, 211, 231, 282
dopamine transporter 241, 243-4, 256, 284-5, 291
dopaminergic 137, 142
Down's syndrome 10
DRD2 90, 132, 134-5, 138-9, 141-3, 145, 164-5, 215, 242-3, 245, 247-8, 285
dreams 102, 137
drinking 61, 175, 196
drug abuse, addiction 18, 34, 41-2, 61, 66, 69-70, 74, 86, 92-95, 131, 134, 139-40, 142, 160, 164, 169, 173-6, 189, 193, 198-203, 205, 211-2, 215, 223-224, 231, 233, 238-9, 241, 243, 246
drunk driving 140, 175
Diagnostic and Statistical Manual (DSM) -III 46, 94, 284-5
DSM-IIIR 187, 285
DSM-IV 205, 285
dyslexia 39, 102, 123

E

easily annoyed 183
eating disorders 169
Echolalia 82
Effexor 273, 275
Eldridge, Roswell 18, 27, 177
electrophoresis 110, 112-3, 121, 128, 211, 220, 241, 284-5, 290
English (academic subject) 197
English medical journal 49, 90
English psychiatrist 74
English TS group 146
English workers 146
Enock, Jay 53-4
environmental factors 9, 62, 80, 93, 183, 197, 249, 288
enzymes 11, 49, 83, 97, 109, 111, 113, 1124, 125, 129, 130, 151, 207

epiphenomena 11, 285
Epstein, Charles 57-8
estrogen 143
eugenics 14, 65, 67, 199
exhibitionism, exhibitionist 18, 25-27, 177, 181, 194, 207
exon mutation 221, 249
exon(s) 112, 114-5, 120-1, 123-4, 126-7, 130, 132, 218, 220-1, 223, 249, 285

F

family history 40-1, 46-7, 54, 70, 80, 90, 111, 231-2, 289 (see *Controlled Family History Studies*)
family study 59, 62, 69-70, 86, 100-1, 168, 198
family therapy 33-5
feed back inhibition 237
Ferry, Linda 202
fetishism 178
Fifth TSA Sponsored Genetic Workshop 87
finger sign 194
firefights 137
fires 25, 33, 183-4
First International Congress on Tourette Syndrome 118
first patient 17, 277
First TSA Genetic Workshop 87
First World Congress of Psychiatric Genetics 74
flashbacks 94, 137
flashers 26
fluvoxamine 274-5
founder effect 109
fragile X-syndrome 221
French workers 146
Freud 9, 36

G

G´A mutation 216, 218, 223, 286
G´A or G´T 224
G´T mutation 216, 219-20, 224-5
Gade, Radhika 202
gamblers, gambling 146, 205-6, 212, 215, 223-4, 238
Gelernter, Joel 134, 164-5, 231, 232
gene frequency 165, 194
Gene Mapping Conference 74
general anxiety 86, 188, 191, 242, 245-6, 273
generalized anxiety disorder 227-8
genetic control 158, 181
Genetic Diseases in Man 114
genetic loading technique 157, 168-9, 177, 180, 183, 198, 200, 232-5
Genomics 76, 219
Gerald, Park 14, 15, 100
Gericke, George 109, 113, 119-20, 122-126, 128-9, 212-3, 215-7, 286
Gilles de la Tourette syndrome 7, 42, 58, 166-7, 286, 291

glucocorticoid 83, 105, 211 (see *GREs*)
Golden, Gerald 100
Goldman perimeter 53
gonadotrophic hormone 143, 286
good student 196-7
Goodman, Richard 77, 114
Gordian knot 101
graduate school 199
grants 11-2, 58, 67, 99, 201, 251-4
GREs 83, 105-6, 127, 210-1 (see *glucocorticoid*)
Grey, Mark 128, 130
Griffin Printers 81
grimaces 17
growth hormone 143, 147
GTP 209
GTPase 209-10
Gts genes 7-8,18, 29-31, 37, 39, 42, 45, 50, 53-55, 58, 61-3, 67, 69, 71, 73, 80, 86-88, 90-2, 94, 97-99, 102, 104, 117-119, 123, 131, 135, 149-150, 153, 157-60, 170-1, 173-177, 180-1, 185, 187, 189-90, 193, 195, 199-200, 227-9, 231, 255, 257, 286
Gts-ADHD gene 167, 188
GTT repeats 105-7
guanfacine 279
Gupta 97, 128

H

H-ras 209-10
Haldol (haloperidol) 18, 26, 36, 39, 40, 42, 91-2, 142, 276-7, 280, 283
Hamer, Dean 179
Hanin, Israel 22
haplotype, haplotyping 134, 141-3, 286
Harvard Medical School 14
Harvey, Dr. 209
Hastings Center 14-5, 57
Hebebrand 146
height 90, 141, 143, 211
heme protein 114
hemoglobin 10, 83, 114-5, 286-7, 289
hemoglobinopathies 114-5, 256
Hérault 209
heroin 173
Hi, I'm Adam. A Child's Book About Tourette Syndrome 81
higher education 199
Hilkevich, John 82
Hill, Shirley 73
histidine 114-5, 120-1, 123-4, 127, 221, 287
HLA antigens 22
homosexuality 70, 178-81
Hope Press 80-1, 117, 157, 253
hostilely withdrawn 102
HTO3 clone 50-1, 73-4, 103, 128, 130, 287
Hudson, James 85-6, 94

Hughes, Susan 81, 277-8
hunger-stat 142
Huntington's disease 7, 18, 91, 133, 207, 221
hypersexual 177, 181, 193-195, 198, 200, 208
hypothalamus 147, 178, 287

I

IDO 97-8, 122-3, 128, 130, 287 (see *indoleamine dioxygenase*)
illicit drug 174
imipramine 280
impulse disorder 212
impulsive, impulsivity 25, 59, 193, 205-208
indoleamine dioxygenase 97, 287 (see *IDO*)
insomnia 102, 137, 273, 275, 280
International Congress of Human Genetics 119, 125
International Society for Biomedical Research in Alcoholism 169
International Symposium 22
introns 120, 126, 132, 211, 216, 218, 220-2, 225, 249, 287
IQ 199
iron 114, 286
Irons, Ed 218
irritable, irritability 59, 201, 206, 273
irritable bowel syndrome 85, 160, 169, 170, 189, 287
Israeli Defense Force 119
Italy 139, 201

J

Jankovitch 153
Jerry L. Pettis V.A. Hospital 92, 288
Johannesburg 217, 225
Johns Hopkins University 67, 101
Johnson, Pat 141
Journal of Alcoholism: Clinical and Experimental Research 73
Journal of Clinical Psychiatry 71
Journal of Developmental and Physical Disabilities 154
Journal of Pediatrics 153
Journal of the American Academy of Child and Adolescent Psychiatry 40, 166
Journal of the American Medical Association (JAMA) 40, 89, 95, 96, 131, 134, 165, 287

K

Kaiser plan 196, 198
Kalahari reaction 128
Kerbeshian, Jacob 92
Kevles, Daniel 67
Kidd, Ken 18, 29, 42-3, 57, 134, 163-4, 231
Kirsten, Dr. 209
Knell, Ellen 71, 167
Korea 199
Kovacs, Bruce 146, 286
Kruger National Park 114

Kurlan, Roger 43, 85, 87, 100, 163, 165, 231, 256
kynurenine 109

L

LA/TSA 18-19, 22-23, 36, 287
Lancet 49, 146
LD 167
learning disabilities 21, 59, 100, 119, 166, 189, 193, 195, 199, 210
learning disorders 39, 70, 86, 99, 166-7, 189-91, 197, 199
learning problems 39, 118, 189-90, 210, 233, 239, 246
Lesch-Nyhan syndrome 207
Leckman, James 42, 57, 59, 101, 164, 165, 167, 227, 231
LeGro, Rick 147
LeMoal 137
Lemon, Jack 18
Lesieur, Henry 205
leukemia virus 209
LeVay, Simon 178
Levi, Sue 26, 57, 59, 81
Library of Congress 81
limbic system 65, 79, 145, 193, 287, 290
Lindberg, George 131
Lindsey, Mrs. 9
linear analysis of variance 245
linkage 29-30, 43, 55, 73, 75-6, 87, 90-1, 93, 105, 118-9, 123, 133, 146, 150-2, 162-3, 165, 179, 207, 232, 249, 255, 288
linkage disequilibrium 132-4, 211, 216, 218, 249, 287
Loma Linda 92, 202, 288
Los Angeles school district 90
Lowe, Tom 40-1
LSD 173
Luvox 273-5
lying 33, 183

M

MacMurray, Jim 92-5, 117, 137, 139, 141, 164, 196, 215, 241-2, 288
mania 47, 66, 102, 187, 189-91, 234-5, 239, 242, 245, 246, 273
Maniatis 83
manic, maniclike behavior 59, 187, 233
manic-depression 9, 62, 70, 74-5, 86, 91, 94, 123, 150, 187, 198-9, 283
Manic depression gene 75
MAO inhibitors 207
MAO-A 207
MAO-B 207
Mapping Our Genes 65
marijuana 173
masochism 178
math (academic subject) 197
Mayer 209

McKusick, Victor 67
McLean Hospital 85
MDSO 26
Medicine 101-2
melatonin 273, 280
memory 18, 199, 238-9
Mercer, Karen 129, 157, 287
Merkulov 211
Merkulova 211
methyl transferase 123, 126
Mexico 199
Michels 15
migraine 85
Minderaa 99, 100
MMPI 45
MNS 30, 73, 118
Moban 273, 277
modifier, modifying gene 76, 90, 92, 94-6, 98, 131, 146, 256
Mohandas 51
molecular biology 2, 202, 208
molecular genetic loading technique 232-3, 235
molindone 277
Mother's Age at First Birth 196
Motulsky, Arno 10, 65, 67, 77, 199
mugging 183
Muhleman, Donn 50, 83, 97, 103, 107, 113-5, 121-123, 127, 216, 218, 220, 253, 285, 288
Myers 83
myotonic dystrophy 221

N

NADP 129
Najfeld, Vesna 97
National Institute for Health Statistics 141
National Institute of Alcohol Abuse and Alcoholism 95, 253, 288
National Institute of Drug Abuse 8, 241, 252-3, 288
National Institute of Mental Health 14, 253
National Institutes of Health (NIH) 8, 79, 252, 288
National Neurological Research Bank 93
Nature 13, 73, 76, 91
Nazi, Nazism 14, 65, 199
NBT 128-9, 225
Nee 27
nefazodone 275-6
Netherlands 109, 207
neurofibromatosis 150, 210
neurotransmitters iii, 119, 147, 151, 171, 207, 209-10, 237, 241, 248, 250, 273, 275, 285, 288, 290-1
New England Journal of Medicine 29, 47, 54, 94-96
nicotine 201-2, 253, 280-1
NIDA 252, 288
night terrors 94, 153

NIH Study Sections 218
nitro blue tetrazolium 129
Noble, Ernest 89, 134, 142, 203
norepinephrine 123, 207, 237-9, 241-2, 275, 284-5, 288, 291
Nöthen 232

O

O'Brien, John 11
ob gene 142
obesity 61, 75, 86, 141-2, 193, 211
obsessive thoughts 90, 288
obsessive-compulsive 19, 21, 47, 53-4, 59, 62, 71, 75, 78, 85-7, 94, 99, 102, 118-9, 125,
        168-9, 175, 178, 189-91, 198-9, 210, 227-8, 231, 233-5, 238-9, 241-2, 245-6,
        248, 257, 273-7, 288
odds ratios 175
OLA 219, 288
oligomer 84, 114-5, 120-1, 211, 219-20, 289
oligonucleotide ligase assay (OLA) 219, 288
oligonucleotides 83-4
opiates 173
opioid receptors 254
oppositional behavior 25, 45, 242
oppositional defiant 33, 185, 189, 233, 235, 239, 245-8, 257, 273, 277
Oppositional Defiant Disorder (ODD) 183, 185
Orap 276-7, 279
Orientals 134
Oxford University Press 78
oxidases 129, 207, 289
oxygen 97, 114, 129, 221, 286, 289, 291
oxygenase 50, 97, 109, 128-9, 225, 287, 289, 291

P

Pagemaker 81
palindrome 106
panic 137, 164, 228, 246
panic attacks 17, 42, 70, 75-6, 85, 90, 93-4, 102, 118, 123, 131, 150, 164, 189, 191, 193,
        199, 205, 228, 242, 273
Panic Disorder 62, 227-8
paper(s) 11-3, 18, 22, 26, 29, 40-3, 45, 47, 49, 54, 57-60, 62, 65, 67, 71, 73-7, 86, 89, 94-
        7, 99-102, 113, 118-9, 128-9, 131, 134, 139, 145-6, 152-5, 157, 165, 168-9, 183,
        193-4, 199, 207, 211-3, 219, 226, 228-9, 231, 243, 251-2, 254-5, 257, 285
Parkinson's disease 131, 285
paroxetine 274
patent 113, 124-6, 212, 217-8, 225
Pauls, David 42-3, 57-9, 61-3, 65-70, 75, 77, 85-7, 99-102, 159-60, 163-8, 174, 183, 187,
        193, 227, 231, 253, 257
Paxil 273-4
Pc1 Duarte 93-4
PCR 83-4, 107, 114, 120-1, 124. 126, 134, 145, 216, 219-21, 241, 283, 289
Pediatrics 153

pedigree 18-20, 27, 30-1, 47, 54, 73, 75, 79, 87, 99, 102, 146, 149-53, 169, 179-80, 208, 251, 289
pedophilia 178
penetrance 18-9, 29, 31, 149, 228, 289
Perisco, Tony 241
Pert, Candice 254
pervasive developmental disorder (PDD) 75, 92, 289
phenylketonuria 207
phobias 45, 47, 59, 62, 86, 102, 118, 164, 168, 189, 191, 199, 210, 227-8, 233, 246, 257, 273
Phobic Disorder 227-8
physical abuse 35, 183
Plank, Max 254
Plenum Press 77
POINTER 29
polygene, polygenic 147, 149-152, 210, 222, 225, 232, 235, 240, 245, 248-50, 256, 289
polygenic set 210, 223, 235, 240, 245
polysubstance abuse 139-40, 42
poor parenting 61, 93, 183
Pope 85-6, 94
Post-Traumatic Stress Disorder (PTSD) iii, 85-6, 94, 98, 131, 137-8, 211, 289
poverty 14, 183
Pretoria 109, 113, 118, 120, 124-5, 215-6, 286
prolactin 146-7
Prolixin 277
promoters 83-4
Prozac 273, 276
psychedelics 173-4
Psychiatric Clinics of North America 47
psychosomatic 45, 169, 171, 290
Puerto Rico 199
purse snatching 183

Q

questionnaires 46-7, 58, 157, 169, 205, 232, 251

R

Raeburn, Paul 66
rage 25, 33, 35, 45, 273, 277-8
rape 207
Rappaport, Judy 119
ras gene 209-10
reading problems 62, 189-91, 239, 242, 245-6
"real" mutation 132-4, 216, 218
rebuttal 43, 58-999
redox 129, 225, 290
reduction-oxygenation 129
regulatory DNA 97
regulatory region 83-4, 98, 103-5, 107, 115, 117, 127
repeat 105-7, 145, 221, 225, 240-2, 291
reproduction 147

resentment 20, 183
restriction endonucleases 121, 128, 133, 144, 219-20, 238, 285, 290-1
Riddle, Mark 163-4
Ring, Rob 241
Risperdal 273, 276-8
risperidone 276-7
Ritalin 39-42, 90, 278
rituals 92, 102, 232
robbery 183
Robertson, Mary 85, 99-100
Robins, Lee 46
Rogeness 237
Rohaidy 153
Rosenthal, Richard 205
Rugle, Loreen 205
running away from home 19, 183
Russian 211
RYAN — A Mother's Story of Her Hyperactive/Tourette Syndrome Child 81, 278

S

Sacks, Oliver 85, 87
sadism 178
Salk Institute 178
sarcoma 209
sarcoma virus 209
schizoid 47, 62, 91, 102, 189-91, 233-5, 246
schizophrenia 7, 9, 36, 74-5, 91, 94-5, 123, 134, 145-6, 150, 223-5, 276, 285
Schmid 50
school ii, 9-10, 14, 21, 36, 41, 53, 90, 199, 231, 241, 277-8
school, carrying knife to 19
school, dropping out 199, 239
school expulsion 33, 140
school, missing 183
school performance 21, 196-7, 239, 246
school problems 195
School of Public Health
science (general) i, ii, 5, 7, 12, 19, 53, 62, 66-7, 82, 155, 164, 168, 251-2, 254-5, 289
science (academic subject) 9, 197
Science 74, 91, 94, 135, 178, 208
Science for the People 14
Science News 87
Science Writer's Conference 131
Scientific Autobiography and Other Papers 254
Seattle 10, 65, 74
Second World Congress of Psychiatric Genetics 123, 125, 134
selection 58, 166, 181, 188, 193-195, 199-201
Seligman, Adam 82
Seligman, Muriel 18, 82
semidominant-semirecessive 30, 54, 90, 118, 150, 256
sensation seeking 237
separation anxiety 59, 169

serotonin 49-50, 54, 58-9, 65, 73, 78, 83, 86-7, 89, 91-2, 94-5, 97, 99, 118-9, 122-3, 126, 147, 153, 169-71, 176, 180, 207, 225, 241-2, 248, 252, 273-6, 280, 287, 290-1
sertraline 273-4
Serzone 273, 275-6
sex, aversion to 181
sex chromosomes 13
sex drive 177-8, 180
sex, excessive interest in 194
sex, forcing 183
sex (gender) 13, 141, 180
sex offenders 20, 26
sex, precocious interest in 194
sex, thoughts 25, 178, 194
sexual abuse 26, 183
sexual activity 189, 193
sexual behavior 22, 91, 95, 160, 177-8, 180-1, 183, 189, 194, 198, 212, 233-4, 273
sexual contact 181
sexual disinihibition 193-4
sexual disorder 257
sexual dysfunction 275
sexual exhibitionism 18
sexual impulses 177
sexual partner 181
sexual preference 180
sexual problems 177, 191, 246
sexual touching 177, 194
sexually dimorphic 290
sexually dimorphic nuclei 178
Shapiro, Arthur 45
sickle cell 10, 194
Singer, Harvey 101-2, 163
sleep 280
sleep apnea, 86, 153, 157
Sleep Behavior Questionnaire 102
sleep disorders 47, 62, 87, 94, 102, 118, 189, 191, 233, 257, 280
sleep disturbance 99
sleep laboratory study 153
sleep problems 153, 239, 245-6, 280
sleep regulation 153
sleep, REM 153
sleep structure 280
sleeping pills 173
Smith, Myora 51
smoking 45, 196-7, 201-3, 205, 223-4, 238
Sobell, Janet 134
sobering up 175
social phobias 86, 164, 227-8
social studies (academic subject) 197
socially withdrawn 102
sodium valproate 278
Sokoloff 145

Soma 273, 279
somatiform disorder 75, 290
somatization 189, 191, 234, 242, 245-6
South Africa 107, 109, 117-8, 125, 128, 150, 286, 289
South African Congress of Human Genetics 113, 213
South African Society of Human Genetics 109
special education 231
Speck, Richard 13
spectrum disorder(s) 31, 37, 53, 59-61, 63, 68, 71, 74-5, 80, 84-7, 93-4, 99-101, 109,
    111-2, 118, 123, 125, 131, 138, 150, 165, 169, 189-90, 194-5, 199, 205-6, 215,
    227, 232, 245-6, 248, 252, 255, 257, 273-5
speech, delayed 92
speech disorders 166-7
speech problems 164, 166, 168
speed 139, 173
spiteful 183
SSRIs 181, 273-6, 290
stealing 33, 35, 183
Strauss, Gordon 85
stress 86, 94, 131, 137-8, 187, 211, 289
stuttering 62, 99, 102, 118, 164, 166-7, 189, 191, 233-, 239, 245-6, 248
substance abuse 168, 175, 191, 198-201, 241, 246, 248
Sudden Infant Death Syndrome (SIDS) 153-4, 290
suicide 49, 187, 198, 215, 223, 255
Sverd, Barbara 154
Sverd, Jeff 74, 92, 100, 154-5, 227

T

tandem repeat 145, 291
TATA box 104, 127
Tay-Sachs disease 11, 194
TDO2 50-1, 58, 73-6, 83-4, 89, 91, 94, 97-9, 103, 105-7, 109-15, 117, 119-30, 133-4,
    150, 169, 211-3, 215-8, 221, 223, 225, 256, 291
Tegretal 278
temper, losing 183
temper, short 33, 207, 273
temper tantrums 35, 45, 273
Tenex 273, 279
testosterone 143, 180, 286
Textbook of Hematology 114
The Boy Who Couldn't Stop Washing 119
The Gene Bomb 200
The Genetics of Human Behavior – Lessons for Two Societies 61
The Scientist 254
The Silent Intruder 18
The Ticking Link 87
Tic Talk 21
tics ii, 7, 17-21, 30-1, 36-7, 39-43, 47, 63, 74, 76, 90, 100, 119, 125, 148, 157-8, 164-8,
    174-5, 187-90, 205, 231-3, 239, 245-6, 253, 273, 277-9
tics, chronic 62, 149, 151, 165-7, 191, 228-9, 291
tics, motor 17, 26, 29, 33, 40-1, 87, 92, 99, 149, 151, 165

tics, muscle 26, 291
tics, vocal 26, 29, 33, 87, 92, 99, 291
Tillman's reagent 225
Tilly 83
Tone 97
Tourette syndrome (TS) ii, 5, 7-9, 11-2, 15, 17-23, 25-7, 29-31, 33-7, 39-43, 45-7, 49-50, 53-5, 57-63, 65-71, 73-83, 85-95, 97-107, 109-14, 118-23, 125, 127, 130-1, 133-5, 137-8, 145-7, 149-50, 153-4, 157-60, 163-71, 173-4, 177-81, 183-4, 187-91, 193-6, 198, 200-1, 205-6, 209-13, 215, 218, 220-1, 223-5, 227-9, 231-3, 235, 238-43, 245-6, 248-9, 251-3, 255-7, 273-81, 285-7, 291
Tourette Syndrome and Human Behavior 5, 8, 47, 78, 109, 194, 273, 283
Tourette Syndrome Association (TSA) 8, 18-9, 22-3, 26, 30, 36-7, 41, 54-5, 57, 59, 68, 81, 87, 99, 118-9, 123, 163-4, 252, 255, 257, 287, 291
Tourette Syndrome: Current Controversies 85
Tourette syndrome (TS) spectrum disorder 53, 86-7, 93-4, 101, 109, 111-2, 165, 169-70, 205, 273-5
Tourette Syndrome Symposium 118
Tourtellotte, Wallace 93
tranquilizers 173
transporter 151, 240-4, 256, 284-5, 291
tryptophan 49-50, 54, 58, 97, 109, 114, 119, 129-30, 283, 287, 290-1
tryptophan 2,3-dioxygenase 50, 291
tryptophan dioxygenase 252, 291
tryptophan hydroxylase 50, 122
TS proband(s) 42, 62, 71, 118, 146, 157-9, 163-7, 171, 174, 177-8, 187-90, 223, 227-8, 235, 238-9, 242-3, 245
Turner's syndrome 10
twin studies 158, 173, 179
type I statistical error 43, 254, 291
type II statistical error 43, 63, 69-70, 165, 167, 254, 255, 291
tyrosine 237
tyrosine hydroxylase 237

U

UCLA 51, 85, 89
Uhl, George 241
University (Uni) High 9, 10
University of California Press 79
University of Illinois 9, 10
University of Washington 10, 67
University of Oregon 90

V

valproic acid 278
Vandenberg, David 241
variance 245, 256
venlafaxine 275
veteran(s) 94, 137-8
Vietnam 94, 137
vindictive 183

violence, violent 13-4, 25, 137
violent crime 140
violent tantrums 35
visual field studies 54

W

Walkup, John 101
Wall Street Journal 89
Wallace, 93
Wallace, Bruce 202, 219
Walzer, Stanley 14
Washington Congress (see *International Congress of Human Genetics*)
Washington, D.C. 99, 125
Washington Post 135
Washington, Tacoma 10
Washington University Medical School 29, 46
Wasmuth, John 51
Watson and Crick 193
weapons 183
weight 59, 141-3, 275
weight problems 53
Wexler, Milton 18
Wexler, Nancy 18
Wilson, J.R. 7
Wingerson, Lois 65
withdrawal, social 91, 276
withdrawal symptoms 139, 169, 174
workaholism 53, 257

X

X-chromosome 149, 179, 207
XO chromosome 13
XX chromosome 13
XXY chromosome 13-4
XY chromosome 13
XYY chromosome 12-4
XYY affair 12-3, 61
XYY syndrome 12

Y

Yale 18, 29, 41, 59, 66, 69, 71, 75, 99, 134-5, 163-4, 227, 253, 255, 257
Yale Child Study Center 40, 42, 255

Z

Zoloft 273-4
Z score 141, 143